# Part IV: Electronic Devices
# From
# Circuit Analysis First Edition

Allan H. Robbins and Wilhelm C. Miller

NELSON EDUCATION

# NELSON / EDUCATION

ISBN-13: 978-0-17-643832-6
ISBN-10: 0-17-643832-7

*Consists of Selections from:*

*Circuit Analysis with Devise: Theory and Practice*
Robbins/Miller
ISBN 0-4018-7984-5, © 2004

# Contents

......................................................................................................................................

......................................................................................................................................

# VI

In previous chapters, we dealt with basic circuit analysis. In this section, we turn our attention to the second major topic area of the book—electronic principles and practices.

The electronic devices covered in this book are *semiconductor solid state* devices—that is they are made from solid crystalline semiconductor material. To understand how they operate requires an understanding of elementary atomic theory. Although we introduced the basics of this theory in Chapter 2, some additional ideas are needed. We begin with these. Following this, we examine various devices including diodes, transistors, operational amplifiers, etc. We then look at the application of these devices in various important circuits throughout the remainder of the book.

In keeping with the trend in teaching electronics today, less time is spent on the detailed analysis of transistor biasing techniques than in the past and more is devoted to the use of op-amps in small signal amplifiers. ■

## ■ KEY TERMS

Anode/Cathode

Barrier Potential

Biasing

Diode

Donor/Acceptor Atoms

Electron-Hole Pair

Intrinsic/Extrinsic Material

Majority/Minority Carriers

*n*-type and *p*-type Semiconductor
  Material

Negative Temperature Coefficient
  (NTC)

*p-n* Junction

Saturation Current

Tetravalent, Trivalent, Pentavalent
  Atoms

## ■ OUTLINE

## ■ OBJECTIVES

On completion of this chapter, you will
be able to

- sketch the symbolic representation
  of an atom, with particular attention
  to the valence shell,

- explain what is meant by energy
  levels, energy bands, the conduction band, the valence band, and
  energy gaps,

- compare the energy gaps of insulators, semiconductors, and conductors,

- describe how electron-hole pairs
  are created in semiconductors,

- explain what is meant by the terms
  *trivalent, tetravalent,* and *pentavalent*
  as they relate to atomic structure,

- describe the use of doping to foster
  the creation of conduction electrons
  and holes,

- describe electron current and how it
  accounts for conduction in *n*-material,

- describe how holes provide the
  mechanism by which electrons pass
  through *p*-material,

- describe what is meant by majority
  carriers and minority carriers,

- describe the important aspects of a
  *p-n* junction, including the depletion
  region and the barrier potential,

- identify the terminals of a diode and
  state the barrier potential for a typical diode,

- describe how conduction takes place
  through a forward-biased junction,

- describe why a reverse-biased
  junction blocks current,

- describe the basics of reverse
  junction breakdown and junction
  capacitance.

# Introduction to Semiconductors

24

S emiconductor materials are the heart of solid-state electronics. From them, we fashion important devices such as diodes, transistors, and integrated circuits, and from these, we build computers, cell phones, home theatre systems, and the like. The most commonly used semiconductor material is silicon (Si), although germanium (Ge) is used in certain applications. Thus, most of our focus is on silicon.

**Intrinsic** (pure) semiconductors are materials that have properties between those of conductors and insulators—i.e. they conduct electricity better than insulators but not as well as conductors. However, by suitable "doping", we can alter their characteristics and fabricate the devices that we require from the modified materials. To understand how this is done and how such devices operate, you need an understanding of elementary atomic theory. Thus, we begin with a review of the atom. We then introduce energy levels, bonding, and the concept of electron and hole currents. Next, we describe doping and the *p-n* junction. The concepts of majority carriers and minority carriers are then described and the mechanism of charge flow in doped materials is studied. Finally, the simplest useful semiconductor device, the junction diode is described. We conclude with a look at forward and reverse biasing, thus setting the stage for our study of diodes in Chapter 25. ■

## 24.1 Semiconductor Basics

Consider Figure 24–1. As noted in Chapter 2, an atom consists of a positively charged nucleus of protons and neutrons surrounded by a cloud of orbiting negatively charged electrons. In its normal state, each atom has an equal number of protons and electrons and thus, is neutral, i.e., uncharged. Electrons are grouped into shells, designated *K, L, M, N,* etc. The last occupied shell is called the valence shell, and electrons in this shell are valence electrons. Materials are categorized electrically as conductors, insulators, or semiconductors, depending on how many electrons they have in their valence shell. Materials with 1 valence electron are conductors, those with 8 are insulators and those with 4 are semiconductors. Atoms with 4 valence electrons are called **tetravalent** atoms—thus, semiconductors are tetravalent materials.

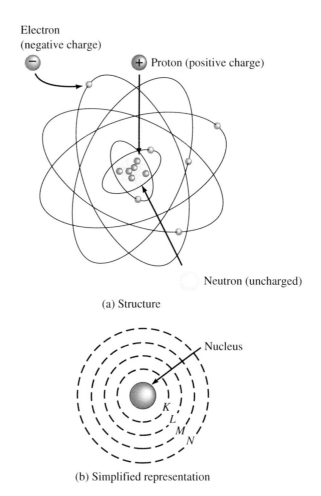

Electron
(negative charge)

+ Proton (positive charge)

Neutron (uncharged)

(a) Structure

Nucleus

*K*
*L*
*M*
*N*

(b) Simplified representation

**FIGURE 24–1** Bohr model of the atom. Although this is a somewhat simplified picture, it is adequate for our purposes.

Two semiconductor materials, silicon (Si) and germanium (Ge), are of particular interest to the electronics industry. Of these, silicon is by far the most widely used because of its superior electrical properties. An important characteristic of both Si and Ge is that they tend to form crystals in their intrinsic state. This crystalline structure leads to some important electrical properties, as you will soon see.

## Energy Levels of Orbiting Electrons

The electrons of Figure 24–1 travel about the nucleus at incredible speeds, making billions of trips per second. This means that they posses energy. A study of atomic physics shows that electrons with greater energy orbit at greater distances from the nucleus than those with less energy—see sidebar note. This means that valence electrons have the greatest energy of all. Studies also show that orbiting electrons can exist only at certain discrete energy levels—thus, only those orbits corresponding to these levels (the shells of Figure 24–1) are possible. Figure 24–2 symbolically illustrates the energy level associated with each shell for an isolated atom. Note the energy gaps between levels. These are called *forbidden* zones. No electron can orbit in a forbidden zone, although it may pass through such a zone if it changes orbit.

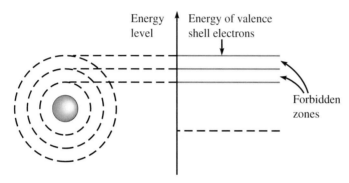

**FIGURE 24–2** Energy levels for an isolated atom.

## Energy Bands

Figure 24–2 suggests that an atom has discrete energy levels. However, single atoms do not exist in isolation. When atoms group together, the electrical forces of attraction and repulsion between adjacent atoms slightly alter the radiuses of orbiting electrons, causing the energy levels to widen into bands. Figure 24–3 illustrates bands for the three electrical classes of materials, insulators, semiconductors, and conductors. (Since we are only interested in valence electron energy levels, we have shown only their valence energy bands.) However, a new energy band, denoted the *conduction band*, has been added to each.

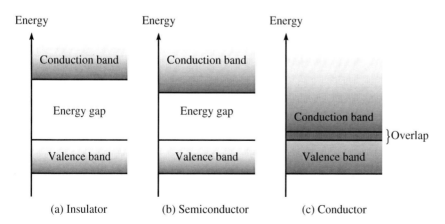

**FIGURE 24–3** Conduction and valence bands for an insulator, a semiconductor, and a conductor.

## The Conduction Band

As you saw in Chapter 2, electrons may be dislodged from atoms by the application of external energy. For example, for a metal like copper, huge numbers of valence electrons can gain sufficient energy from heat at room temperature to escape from their parent atoms and wander randomly from atom-to-atom throughout the material. Termed *free electrons,* they are (as you saw in Chapter 2) the electrons that take part in the conduction process, thus, they are also called *conduction electrons.* Since conduction electrons have more energy than those electrons that are still bound to their parent atoms, we have added an energy band (the conduction band) above the valence energy band to accommodate them.

The space between the valence band and the conduction band is called the *energy gap.* It represents the amount of energy, usually specified in electron volts (eV) (see sidebar note), that is required to break an electron free and move it into the conduction band. Now let us consider each class of material in turn.

**Insulators**   For insulators (Figure 24–3(a)), the energy gap is quite large. This means that considerable energy is needed to move an electron from the valence band to the conduction band. Because of this, insulating materials have very few free electrons and thus, their conductivity is nearly zero.

**Semiconductors**   The energy gap for semiconductors is much narrower than for insulators, typically around 1 eV. This is low enough that some valence electrons gain sufficient energy from heat alone (even at room temperature) to jump from the valence band to the conduction band (Figure 24–3(b)). Enough free electrons are created in this manner that semiconductors can actually conduct (although not well). As a result, semiconductors have electrical properties that are somewhere between those of a conductor and an insulator.

**Conductors**   For conductors, the valence band and the conduction band overlap, Figure 24–3(c). In the overlap region, electrons in the valence band are also in the conduction band and thus, conductors have enough free electrons to permit easy conduction. Consequently, such materials have high conductivity.

## Silicon and Germanium Atoms

Let us look specifically at semiconductors. Consider first a silicon atom. As shown in Figure 24–4(a), it has 14 orbiting electrons with 4 in the valence shell. Since we are interested only in valence electrons, we can simplify the representation to that of (b). The central group of charges contains the 14 positive charges ($14p^+$) of the nucleus plus the 10 electrons of the inner shells for a net positive charge of $4p^+$. Now consider a germanium atom (not shown). It has 32 protons and 32 electrons, its valence shell is shell $N$ and all inner shells are full. Since its valence shell contains 4 electrons, it can also be reduced to the simple representation of (b).

### NOTES . . .

**The Electron Volt**

Throughout this text, we generally use the SI unit of energy, the joule. However when dealing with energy levels of atoms, this is too large a unit. In atomic physics, energy is usually expressed in electron volts (eV). Recall from Chapter 2, Equation 2–3, energy is given by $W = QV$. Let $Q = e$ (the charge on an electron). If the electron is moved through a potential difference of $V$ volts, then the energy change is $W = eV$ electron volts. Specifically, if $V = 1$ V, then $W = 1$ eV. Since $e = 1.602 \times 10^{-19}$ coulombs, 1 eV $= 1.602 \times 10^{-19}$ joules.

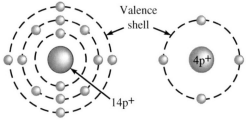

(a) Basic representation    (b) Simplified representation.
The net core change is 4p+

**FIGURE 24–4**   A silicon atom.

## Covalent Bonding

In Chapter 2, we noted that a valence shell is full when it contains 8 electrons. Semiconductors contain 4. However, when crystals of silicon or germanium solidify, their atoms arrange themselves and bond together in such a manner as to fill all valence shells by sharing valence electrons with adjacent atoms. This is called *covalent bonding* and is illustrated symbolically in Figure 24–5. Note that each atom bonds with 4 neighboring atoms to gain the 4 required electrons. Since all valence shells are full, the material acts like an insulator. (Actually, thermal energy changes the situation somewhat so that this picture is true only at a temperature of 0 K as described in the next section.)

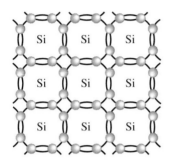

FIGURE 24–5   Covalent bonding. Each atom shares valence electrons with its four neighbors. Since all valence shells effectively posses 8 electrons, they are full.

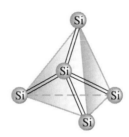

FIGURE 24–6   Si and Ge form three-dimensional tetrahedral shaped crystal. The double lines represent (symbolically) the shared valence electrons.

**N O T E S . . .**

**Crystalline Structure**

Although we have shown the bonding of atoms in a two-dimensional array, silicon and germanium crystals actually form as 3-dimensional tetrahedral-shaped structures as depicted symbolically in Figure 24–6. (A tetrahedron has four planer, triangular-shaped faces.) When a block of silicon (or germanium) solidifies, the four atoms at the apexes covalently bond with those of other crystals, creating a periodic lattice that gives these materials their important electrical properties. Obviously, Figure 24–6 is a rather complex representation; fortunately however, we never actually have to use it since all of the important ideas that we need can be obtained from the simpler representation of Figure 24–5.

## Electron-Hole Pairs

As noted above, at absolute zero temperature, all electrons are tied up in covalent bonds and there are no free electrons. However, as temperature is increased, some electrons in the valence band gain sufficient energy to break free and move into the conduction band. The vacancy left by a departing electron is called a *hole,* and each electron that moves into the conduction band leaves a corresponding hole in the valence band, creating an **electron-hole pair.** However, the life of a free electron is relatively short and soon after it jumps to the conduction band, it falls back into one of the available holes. This process is called *recombination.* Because of continual recombination and regeneration, at any given time, there are of the order of $10^{10}$ electron-hole pairs/cm$^3$ in silicon and $10^{12}$ in germanium at room temperature. This means that statistically (at room temperature) there are this many free electrons in their respective conduction bands. Note also that the atoms that have momentarily lost an electron are left with a net positive charge and are thus *positive ions.* However, the material still has no net charge because each positive ion bound in the lattice is balanced by a free electron elsewhere in the material.

## Electron Current and Hole Current

Although the numbers of free electrons indicated above may seem large (see sidebar note), the numbers are actually quite small and thus, intrinsic silicon and germanium are very poor conductors. Nonetheless, a small amount of conduction does take place if an external source of emf is applied, although the details are somewhat different than for conductors since both an electron current and a hole current occur.

## 24.2 Conduction in Semiconductors

**N O T E S . . .**

**A Comparison**

Silicon has of the order of $10^{10}$ free electrons/cm$^3$ at room temperature, while copper has of the order of $10^{23}$. This means that copper has $10^{23}/10^{10} = 10^{13}$ times as many free electrons per unit volume as silicon. Thus, compared to a good conductor like copper, intrinsic silicon has relatively few free electrons and as a result, quite poor conductivity. Similarly for germanium.

## NOTES . . .

### Two Viewpoints on Holes

We now have two viewpoints on holes. On the one hand, we can view holes simply as a means whereby electrons move through a semiconductor material from the negative source terminal to the positive. On the other, we can view the holes as being positive charges that move through the material from the positive source terminal to the negative. Both viewpoints are useful and in what follows, we will use whichever is convenient.

Figure 24–7 illustrates the process. As indicated, electrons are attracted to the left (toward the positive terminal of the battery). However, only those electrons in the conduction band are free to move. This movement of electrons constitutes a current (referred to as *electron* current). Now consider the electrons that remain in the valence band. These cannot move in the same manner as conduction electrons since they are still bound to the parent atom and do not have enough energy to break free. However, as indicated in (a), the hole created by the displaced free electron exists in a valence band orbit and an electron from a neighboring atom may wander into it, filling the hole. When this happens, another hole is created as in (b). The process repeats itself, with the result that, as valence band electrons shift left into vacant holes, the holes effectively shift right as indicated by the progression in Figures 24–7(a), (b) and (c). Since a hole represents the absence of a negative charge in an otherwise neutral material, the moving holes look like moving positive charges. Since moving charges represent current, the movement of holes constitutes a current (referred to as *hole current*)—see sidebar note. Since there are equal numbers of free electrons and corresponding holes, the electron current is exactly equal to the hole current.

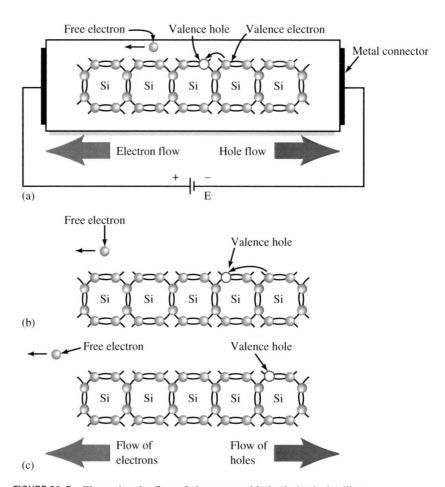

**FIGURE 24–7**   Illustrating the flow of electrons and holes in intrinsic silicon.

### The Effect of Temperature

As temperature is increased, more electrons move into the conduction band. This increases the conductivity of the material and reduces its resistance. Consequently, semiconductors have a **negative temperature coefficient (NTC)**. (In contrast, metals like copper have positive temperature coefficients since their resistance increases with temperature.)

A semiconductor in its intrinsic state is of little use. However, when impurities of the appropriate type and amount are added in the molten state, the properties of the material change dramatically. The addition of as little as 1 part per million (ppm) will foster the creation of a large number of holes or electrons, resulting in increased conductivity and greatly reduced resistivity. The process of adding impurities is referred to as *doping*. (Doped material is referred to as **extrinsic material.**) Doping can be used to create either ***n*-type** or ***p*-type** material.

### 24.3 Doping

### *n*-Type Semiconductor

An *n*-type semiconductor is a semiconductor that has more free electrons than holes. It is created when intrinsic semiconductor is doped with atoms containing 5 electrons in their valence band. (Such atoms are called **pentavalent atoms** and include phosphorous (P), arsenic (As), and antimony (Sb)). To illustrate, consider again Figure 24–5. If the central atom of silicon (which has 4 valence electrons) is replaced by an atom of arsenic (which has 5 valence electrons), there will be 9 valence electrons available for bonding instead of the required 8. Thus, there is an extra electron not needed for the bonding process (Figure 24–8). (The material however, is still electrically neutral.) The arsenic atom, which provides the additional electron, is referred to as a **donor atom.** Because the extra electron is loosely bound, thermal energy may dislodge it, turning it into a free (conduction) electron. If you add 1 ppm of impurity, statistically every millionth atom will have an excess electron. For silicon (which has about $10^{23}$ atoms/cm$^3$), this adds about $10^{17}$ additional electrons/cm$^3$, greatly increasing the available free electrons and hence, the conductivity. Note that no new holes are created, i.e., the only holes present are the thermally-generated ones.

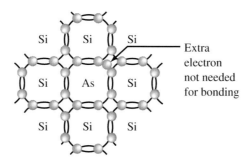

**FIGURE 24–8**   *n*-type material is created when intrinsic semiconductor is doped with pentavalent atoms. The extra electrons from the arsenic atoms are able to move freely throughout the material like free electrons do in a metal such as copper.

### Majority Carriers and Minority Carriers

Recall intrinsic semiconductor has equal numbers of free electrons and holes. When we added the donor impurity, we got huge numbers of additional free electrons but no new holes. As a result in *n*-material, free-electrons vastly outnumber holes. Thus when a source is connected, electrons and holes move through the material as you saw in Figure 24–7, but since there are so many more electrons than holes, most of the conduction takes place as conduction electron flow (Figure 24–9). For this reason, in *n*-material, electrons are called **majority carriers** and holes are called **minority carriers.**

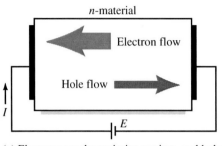
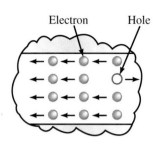

(a) Electrons are the majority carriers, and holes
    are the minority carriers

(b) Conceptual representation.
    Note that most of the
    carriers are electrons

**FIGURE 24–9**    Conduction in *n*-type material.

### *p*-Type semiconductor

A *p*-type semiconductor is a semiconductor that has more holes than conduction electrons. It is created when intrinsic material is doped with **trivalent atoms** (atoms with three electrons in their valence band such as boron (B), aluminum (Al) and gallium (Ga)). To illustrate, consider Figure 24–10. Since boron has only three electrons in its valence shell, the covalent bond is missing an electron, i.e., a hole has been created. This valence hole will readily accept an available electron, thus permitting the hole to "move" through the material. The boron atom is referred to as an **acceptor atom.**

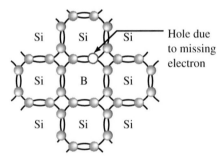

**FIGURE 24–10**    *p*-type material is created when intrinsic semiconductor is doped with trivalent atoms. The valence hole permits the acceptance of free electrons. Thus, the extra hole from the boron atom is free to move throughout the material similarly to what we saw in Figure 24–7.

Note that each acceptor atom creates a hole that is not counterbalanced by a new free electron. Thus, in *p*-material, holes vastly outnumber free electrons. Consequently, when an external voltage source is applied, there are many more holes that "move" through the material than there are electrons—thus, holes are the majority carriers and electrons the minority carriers in *p*-material (Figure 24–11).

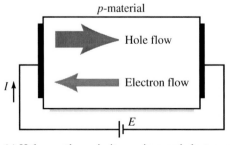
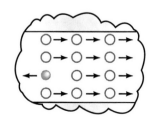

(a) Holes are the majority carriers, and electrons
    are the minority carriers

(b) Conceptual representation

**FIGURE 24–11**    Conduction in *p*-type material.

We now turn our attention to the ***p-n* junction.** A *p-n* junction is created when semiconductor material is fabricated with an abrupt transition from *p*-type to *n*-type material. However, junctions must be created by some sort of molten or diffusion process that maintains the continuous lattice structure of the material—you cannot simply push two pieces of material together to form a junction—see Notes.

## 24.4 The *p-n* Junction

## NOTES . . .

### Fabricating a *p-n* Junction

One way to create a *p-n* junction is by diffusion—you can diffuse donor impurities into *p*-material or acceptor impurities into *n*-material. The basic process is illustrated in Figure 24–12. Here, an *n*-type material is heated to a high temperature (about 950° C) in the presence of boron gas, causing boron impurities to diffuse into the *n*-material. The process is continued until sufficient boron atoms bond with the silicon atoms to create a region of *p*-material. Since the procedure is done at high temperature, the desired *p-n* junction is created while maintaining the required crystalline structure of the semiconductor.

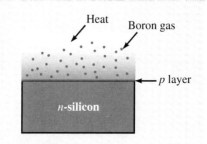

**FIGURE 24–12**   Fabricating a *p-n* junction by the diffusion process.

Although you cannot create a *p-n* junction by simply butting two pieces together, it is instructive to imagine that you can. Consider isolated *n*-type and *p*-type wafers (Figure 24–13). (Only majority carriers are depicted for each.) These carriers move about randomly in their respective materials under the influence of thermal energy.

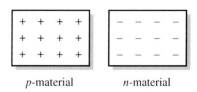

**FIGURE 24–13**   Isolated wafers with only majority carriers depicted. Both materials are electrical neutral.

### Depletion Region and Barrier Potential

Now (conceptually) bring the two pieces together (Figure 24–14(a)). As they touch, some of the free electrons in the *n*-material diffuse across the junction into the holes in the *p*-material. Since the *p*-material was initially neutral, these additional electrons create a region of negative charge in the *p*-material near the junction. Note also that, since the electrons originate from an initially neutral *n*-material, their departure creates a region of positive charge in the *n*-material. The process continues until equilibrium is reached. Since the region straddling the junction has been depleted of majority carriers, it is called the *depletion region*. Figure 24–14(b) shows an expanded (conceptual) view. Since initially neutral atoms in the *n*-material have lost an electron, they are short one negative charge each and thus, are positive ions. Conversely, initially neutral atoms in the *p*-material have gained an electron and are thus negative ions. These separated charges produce an electric field in the depletion region in much the same manner as the charges on a capacitor's plates produce an electric field in the space between them. In fact, the separated charges create a voltage across the junction called the *junction* or **barrier** voltage (or **potential**) $V_B$. For silicon, $V_B$ is approximately 0.7 V at 25° C, while for germanium it is approximately 0.3 V. (However, this barrier voltage cannot be used as a voltage source—i.e., if you connect a load across a *p-n* junction, it will not force current through the circuit as does a battery. It is best simply to think of $V_B$ as a barrier voltage that must be overcome by an applied external source in order to force current through the device.) The polarity of $V_B$ is as indicated in Figure 24–14.

Depletion region

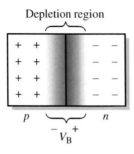

$p$          $n$

$-V_B+$

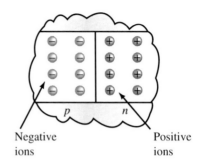

Negative                                    Positive
ions                                        ions

(a) *p-n* junction. Red represents      (b) Conceptual representation of the
   a region of positive charge             depletion region. Since atoms in
   while blue represents a region          the *p* material near the junction
   of negative charge. (The                have gained an electron, they
   junction width has been                 form negative ions, while atoms
   exaggerated for purposes                in the *n* material have lost an
   of illustration.)                       electron and form positive ions.

**FIGURE 24–14**   Conceptual joining of the two wafers to create a *p-n* junction. The migration of majority carriers across the junction results in a depletion region and a barrier potential $V_B$.

## 24.5 The Biased *p-n* Junction

The *p-n* junction is the basis for several important devices, the simplest of which is a two-terminal device called a **diode** (Figure 24–15). For reasons discussed below, a diode is a unidirectional device that passes current easily in one direction (in the direction of its arrow (c)), but blocks it in the other. Thus, when **forward biased** as in (d), the diode conducts easily, but when **reverse biased** as in (e), it doesn't. (Actually, there may be a small leakage current when reverse biased, but it is so small that it is usually negligible as described next.) The *p* end is called the **anode** and the *n* end is called the **cathode.**

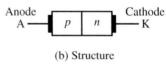

Anode                                Cathode
A ——[ *p* | *n* ]—— K

(b) Structure

A ————▶|———— K

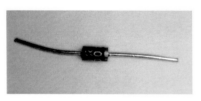

(a) Photo of a diode. The gray body       (c) Symbol. The arrow indicates the
    band denotes the cathode end             direction that it passes current

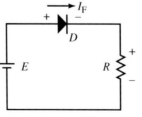

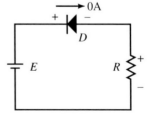

(d) Forward-biased case                    (e) Reverse-biased case

**FIGURE 24–15**   The diode is a unidirectional device that passes current only in one direction.

### The Reverse-Biased *p-n* Junction

For reverse biasing, the positive terminal of the source is connected to the *n*-material and the negative terminal to the *p*-material (Figure 24–16). Note that the depletion region has widened. This is because the positive terminal of the voltage source attracts electrons (the majority carriers) in the *n*-material toward its positive terminal, drawing them away from the junction, while at the same time, holes in the *p*-material (its majority carriers) are drawn to the negative terminal, again away from the junction. As you can see, no majority carriers are attracted toward and, hence, across the junction—thus, the majority current is zero.

Now consider minority carriers. Due to thermal energy, a small number of electron-hole pairs are created in each material. Because of their random motion, some of these will wander into the depletion region. For reasons that we won't go into (it requires a closer look at conduction band energy levels), all *p*-side minority electrons that enter the depletion region are swept through to the *n*-side. Similarly, all minority holes from the *n*-side that enter the depletion region are swept across into the *p*-side. This movement of charge constitutes a current. However, there are so few minority carriers in each material that the current, called **saturation current** $I_s$, is very small. (For example, saturation current for a typical signal diode is of the order of a few nanoamps to a few microamps.) Since minority carriers are generated by heat energy (not doping), saturation current is dependent on temperature (as we discuss more fully in Chapter 25).

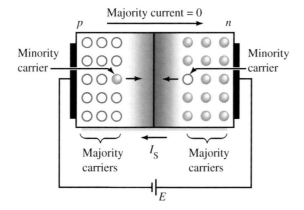

**FIGURE 24–16**   Reverse biased *p-n* junction. Since so few minority carriers are present, $I_s$ is very small, typically in the nA range for signal diodes.

### The Forward-Biased *p-n* Junction ($E > V_D$)

For forward-biasing, the positive terminal of the source is connected to the *p*-material and the negative terminal to the *n*-material, Figure 24–17. First consider the *n*-side. There are many free electrons (majority carriers) in the *n*-material, and these are repelled away from the negative terminal and attracted toward the positive terminal by the potential of the source—thus, they are propelled toward the junction. If the source voltage is greater than the barrier potential, many will acquire sufficient energy to cross where they recombine with holes to fill bonding sites in the *p*-material. (The battery provides a continuous supply of electrons at the negative terminal to replenish them.) Now consider those electrons that have crossed the junction. Because of the source potential, they drift from hole-to-hole in the valence band (as depicted earlier in Figure 24–7). From this, we see that current in the *n*-material is an electron current while the current in the *p*-material is a hole current—that is, conduction in each material is by means of its majority carriers. This current is referred to as $I_{majority}$. There is also a small amount of minority current (opposite in direction to the majority current in each material). Total current $I_D$ (Figure 24–17) is thus composed of both majority and minority current. However, minority current is so small, it can usually be neglected. Thus, for all practical purposes, diode forward current consists of majority current only—that is, $I_D \approx I_{majority}$. The voltage across the diode is approximately the barrier voltage. This is illustrated in Figure 24–18 for a silicon diode: here, $V_D \approx 0.7$ V.

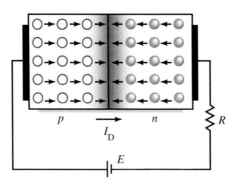

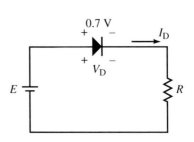

**FIGURE 24–17**   Forward-biased *p-n* junction. Although there is a small amount of minority current, for all practical purposes $I_D \approx I_{majority}$.

**FIGURE 24–18**   Forward-biased silicon diode.

## 24.6 Other Considerations

### Junction Breakdown

When a reverse biased diode is subjected to too much voltage, its junction breaks down. When this happens, large reverse current results. There are two breakdown mechanisms.

**Avalanche Breakdown**   As voltage is increased, minority carriers in the depletion region are accelerated to such velocities that when they collide with atoms in the crystal structure, electrons are knocked free, creating additional electron-hole pairs. These electrons are in turn accelerated and the process feeds upon itself until an "avalanche" of electrons results. Until breakdown occurs, the current is very small, but after breakdown, it is very high and, if not limited by the external circuit, will destroy the diode. The voltage at which this breakdown occurs is called *peak inverse voltage (PIV)* or *peak reverse voltage (PRV)*. (We look at it in more detail in Chapter 25.)

**Zener Breakdown**   If the semiconductor material is heavily doped, the depletion region narrows. This increases the electric gradient field at the junction, and at some applied voltage, the force on the electrons is so great that they are literally torn from orbit. This phenomenon is referred to as *Zener breakdown* and the voltage at which it occurs is called the *Zener voltage $V_Z$*. Diodes specifically developed to utilize this effect are called *Zener diodes*. We consider them also in Chapter 25.

### Junction Capacitance

The structure of a reverse-biased *p-n* junction is similar to a capacitor in that its depletion region behaves as a dielectric (insulator), while its *n* and *p* regions because they are conductive, act like capacitor plates. As you have already seen, the thickness of the depletion region depends on the applied reverse voltage—

the larger the voltage, the wider the region. As you learned in Chapter 10, increasing the distance between capacitor plates decreases its capacitance—thus you can see that increasing reverse voltage lowers junction capacitance (and vice versa). The capacitance of a reverse-biased diode is very small, typically of the order of 5 to 100 pF. At low frequencies this represents a very large reactance $X_C = \dfrac{1}{2\pi f C}$ that has little effect on circuit operation. However, at high frequencies, $X_C$ may become small enough that you have to take it into account. Some diodes (called *varistor diodes* or *EPICAP diodes*) are designed specifically to take advantage of this voltage controlled capacitance. We consider them in Chapter 25.

## PROBLEMS

### 24.1  Semiconductor Basics

1. What is meant by the term *valence electron?*

2. Consider the copper atom of Figure 2–4 (Chapter 2). Which has the greater energy, an electron in the *M* shell or an electron in the *N* shell? Why?

3. Sketch an energy level diagram for gold.

4. If the energy gap for a certain material is $1.762 \times 10^{-19}$ J, how many eV are needed to move an electron from its valence band to its conduction band?

5. How does the energy gap for a semiconductor compare to that of an insulator? Of a conductor? Use sketches to answer this question.

6. Sketch a germanium atom. Indicate the number of protons in its nucleus and the number of electrons in each shell.

7. A carbon atom nucleus contains 6 protons and 6 neutrons.

    a.  How many electrons are in a neutral carbon atom?

    b.  How many electrons are in its outermost shell?

    c.  Based on the answer of part b, carbon would be classified as what type of atom, *trivalent, tetravalent,* or *pentavalent?* Explain your answer.

### 24.2  Conduction in Semiconductors

8. Copper has many more free electrons per unit volume than does intrinsic semiconductor. By what factor (approximately) are the numbers of the free electrons in copper larger than they are in intrinsic germanium at room temperature? Contrast this to silicon.

9. a.  Explain what is meant by the term *positive temperature coefficient* and give an example of a material that has a PTC.

    b.  Explain what is meant by the term *negative temperature coefficient* and give an example of a material that has an NTC.

10. The valence electrons of germanium are located at a greater distance from the nucleus than those of silicon. What effect does this have on the conductivity of the germanium (as compared to silicon) when temperature rises? Explain.

11. Describe hole current in intrinsic semiconductor, i.e., describe the means by which valence electrons move through the material.

### 24.3  Doping

12. What do the terms *intrinsic* and *extrinsic* mean as applied to semiconductors?

13. a.  *p*-type impurity consists of _____ (tri, tetra, penta)-valent atoms.

    b.  *n*-type impurity consists of _____ (tri, tetra, penta)-valent atoms.

14. How does the addition of an impurity affect the resistivity of a semiconductor such as silicon?

15. In *p*-type material, _____ (holes, electrons) are the majority carrier.

16. In *n*-type material, _____ (holes, electrons) are the minority carrier.

17. Charges moving in the external wires connected to a *p-n* junction are (holes, electrons).

18. If you add aluminum as an impurity to intrinsic silicon, what type of extrinsic material results?

19. Explain how the addition of antimony increases the number of free electrons in intrinsic silicon without increasing the number of holes.

### 24.4  The *p-n* Junction

20. Why can you not create a *p-n* junction by simply pressing wafers of *p*-type and *n*-type material together?

21. The barrier potential of a silicon *p-n* junction at 25° C is approximately _____ V.

22. When a *p-n* junction is constructed, it results in a device called a/an

_____ .

23. If a voltmeter is placed across an unbiased silicon *p-n* junction at a temperature of 25° C, it will measure

    a. −0.7 V                              b. +0.7 V

    c. 0 V                                  d. −0.3 V

    e. +0.3 V

24. For the *p-n* junction of Figure 24–19, what type of semiconductor material is used and which is the *p*-side. Explain your reasoning.

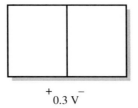

+    −
0.3 V

**FIGURE 24–19**

### 24.5  The Biased *p-n* Junction

25. Describe why forward biasing a junction narrows the depletion region.

26. Figure 24–20 shows an example of a _____ (forward/reverse) - biased diode. Its current will be _____ (large/small).

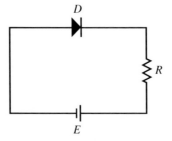

*D*

*R*

*E*

**FIGURE 24–20**

27. In a forward-biased diode, the current consists mainly of _____ (majority/minority) carriers.

28. In a reverse-biased diode, leakage current is referred to as _____ carrier current.

29. For the diode of Figure 24–21, sketch the schematic, label the anode and cathode, and indicate the direction of conventional current through the device when forward biased.

**FIGURE 24–21**

30. Redraw Figure 24–18 assuming a germanium diode.

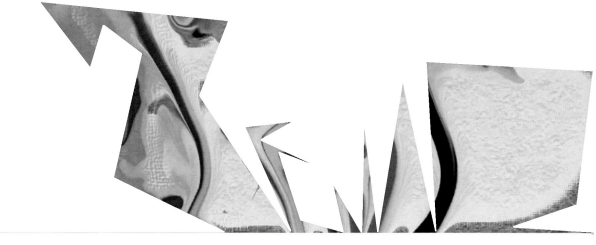

■ **OBJECTIVES**

After studying this chapter, you will be able to

- analyze simple diode based circuits using the basic diode models,

- sketch the characteristic curve of a real diode and describe the important considerations relative to its forward- and reverse-biased regions,

- interpret the data presented on diode spec sheets,

- describe the operating characteristics of a zener diode,

- interpret the data presented on zener diode spec sheets,

- describe and analyze the basic zener voltage regulator circuit,

- describe the characteristics and the application of varactor diodes,

- explain and analyze the operation of half-wave and full-wave rectifier circuits,

- describe basic power supply filtering,

- analyze basic filter circuits to determine ripple and dc output voltage for full-wave and half-wave circuits,

- determine ripple factor for filtered power supply waveforms,

- use PSpice and MultiSIM to analyze diode based circuits.

# 25

There are many types of commercial diodes, including the basic junction diode, the zener diode, the varactor diode, the photodiode, and so on. There are also variations within families. For example, within the basic diode family, there are rectifier diodes (intended for heavy current, low frequency applications) and signal diodes, (intended for low current, high frequency applications). However, all share the basic $p$-$n$ junction structure studied in Chapter 24, and thus have certain characteristics in common. In this chapter, we first look at these characteristics. We then examine some of the specialty diodes. Finally we look at the application of diodes in power supply circuits.

When studying diodes, it is customary (as in many other areas of electronics) to create models to help understand their operation and application. Often, devices can be modeled in several different ways. For example we sometimes start with a simple model to explore a device's main characteristics. Then, when we have a good understanding of these, we refine the model to take into account the things that we have ignored. This is how we approach the diode. We develop three different models, then, for any given problem, select the one that best suits the task with which we are faced. We begin with the ideal model. Here, we consider only the device's fundamental behavior and neglect everything else. ∎

TRADITIONALLY, AM RADIOS HAVE USED diode detection to separate the low frequency broadcast information (i.e., voice and music) from the high frequency radio wave carrier on which it rides. However, the path from early radio to modern radio contains some unusual devices. One of the most unusual was the "coherer." The coherer consisted of a pile of metal filings lying loosely in a glass tube between metallic electrodes. It was connected between the antenna and other circuitry and when a radio signal was received, its resistance dropped dramatically, allowing the passage of current. However, since the coherer did not resume its original high resistance, it was fitted with a tapping device that shook the filings loose again, returning it to its high resistance state. As crazy as it sounds, the device actually worked—it was the detector used by Marconi on his first successful transatlantic radio experiments in 1901. ∎

## 25.1 Diode Models

### The Ideal Diode

As you saw in Chapter 24, the fundamental characteristic of a diode is that it passes current easily in one direction but blocks it in the other. This behavior can be modeled by means of a switch (Figure 25–1). When forward-biased as in (a), the diode looks like a closed switch and thus can effectively be replaced by a short circuit, while when reverse-biased (b), it looks like an off switch and can be replaced by an open circuit. This representation is called the **ideal model.** For the forward case, $V_D = 0$ V (since the diode looks like a short), while for the reverse case, $I_D = 0$ (since it looks like an open).

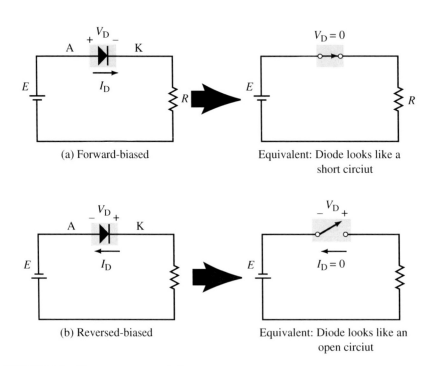

(a) Forward-biased                Equivalent: Diode looks like a short circiut

(b) Reversed-biased               Equivalent: Diode looks like an open circiut

**FIGURE 25–1**   The ideal diode model.

**EXAMPLE 25–1**

For Figure 25–2(a), determine diode voltages and circuit currents for the forward and reverse biased cases.

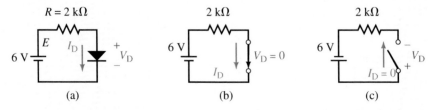

(a)               (b)               (c)

**FIGURE 25–2**

### Solution

**Forward-biased case (b):** Since the diode looks like a short, $V_D = 0$ V and $I_D = E/R = (6\text{ V})/(2\text{k}\Omega) = 3$ mA.

**Reverse-biased case (c):** Since the diode looks like an open circuit, current is zero and thus the voltage across $R$ is also zero. KVL yields $V_D = 6$ V.

## Ideal Diode Characteristic Curve

The behavior described above can be shown graphically. When forward-biased, the diode has zero volts across its terminals regardless of current. This plots as a vertical line (Figure 25–3). When reverse-biased, the diode has zero current, regardless of voltage. This plots as a horizontal line. The resulting graph is called a V-I **characteristic curve.**

## An Application

A simple application of a diode is the inexpensive two-level light dimmer circuit used in some table and floor lamps (Figure 25–4). When you switch the lamp on, contact 1 closes yielding the circuit of Figure 25–5(a). During the positive half cycle, the diode is forward-biased and conducts. During the negative half cycle, however, it is reverse-biased and does not. Since current results during only half the cycle, the light is dim. When you move the switch to its next position, you get circuit (b). With conduction over the full cycle, you get full rated current and the lamp is bright.

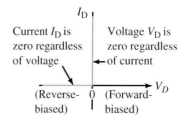

**FIGURE 25–3**   Characteristic curve for an ideal diode.

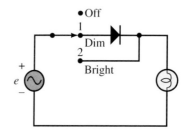

**FIGURE 25–4**   Dual level light dimmer circuit. Use a rectifier diode for this circuit.

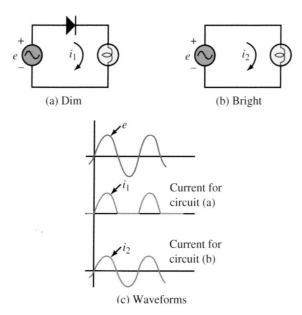

(a) Dim         (b) Bright

Current for circuit (a)

Current for circuit (b)

(c) Waveforms

**FIGURE 25–5**   Operation of the light dimmer circuit.

## The Second Approximation

The ideal model is of limited value for numerical analysis. The second approximation yields an improvement by incorporating the barrier potential $V_B$. The forward-biased case is shown in Figure 25–6(b). Here the actual diode is represented as an ideal diode in series with a dc source equal to the barrier potential (approximately 0.7 V for silicon and 0.3 V for germanium)—see Note. Before the diode can conduct, the externally applied voltage must overcome this voltage. The characteristic curve is illustrated in (c). As you can see, current is zero when $E < V_B$ (i.e., below the knee of the curve), but when the applied voltage exceeds the barrier potential, the diode turns on and conduction takes place. Since the ideal diode part of the equivalent looks like a short circuit, voltage $V_D$ remains constant at approximately 0.7 V (referred to as the *nominal voltage* of the diode), regardless of current. This yields a vertical line.

## NOTES . . .

1. Voltage $V_B$ shown in Figure 25–6 is not a source of emf. As noted in Chapter 24, it represents the junction (barrier) voltage of the diode and as we saw in Figure 24–18, it is the voltage that must be overcome by the external source to permit forward current.

2. Germanium diodes are seldom used in practice. Thus unless otherwise noted, all diodes used from here on are silicon.

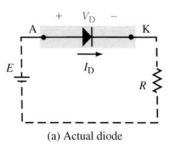
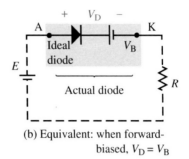

(a) Actual diode

(b) Equivalent: when forward-biased, $V_D = V_B$

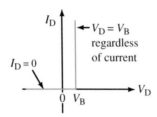

(c) Characteristic curve

**FIGURE 25–6** Second diode approximation.

**EXAMPLE 25–2**

Using the second approximation, analyze the circuit of Figure 25–2(a).

**Solution** See Figure 25–7. For the forward-biased case, (a),

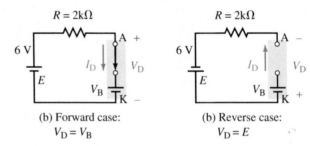

(b) Forward case:
$V_D = V_B$

(b) Reverse case:
$V_D = E$

**FIGURE 25–7**

$$I_D = \frac{E - V_D}{R} = \frac{6 \text{ V} - 0.7 \text{ V}}{2 \text{ k}\Omega} = 2.65 \text{ mA}$$

For reverse bias (b), $I_D = 0$ and the voltage across $R$ is thus zero. KVL yields $V_D = 6$ V as in Example 25–1—thus, $V_B$ has no effect here.

PRACTICE PROBLEMS 1

1. Repeat Example 25–2 for a germanium diode.
2. Add a 3-k$\Omega$ resistor across the diode of Figure 25–2 and solve for $I_D$ for the forward-biased case. Hint: Use Thevenin's theorem.

*Answers*
1. Forward: 2.85 mA, 0.3 V; Reverse: 0 mA, 6 V
2. 2.42 mA

### The Third Approximation

Semiconductor material has some resistance (recall Chapter 24), which can be incorporated as in Figure 25–8(b) to yield the third model. This resistance (called $r_f$) is quite small and ranges from a few ohms to several hundred ohms for commercially available diodes. When $E$ exceeds $V_B$, the resultant current causes a drop across $r_f$ and $V_D$ increases slightly as current is increased, resulting in a sloped characteristic as in (c). For the reverse-biased case (not shown), the diode looks like an open circuit, current is zero, and thus, $r_f$ has no effect. (We look at $r_f$ in more detail in Section 25.2.)

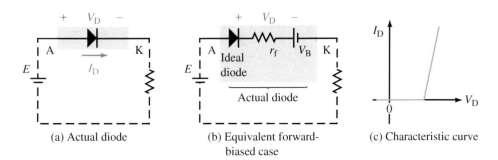

| (a) Actual diode | (b) Equivalent forward-biased case | (c) Characteristic curve |

**FIGURE 25–8**   Third diode approximation. The resistance $r_f$ shown in (b) is studied in Section 25.2.

Real diodes differ somewhat from our models. Figure 25–9 shows the characteristic of a typical silicon diode. To help understand it, let us consider each region in detail.

## 25.2  Diode Characteristic Curve

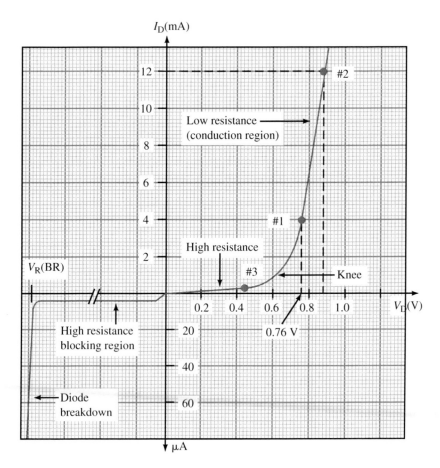

**FIGURE 25–9**   Characteristic curve of a real silicon diode.

### The Forward Region

For low **forward voltage,** resistance is high since the depletion region at the *p-n* junction is relatively wide. Thus, current is low. As source voltage is increased, the depletion region narrows, and by the time that the *knee* of the curve is reached, it has been significantly reduced. As source voltage is increased further, more carriers become available until finally, the *conduction region* is reached. Note that voltage $V_D$ is approximately 0.7 V here, but because of the internal voltage drop of the diode (due to its resistance $r_f$), $V_D$ increases slightly as current increases. For a real diode, $V_D$ may increase up to $\approx$ 1V under load.

Since resistance changes as you move along the curve, you must treat it as dynamic resistance. As noted in Chapter 4, Section 4.7, dynamic resistance is the inverse of the slope of the *V-I* curve. Thus, as shown in Figure 25–10,

$$r_f = \frac{\Delta V}{\Delta I} \qquad \qquad \textbf{(25–1)}$$

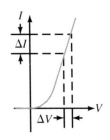

**FIGURE 25–10**    $r_f = \Delta V/\Delta I.$

To illustrate, consider the region between points #1 and #2, i.e., the conduction region of Figure 25–9. Voltage $V_D$ at 12 mA is 0.88 V and at 4 mA it is 0.76 V. Thus,

$$r_f = \frac{\Delta V}{\Delta I} = \frac{0.88 \text{ V} - 0.76 \text{ V}}{12 \text{ mA} - 4 \text{ mA}} = 15 \ \Omega$$

Similarly, between the origin and point #3 you find $r_f = \dfrac{\Delta V}{\Delta I} = \dfrac{0.44 \text{ V} - 0 \text{ V}}{0.2 \text{ mA} - 0 \text{ mA}}$
$= 2.2 \text{ k}\Omega$

In practice, forward-biased diodes are almost always operated in their conducting regions, which means that their dynamic resistances will be relatively low. (This is the resistance that we included in our third model shown in Figure 25–8.)

### The Reverse Region

For small reverse voltages, current is extremely small. (In Figure 25–9, we have expanded the current scale by a factor of 1000 to make it readable—thus, the current in the third quadrant is scaled in $\mu$A instead of mA.) As reverse voltage is further increased, you reach a point $V_{R(BR)}$ at which the diode breaks down and current increases rapidly. As noted in Chapter 24, this voltage is called the *peak inverse voltage* (PIV), *peak reverse voltage* (PRV), or simply $V_{R(max)}$. If this voltage is exceeded, the diode may be permanently damaged. (Some diodes, called zener diodes, are designed to operate beyond this point. We examine them in Section 25.4.) The resistance of the diode (before it breaks down) is very large, typically of the order of 10 M$\Omega$.

### Before We Move On

In reality, you will likely never need to compute resistance using Equation 25–1. However the concepts are important, as you will see in later sections. Note also that our third model describes the behavior of a real diode extremely well, except around the knee of the curve and at reverse breakdown. In practice, however, you do not normally operate a diode in either of these regions anyway.

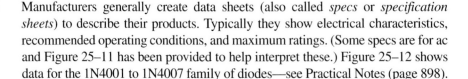

## 25.3  Diode Data Sheets

Manufacturers generally create data sheets (also called *specs* or *specification sheets*) to describe their products. Typically they show electrical characteristics, recommended operating conditions, and maximum ratings. (Some specs are for ac and Figure 25–11 has been provided to help interpret these.) Figure 25–12 shows data for the 1N4001 to 1N4007 family of diodes—see Practical Notes (page 898).

(a) Actual diode                    (b)

**FIGURE 25–11**   Helping to understand diode ac characteristics.

# 1N4001, 1N4002, 1N4003, 1N4004, 1N4005, 1N4006, 1N4007

1N4004 and 1N4007 are Preferred Devices

## Axial Lead Standard Recovery Rectifiers

This data sheet provides information on subminiature size, axial lead mounted rectifiers for general-purpose low-power applications.

**Mechanical Characteristics**
- Case: Epoxy, Molded
- Weight: 0.4 gram (approximately)
- Finish: All External Surfaces Corrosion Resistant and Terminal Leads are Readily Solderable
- Lead and Mounting Surface Temperature for Soldering Purposes: 220°C Max. for 10 Seconds, 1/16″ from case
- Shipped in plastic bags, 1000 per bag.
- Available Tape and Reeled, 5000 per reel, by adding a "RL" suffix to the part number
- Available in Fan-Fold Packaging, 3000 per box, by adding a "FF" suffix to the part number
- Polarity: Cathode Indicated by Polarity Band
- Marking: 1N4001, 1N4002, 1N4003, 1N4004, 1N4005, 1N4006, 1N4007

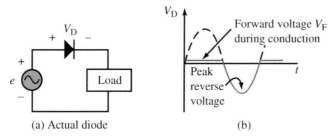

**ON Semiconductor**®

http://onsemi.com

**LEAD MOUNTED RECTIFIERS
50-1000 VOLTS
DIFFUSED JUNCTION**

CASE 59-10
AXIAL LEAD
PLASTIC

**MARKING DIAGRAM**

AL
1N
400x
YYWW

AL      = Assembly Location
1N400x = Device Number
x       = 1, 2, 3, 4, 5, 6 or 7
YY      = Year
WW      = Work Week

**MAXIMUM RATINGS**

| Rating | Symbol | 1N4001 | 1N4002 | 1N4003 | 1N4004 | 1N4005 | 1N4006 | 1N4007 | Unit |
|---|---|---|---|---|---|---|---|---|---|
| *Peak Repetitive Reverse Voltage Working Peak Reverse Voltage DC Blocking Voltage | $V_{RRM}$ $V_{RWM}$ $V_R$ | 50 | 100 | 200 | 400 | 600 | 800 | 1000 | Volts |
| *Non-Repetitive Peak Reverse Voltage (halfwave, single phase, 60 Hz) | $V_{RSM}$ | 60 | 120 | 240 | 480 | 720 | 1000 | 1200 | Volts |
| *RMS Reverse Voltage | $V_{R(RMS)}$ | 35 | 70 | 140 | 280 | 420 | 560 | 700 | Volts |
| *Average Rectified Forward Current (single phase, resistive load, 60 Hz, $T_A$ = 75°C) | $I_O$ | 1.0 | | | | | | | Amp |
| *Non-Repetitive Peak Surge Current (surge applied at rated load conditions) | $I_{FSM}$ | 30 (for 1 cycle) | | | | | | | Amp |
| Operating and Storage Junction Temperature Range | $T_J$ $T_{stg}$ | -65 to +175 | | | | | | | °C |

*Indicates JEDEC Registered Data

**ORDERING INFORMATION**

See detailed ordering and shipping information on page 2 of this data sheet.

**Preferred** devices are recommended choices for future use and best overall value.

**FIGURE 25–12**   Diode data sheet. (*Courtesy of ON Semiconductor*)

PRACTICAL NOTES . . .

1. Diodes are identified by part numbers, usually by a 1N prefix, for example, 1N4001, 1N4002, etc. as indicated in Figure 25–12.

2. Data sheets are typically divided into two main sections. The *Maximum Ratings* section shows limits that you must not exceed when you design your circuit, or else the device may be damaged or destroyed. The *Electrical Characteristics* section shows the typical and max values that you should expect during operation for key quantities, such as forward voltage drop and reverse current.

3. Although Figure 25–12 lists the complete family of 1N400X devices, the 1N4004 and 1N4007 are designated as *preferred* devices and are recommended for new designs.

4. When selecting a diode for a particular task it is important to include a safety margin, for example by choosing a component that is capable of handling at least 20% more current or voltage than the circuit is likely to require. (Some manufacturers of high quality equipment insist on a safety margin of 50%.) A safety factor of this magnitude ensures that the design will remain reliable for many years. In addition, you should use a preferred device if possible (as this reduces costs by cutting down on inventory). Thus, if the reverse voltage of a diode is determined to be 150 V, you might consider using a 1N4003, which has a $V_R = 200$ V. While this is acceptable, it is recommended instead that you use the 1N4004, which is a preferred device and is more likely to be stocked by your supplier.

5. You can get data sheets from the Internet.

Let us look at some of these specifications.

**Reverse Voltage** All diodes in Figure 25–12 are identical except that each has a different maximum reverse voltage rating. For example the 1N4001 can handle a maximum dc voltage of $V_R = 50$ V, while the 1N4007 can handle 1000 V. With ac, the 1N4001 can handle a repetitive sinusoidal voltage with a peak reverse voltage of $V_{RRM} = 50$ V (Figure 25–11), a non-repetitive 60 Hz half sine wave maximum of $V_{RSM} = 60$ V or a continuous sine wave voltage with rms value of $V_{R(RMS)} = 35$ V, while the 1N4007 can handle corresponding values of 1000 V, 1200 V, and 700 V.

**Forward Current** All members of the 1N400X family can handle a maximum **average forward current** of $I_0 = 1.0$ A (also called $I_{F(AVG)}$). However, when you first energize a circuit, you may get a brief current transient (called a *surge* current) that greatly exceeds the normal operating current. All devices can handle a surge current (denoted $I_{FSM}$) of 30 A for one cycle of a 60 Hz sinusoidal waveform.

**Maximum Instantaneous Forward Voltage Drop $v_F$** This is the maximum instantaneous voltage across the forward-biased diode (Figure 25–11), and is guaranteed not to exceed 1.1 V at a current of $I_F = 1$ A.

**Maximum Full-Cycle Average Voltage Drop $V_{F(AV)}$** When averaged over a full cycle, $V_F$ is guaranteed not to exceed 0.8 V at a current of 1 A.

## Temperature Derating

A diode generates heat and if the ambient temperature is high, this heat may not be dissipated fast enough and you may have to derate the device to protect it. For example, diode average forward current is typically specified at an ambient temperature ($T_A$) of 75° C, but if you wish to operate at a higher temperature, you must reduce the amount of current that you draw. Consider Figure 25–13. For the diode represented, if you maintain the ambient temperature at or below 75° C, you can draw 1 A; however if you wish to operate at an ambient of 125° C, you must design the circuit such that its average forward current does not exceed 0.4 A.

## Parameter Shifts

Temperature also affects a diode's *V-I* characteristics, since an increase in temperature creates more thermally generated electron-hole pairs. For the forward case Figure 25–14, the greater number of carriers available results in a larger forward current for a given forward voltage, causing an effective shift of the characteristic to the left as temperature increases (and vice-versa). For both Si and Ge, this shift is about 0.25 mV for each °C change in junction temperature ($T_J$). To illustrate, consider a silicon diode with a barrier potential of $V_B$ = 0.7 V at 25° C. If the junction temperature rises to 65° C (a rise of 40° C), $V_B$ will drop by 40° C × 2.5 mV/°C = 0.10 V to 0.6 V.

For the reverse case, an increase in temperature also causes an increase in current, but here, the current is leakage (i.e., saturation) current. Experience has shown that each 10° C rise in junction temperature results in an approximate doubling of this current. For example, if $I_S$ = 10 nA at 25° C, it will be 20 nA at 35° C, 40 nA at 45° C, etc. as illustrated in Figure 25–15.

## 25.4 Temperature Considerations and Other Effects

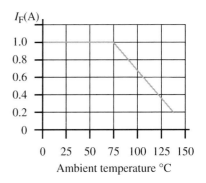

**FIGURE 25–13** Typical derating curve.

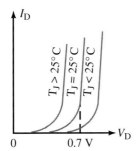

**FIGURE 25–14** Effect of temperature on barrier voltage.

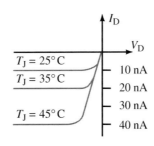

**FIGURE 25–15** Effect of temperature on saturation current.

PRACTICE PROBLEMS 2

1. A silicon diode has a saturation current of 22 nA at 25° C. What is its saturation current at 85° C?

2. Repeat Problem 1 for a germanium diode with 15 μA at 25° C

3. A silicon diode has a saturation current of 0.768 μA at 75° C. What is its saturation current at 25° C?

*Answers*
1. 1.41 μA;  2. 960 μA;  3. 24 nA

### Reverse Recovery Time at Switching

When you switch a diode from its *on* state to its *off* state, the change does not occur instantaneously. The time that it takes (called **reverse recovery time**) is denoted $t_{rr}$ and ranges from a few nanoseconds for switching diodes to a few microseconds for rectifier diodes. The larger $t_{rr}$, the slower is the diode.

### Before We Move On

As you can see, temperature variations produce complex interactions in diode operation. Fortunately, for routine room temperature design you can generally ignore these. However if you wish to design for temperature extremes, you must take temperature effects into account. However, this is beyond the scope of this book and will not be considered here.

## 25.5 The Zener Diode

PRACTICAL NOTES . . .

During manufacture, the zener voltage of commercial devices is set by the amount of doping used. Diodes are available with values of $V_Z$ from a few volts to several hundred volts.

We look now at our first specialty diode, the **zener diode** (Figure 25–16). It is a special purpose diode designed to maintain a relatively constant voltage across its terminals when operated in its reverse-biased region. A typical characteristic is shown in Figure 25–17. The breakover voltage (the voltage at which the curve changes abruptly) is called the zener voltage $V_Z$. $V_Z$ remains nearly constant from $I_{ZK}$ (the knee current) to $I_{ZM}$ (the maximum rated current). This means that a zener diode will maintain a nearly constant voltage across itself as long as its current is kept within these bounds.

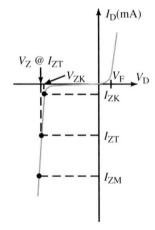

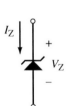

**FIGURE 25–16**   Zener diode symbol.

**FIGURE 25–17**   Characteristic curve of a typical silicon zener diode.

### A Simple Application

To illustrate, let us look at a simple voltage regulator application (Figure 25–18). The job of the regulator is to hold the load voltage constant in spite of variations in input supply voltage and output load current. For this example, we have chosen a 12 V zener. Since the zener maintains (an almost) constant 12 V across itself, the voltage across the load will also remain at 12 V, even if the source voltage and/or the load current vary (within design limits as discussed later).

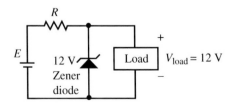

**FIGURE 25–18**   Using a zener diode for load voltage regulation.

### The Zener Diode Spec Sheet

To understand how the circuit of Figure 25–18 works, you need to know more about zener characteristics. Such information can be found on data sheets such as that of Figure 25–19.

**Zeners**
**1N4728A - 1N4752A**

*Vertical text right margin:* Zeners (1N4728A - 1N4752A)

**Absolute Maximum Ratings\*** T$_A$ = 25°C unless otherwise noted

Tolerance: A = 5%

| Symbol | Parameter | Value | Units |
|---|---|---|---|
| P$_D$ | Power Dissipation | 1.0 | W |
|  | Derate above 50°C | 6.67 | mW/°C |
| T$_{STG}$ | Storage Temperature Range | -65 to +200 | °C |
| T$_J$ | Operating Junction Temperature | + 200 | °C |
| R$_{\theta JL}$ | Thermal resistance Junction to Lead | 53.5 | °C/W |
| R$_{\theta JA}$ | Thermal resistance Junction to Ambient | 100 | °C/W |
|  | Lead Temperature (1/16" from case for 10 seconds) | + 230 | °C |
|  | Surge Power\*\* | 10 | W |

\*These ratings are limiting values above which the serviceability of the diode may be impaired.
\*\*Non-recurrent square wave PW = 8.3 ms, TA = 55 degrees C.

**NOTES:**
1) These ratings are based on a maximum junction temperature of 200 degrees C.
2) These are steady state limits. The factory should be consulted on applications involving pulsed or low duty cycle operations.

**DO-41**
COLOR BAND DENOTES CATHODE

**Electrical Characteristics** T$_A$ = 25°C unless otherwise noted

| Device | V$_Z$ (V) | Z$_Z$ @ (Ω) | I$_{ZT}$ (mA) | Z$_{ZK}$ @ (Ω) | I$_{ZK}$ (mA) | V$_R$ @ (V) | I$_R$ (μA) | I$_{SURGE}$ (mA) | I$_{ZM}$ (mA) |
|---|---|---|---|---|---|---|---|---|---|
| 1N4728A | 3.3 | 10 | 76 | 400 | 1.0 | 1.0 | 100 | 1380 | 276 |
| 1N4729A | 3.6 | 10 | 69 | 400 | 1.0 | 1.0 | 100 | 1260 | 252 |
| 1N4730A | 3.9 | 9.0 | 64 | 400 | 1.0 | 1.0 | 50 | 1190 | 234 |
| 1N4731A | 4.3 | 9.0 | 58 | 400 | 1.0 | 1.0 | 10 | 1070 | 217 |
| 1N4732A | 4.7 | 8.0 | 53 | 500 | 1.0 | 1.0 | 10 | 970 | 193 |
| 1N4733A | 5.1 | 7.0 | 49 | 550 | 1.0 | 1.0 | 10 | 890 | 178 |
| 1N4734A | 5.6 | 5.0 | 45 | 600 | 1.0 | 2.0 | 10 | 810 | 162 |
| 1N4735A | 6.2 | 2.0 | 41 | 700 | 1.0 | 3.0 | 10 | 730 | 146 |
| 1N4736A | 6.8 | 3.5 | 37 | 700 | 1.0 | 4.0 | 10 | 660 | 133 |
| 1N4737A | 7.5 | 4.0 | 34 | 700 | 0.5 | 5.0 | 10 | 605 | 121 |
| 1N4738A | 8.2 | 4.5 | 31 | 700 | 0.5 | 6.0 | 10 | 550 | 110 |
| 1N4739A | 9.1 | 5.0 | 28 | 700 | 0.5 | 7.0 | 10 | 500 | 100 |
| 1N4740A | 10 | 7.0 | 25 | 700 | 0.25 | 7.6 | 10 | 454 | 91 |
| 1N4741A | 11 | 8.0 | 23 | 700 | 0.25 | 8.4 | 5.0 | 414 | 83 |
| 1N4742A | 12 | 9.0 | 21 | 700 | 0.25 | 9.1 | 5.0 | 380 | 76 |
| 1N4743A | 13 | 10 | 19 | 700 | 0.25 | 9.9 | 5.0 | 344 | 69 |
| 1N4744A | 15 | 14 | 17 | 700 | 0.25 | 11.4 | 5.0 | 304 | 61 |
| 1N4745A | 16 | 16 | 15.5 | 700 | 0.25 | 12.2 | 5.0 | 285 | 57 |
| 1N4746A | 18 | 20 | 14 | 750 | 0.25 | 13.7 | 5.0 | 250 | 50 |
| 1N4747A | 20 | 22 | 12.5 | 750 | 0.25 | 15.2 | 5.0 | 225 | 45 |
| 1N4748A | 22 | 23 | 11.5 | 750 | 0.25 | 16.7 | 5.0 | 205 | 41 |
| 1N4749A | 24 | 25 | 10.5 | 750 | 0.25 | 18.2 | 5.0 | 190 | 38 |
| 1N4750A | 27 | 35 | 9.5 | 750 | 0.25 | 20.6 | 5.0 | 170 | 34 |
| 1N4751A | 30 | 40 | 8.5 | 1000 | 0.25 | 22.8 | 5.0 | 150 | 30 |
| 1N4752A | 33 | 45 | 7.5 | 1000 | 0.25 | 25.1 | 5.0 | 135 | 27 |

V$_F$ Forward Voltage = 1.2 V Maximum @ I$_F$ = 200 mA for all 1N4700 series

©2001 Fairchild Semiconductor Corporation                    1N4700A Rev. C

**FIGURE 25–19**   A zener diode data sheet. *(Courtesy of Fairchild Semiconductor)*

**INTERPRETATION NOTES . . .**

1. All voltages and currents on zener data sheets such as Figure 25–19 are given as positive values even though you know that operation is in the third quadrant where you would normally expect to see negative values.

2. I$_{ZT}$, I$_{ZK}$ and I$_{ZM}$ in these specs are defined by Figure 25–17.

**Nominal Zener Voltage V$_Z$**   V$_Z$ is the rated zener voltage and is specified at test current I$_{ZT}$.

**Maximum Zener Current I$_{ZM}$**   If this current is exceeded, the diode may be damaged.

**Knee Current I$_{ZK}$**   If I$_Z$ drops below this value, regulation is lost.

**Zener Impedance Z$_Z$ @ I$_{ZT}$**   This is dynamic impedance as defined by Equation 25–1 and determines how much V$_z$ changes as I$_z$ changes. As shown in Figure 25–20, if current changes by an amount $\Delta I_z$, voltage changes by an amount

$$\Delta V_z = Z_Z \times \Delta I_z \qquad (25\text{--}2)$$

Z$_Z$, which is purely resistive and sometimes denoted as R$_Z$, is substantially constant between I$_{ZK}$ and I$_{ZM}$. (Since Z$_Z$ is specified at the test current I$_{ZT}$, it is sometimes denoted as Z$_{ZT}$.) For the devices of Figure 25–19, Z$_Z$ ranges from 2 Ω to 45 Ω.

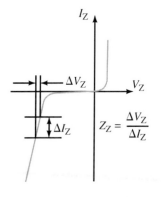

**FIGURE 25–20**   $\Delta V_Z = Z_Z \times \Delta I_Z$. Z$_Z$ is dynamic impedance.

**Power Rating**    Maximum permissible *dc power dissipation* $P_{Dmax}$ is given by

$$P_{Dmax} = V_Z I_{ZM} \text{ watts} \qquad (25\text{--}3)$$

Diodes are commercially available with maximum power ratings from 0.25 W to 50 W.

**Power Derating Factor**    All diodes listed in Figure 25–19 are rated at 1W up to $50°$ C. Above $50°$ C you must derate them by 6.67 mW for each $°$ C rise above $50°$ C. For example, at $85°$ C, $P_{D \text{ derated}} = 1$ W $-$ (6.67 mW/°C) $\times$ ($85°$ C $-$ $50°$ C) $= 0.767$ W. Sometimes derating information is given in the form of a curve as in Figure 25–21.

---

**PRACTICE PROBLEMS 3**

A 500 mW zener diode must be derated when operated above $75°$ C ambient as in Figure 25–21. What is its permissible power rating at $100°$ C?

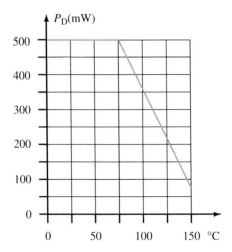

**FIGURE 25–21**

*Answer*
350 mW

**Modeling a Zener Diode**

As a first approximation you can model a zener diode as a voltage source $V_{ZT}$ (Figure 25–22(b)). This is called the *ideal* model. However, a real diode also includes internal impedance $Z_Z$. If you include this, you get the model of (c). It allows you to compute the diode's voltage at any current. To illustrate, note that the voltage at any point in the zener region may be found (relative to the test point) as $V_Z = V_{ZT} + \Delta V_Z$ where $\Delta V_Z$ is given by Equation 25–2. Thus,

$$V_Z = V_{ZT} + (Z_Z \times \Delta I_Z) = V_{ZT} + Z_T (I_Z - I_{ZT}) \qquad (25\text{--}4)$$

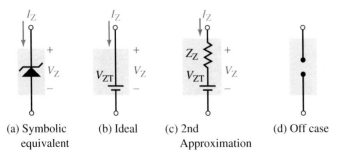

(a) Symbolic equivalent    (b) Ideal    (c) 2nd Approximation    (d) Off case

**FIGURE 25–22**    Zener diode equivalents. If $I_Z$ drops below $I_{ZK}$, the zener looks like an open circuit as in (d).

EXAMPLE 25–3

For a 1N4742A zener, $V_{ZT} = 12$ V and $Z_Z = 9\ \Omega$ @ $I_{ZT} = 21$ mA.

a. Use the second approximation to determine $V_Z$ at $I_Z = 10$ mA and $I_Z = 50$ mA

b. Repeat using the ideal model. Compare results.

**Solution**

a. Since 10 mA and 50 mA are between $I_{ZK}$ and $I_{ZM}$, Equation 25–4 applies. In each case, measure $\Delta I_Z$ from the test point. Thus, for $I_Z = 10$ mA, $\Delta I_Z = 10$ mA $- 21$ mA $= -11$ mA. Substituting into Equation 25–4 yields $V_Z = 12$ V $+ (9\ \Omega)(-11$ mA$) = 11.9$ V. For $I_Z = 50$ mA, $V_Z = 12$ V $+ (9\ \Omega)$ $(50$ mA $- 21$ mA$) = 12.3$ V. Thus, $V_Z$ varies from 11.9 V to 12.3 V.

b. $V_Z = 12$ V regardless of current. (This yields an error of about 2.5% at 50 mA.)

## Application: The Zener Voltage Regulator Revisited

You now have enough information to analyze the regulator circuit of Figure 25–18. First, determine whether the zener is in the *on* state or the *off* state. If it is on, replace it with the desired *on* equivalent from Figure 25–22. If it is *off*, replace it with an open circuit—see Practical Notes.

---

1. In most of what follows, we will use the ideal model. An obvious reason for this is simplicity—the ideal model is extremely easy to use. Another reason has to do with tolerances. Commercial diodes have tolerances typically of ±5% or ±10%. With this level of uncertainty, it is generally unnecessary to worry about the small change in $V_Z$ due to $\Delta I_Z$

2. An easy way to design with zener diodes is to determine the limits imposed by $I_{ZK}$ and $I_{ZM}$ using the ideal model, then design your circuit to stay well within these limits to provide a safety margin. If you do this, even with the uncertainties, your circuit should work safely and satisfactorily.

PRACTICAL NOTES . . .

---

EXAMPLE 25–4

The zener diode of Figure 25–23(a) is a 12 V 1N4742A. Analyze the circuit using the ideal model.

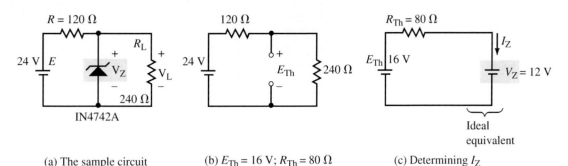

(a) The sample circuit    (b) $E_{Th} = 16$ V; $R_{Th} = 80\ \Omega$    (c) Determining $I_Z$

**FIGURE 25–23**   Analyzing the regulator circuit.

**Solution**   Remove the diode as in (b) and find the Thévenin's equivalent. Here, $E_{Th} = 16$ V and $R_{Th} = 80\ \Omega$. Replace the diode as in (c). Since $E_{Th}$ exceeds the rated zener voltage, the diode is on and $V_Z = 12$ V. Thus, $I_Z = (16$ V $- 12$ V$)/80\ \Omega = 50$ mA. Power dissipation is $P_D = V_Z I_Z = (12$ V$)(50$ mA$) = 0.6$ W, well below the rated value of 1 W. From (a), we see that $V_L = V_Z = 12$ V. Thus $I_L = 12$ V$/240\ \Omega = 50$ mA. Source current is $I_R = I_L + I_Z = 100$ mA and the drop across $R$ is $(120\ \Omega)(100$ mA$) = 12$ V.

In the previous example, all circuit elements are fixed. In practice, both input voltage and load current may vary. Let us look at each of these in turn.

### Input (Line) Regulation

When input voltage $E$ fluctuates, zener current $I_Z$ fluctuates also. If $I_Z$ drops below $I_{ZK}$, you lose regulation; if it rises above $I_{ZM}$, the diode may be damaged. Thus you must not let $E$ drop below $E_{min}$ where $E_{min}$ is the voltage at which $I_Z = I_{ZK}$, and you must not let it rise above $E_{max}$ where $E_{max}$ is the voltage at which $I_Z = I_{ZM}$. To illustrate, consider Figure 25–24. Assuming an ideal zener and noting that $V_L = V_Z$, we see that

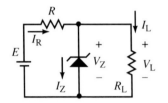

**FIGURE 25–24**

$$I_R = I_Z + I_L = I_Z + \frac{V_Z}{R_L} \qquad (25\text{–}5)$$

and

$$E = I_R R + V_Z \qquad (25\text{–}6)$$

To find $E_{min}$ use $I_Z = I_{ZK}$ in Equation 25–5, while to find $E_{max}$, use $I_{ZM}$.

**EXAMPLE 25–5**

If the zener of Figure 25–24 is a 1N4736A, $R = 330\ \Omega$ and $R_L = 1.5\ \text{k}\Omega$, what is the permissible range of $E$? Use the ideal model.

**Solution**    From the 1N4736A data sheet, $V_Z = 6.8$ V, $I_{ZK} = 1$ mA and $I_{ZM} = 133$ mA.

| Min | From Equation 25–5: | $I_R = 1$ mA $+$ 6.8 V/1500 $\Omega = 5.53$ mA. |

From Equation 25–6:    $E_{min} = (5.53\ \text{mA})(330\ \Omega) + 6.8\ \text{V} = 8.6$ V

| Max | From Equation 25–5: | $I_R = 133$ mA $+$ 6.8 V/1500 $\Omega = 137.5$ mA. |

From Equation 25–6:    $E_{max} = (137.5\ \text{mA})(330\ \Omega) + 6.8\ \text{V} = 52.2$ V

Thus you must keep $E$ between 8.6 V and 52.2 V.

**PRACTICE PROBLEMS 4**

1. Repeat Example 25–5 using a 1N4744A zener diode.
2. For Example 25–5, what value of $E$ yields $I_Z = I_{ZT}$?

*Answers*
1. 18 V; 38.4 V
2. 20.5 V

### Load Regulation

If $R_L$ becomes too small, the load will draw excessive current and the drop across $R$ will cause $V_Z$ to fall below the knee of the curve—thus, the minimum permitted value of $R_L$ is the value at which $I_Z = I_{ZK}$. Alternatively, if $R_L$ becomes too large, the resulting current diverted through the zener may exceed $I_{ZM}$. These considerations set the range for $R_L$. Problems can be solved using basic principles as in Example 25–6. Simply draw the circuit as it looks for each case, then solve.

If the zener of Figure 25–24 is a 1N4736A, $R = 330\ \Omega$ and $E = 24$ V. Determine the permissible range of $R_L$.

**Solution**   From the data sheet, $V_Z = 6.8$ V, $I_{ZK} = 1$ mA and $I_{ZM} = 133$ mA. Consider Figure 25–25. For all cases, $I_R = \dfrac{E - V_Z}{R} = \dfrac{24\ \text{V} - 6.8\ \text{V}}{330\ \Omega} = 52.12$ mA.

Minimum load resistance is the resistance at which $I_Z = I_{ZK} = 1$ mA as indicated in (a). Here, $I_L = I_R - I_Z = 52.12$ mA – 1 mA = 51.12 mA. Thus $R_{L(min)} = 6.8$ V/51.12 mA = 133 $\Omega$. To determine maximum resistance, note that for this particular problem, zener current will not exceed $I_{ZM}$ no matter how large $R_L$ is. To verify, assume an open circuit as in (b). Zener current is

$$I_Z = \frac{24\ \text{V} - 6.8\ \text{V}}{330\ \Omega} = 52.12\ \text{mA},\ \text{which is well below the maximum permit-}$$

ted $I_{ZM}$ of 133 mA.

**EXAMPLE 25–6**

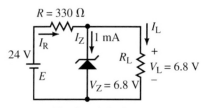

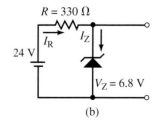

(a) Circuit as it looks for minimum $R_L$

(b)

**FIGURE 25–25**

1. Repeat Example 25–6 using $E = 28$ V, $R = 120\ \Omega$ and a 1N4742A zener diode.

*Answers*
Min $R_L = 90.2\ \Omega$, Max $R_L = 209\ \Omega$

PRACTICE PROBLEMS 5

In practice, line variations and load variations may occur simultaneously. There are several end of chapter problems to help you understand this case.

## Other Zener Applications

Zener diodes may also be used as *limiters* (also called *clippers*), Figure 25–26. (The job of a limiter is to limit the amplitude of a waveform.) During the positive half cycle of circuit (a), as long as the input voltage is below $V_Z$, zener current is extremely small, the drop across $R$ is negligible and $v_o \approx e_{in}$. However, when $e_{in}$ exceeds the zener voltage, the zener conducts and output voltage *clamps* at $V_Z$. During the negative half cycle, the zener is forward-biased and functions as a normal diode Thus, the output voltage will be approximately $-0.7$ V. Now consider circuit (b). Since the zener diode is reversed, it is forward-biased during the positive half cycle, and the output waveform is as shown.

**PRACTICAL NOTES . . .**

While the simple zener regulator described here is adequate for some applications (it is cheap and simple), such regulator circuits are not widely used anymore, as more efficient schemes are available. Some of these are described in Chapter 29.

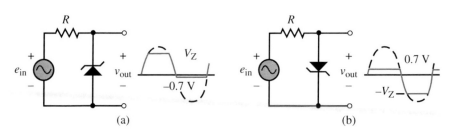

(a)                    (b)

**FIGURE 25–26**

You can also place two zener diodes back-to-back to get clipping on both polarities as shown in Figure 25–27. This scheme is used to protect electronic equipment against transient voltage spikes. As indicated in (b), line voltage spikes larger than the zener voltage are clipped. Special diodes called *transient suppressors* are made for this purpose. They differ from standard zeners in their surge power handling capability—transient suppressors with over a kilowatt of short duration (a fraction of a cycle) surge power handling capability are available.

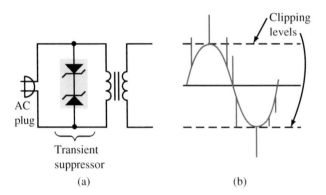

**FIGURE 25–27**   Using a transient suppresor to limit line voltage spikes.

## 25.6 The Varactor Diode

Another special-purpose diode is the **varactor** (also called *varicap, epicap,* or **tuning**) diode. It is, in essence, a voltage variable capacitor that takes advantage of the capacitance inherent in a reverse-biased *p-n* junction. This capacitance, as you saw in Chapter 24, varies with voltage—increasing the voltage across the junction lowers the capacitance and vice versa. Because their capacitance can be varied by means of bias voltages, varactors are used in electronically tuned systems, for example in TV receivers. Typical varactor characteristics are shown in Figure 25–28. Varactors are commercially available with capacitances (denoted $C_T$) that range from about 5 pF to 100 pF.

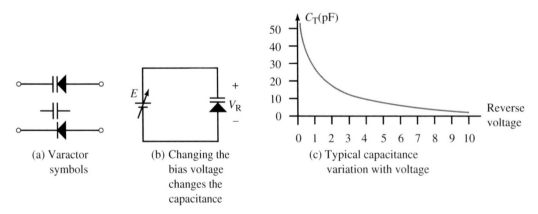

(a) Varactor symbols

(b) Changing the bias voltage changes the capacitance

(c) Typical capacitance variation with voltage

**FIGURE 25–28**   The varactor diode is operated in its reverse-biased mode.

### Varactor Specifications

Figure 25–29 shows a data sheet. The device illustrated is intended for tuning applications and general frequency control. Let us look at some of the data sheet values.

**Capacitance $C_T$**   Nominal capacitance is 29 pF at $V_R = 3$ V. However, because of tolerance, the actual value may fall anywhere between 26 pF and 32 pF. Note the variation of $C_T$ with voltage; at 3 V, $C_T = 29$ pF, but at 10 V, $C_T = 10$ pF. (The diagram looks different than Figure 25–28(c) since a semi-log scale is used here.)

**ON Semiconductor** ™

# Silicon Epicap Diodes

Designed for general frequency control and tuning applications; providing solid–state reliability in replacement of mechanical tuning methods.

- High Q with Guaranteed Minimum Values at VHF Frequencies
- Controlled and Uniform Tuning Ratio
- Available in Surface Mount Package

**MAXIMUM RATINGS**

| Rating | Symbol | MBV109T1 | MMBV109LT1 | MV209 | Unit |
|---|---|---|---|---|---|
| Reverse Voltage | $V_R$ | | 30 | | Vdc |
| Forward Current | $I_F$ | | 200 | | mAdc |
| Forward Power Dissipation<br>@ $T_A$ = 25°C<br>Derate above 25°C | $P_D$ | 280<br>2.8 | 200<br>2.0 | 200<br>1.6 | mW<br>mW/°C |
| Junction Temperature | $T_J$ | | +125 | | °C |
| Storage Temperature Range | $T_{stg}$ | | −55 to +150 | | °C |

**DEVICE MARKING**

MBV109T1 = J4A, MMBV109LT1 = M4A, MV209 = MV209

**ELECTRICAL CHARACTERISTICS** ($T_A$ = 25°C unless otherwise noted.)

| Characteristic | Symbol | Min | Typ | Max | Unit |
|---|---|---|---|---|---|
| Reverse Breakdown Voltage ($I_R$ = 10 µAdc) | $V_{(BR)R}$ | 30 | — | — | Vdc |
| Reverse Voltage Leakage Current ($V_R$ = 25 Vdc) | $I_R$ | — | — | 0.1 | µAdc |
| Diode Capacitance Temperature Coefficient ($V_R$ = 3.0 Vdc, f = 1.0 MHz) | $TC_C$ | — | 300 | — | ppm/°C |

| | $C_t$, Diode Capacitance $V_R$ = 3.0 Vdc, f = 1.0 MHz pF | | | Q, Figure of Merit $V_R$ = 3.0 Vdc f = 50 MHz | $C_R$, Capacitance Ratio $C_3/C_{25}$ f = 1.0 MHz (Note 1) | |
|---|---|---|---|---|---|---|
| Device | Min | Nom | Max | Min | Min | Max |
| MBV109T1,<br>MMBV109LT1,<br>MV209 | 26 | 29 | 32 | 200 | 5.0 | 6.5 |

1. $C_R$ is the ratio of $C_t$ measured at 3 Vdc divided by $C_t$ measured at 25 Vdc.

**MMBV109LT1** is also available in bulk packaging. Use **MMBV109L** as the device title to order this device in bulk.

---

**MBV109T1**
**MMBV109LT1** *
**MV209** *

\* ON Semiconductor Preferred Devices

---

26–32 pF
**VOLTAGE VARIABLE**
**CAPACITANCE DIODES**

---

CASE 419–04, STYLE 3
SC–70/SOT–323

CASE 318–08, STYLE 6
SOT–23 (TO–236AB)

CASE 182–06, STYLE 1
TO–92 (TO–226AC)

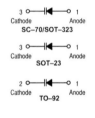

3 ○——▷|◁——○ 1
Cathode         Anode
SC–70/SOT–323

3 ○——▷|◁——○ 1
Cathode         Anode
SOT–23

2 ○——▷|◁——○ 1
Cathode    TO–92    Anode

---

© Semiconductor Components Industries, LLC, 2001
**March, 2001 – Rev. 1**                                    1                              Publication Order Number:
**MBV109T1/D**

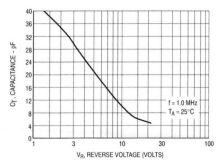

**Figure 1. DIODE CAPACITANCE**

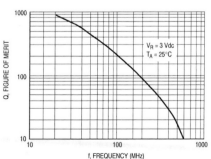

**Figure 2. FIGURE OF MERIT**

**FIGURE 25–29**  Data sheet. *(Courtesy of ON Semiconductor)*

**Figure of Merit (Q)**   An important consideration in tuned circuits is $Q$. To have a sharp tuning characteristic, you need a large $Q$. For this device, at $V_R = 3$ V and $f = 50$ MHz, $Q$ has a minimum value of 200, which is comfortably high. However, $Q$ is frequency dependent, and falls as frequency goes up.

**Capacitance Ratio $C_R$**   The capacitance ratio (also called the *tuning ratio*) tells you by what factor $C_T$ changes over its range. For example, the ratio $C_3/C_{25}$ is the ratio of capacitance at 3 V to capacitance at 25 V. Thus, if, $C_3/C_{25} = 6$, the capacitance at 3 V is 6 times the capacitance at 25 V. For this particular device, $C_R$ lies somewhere between 5.0 and 6.5. The larger the ratio, the more $C_T$ changes with voltage, thus, the coarser is its tuning.

**Capacitance Temperature Coefficient**   The capacitance temperature coefficient (300 ppm/°C) tells you that capacitance changes by 300 millionth of its normal value per °C change. Thus, if $C_T = 29$ pF then $C$ changes by $\Delta C = (300 \times 10^{-6})(29 \text{ pF}) = 0.0087$ pF/°C. Since $C_T = 29$ pF at 25° C, it will equal $C_T = 29$ pF $+ (0.0087)(100° \text{ C} - 25° \text{ C}) = 29.7$ pF at 100° C. Thus, $C_T$ is relatively insensitive to temperature.

For the varactor diode of Figure 25–29, at what temperature will nominal $C_T$ equal 30 pF?

*Answer*
$\approx 140°$ C

## A Varactor Tuning Application

As you saw in Chapter 21, the resonant frequency of a tank circuit may be controlled by means of a variable capacitor as illustrated in Figure 25–30(a). An alternate scheme using a varactor is shown in (b). By varying the potentiometer, you vary the bias voltage and thus the capacitance of the varactor. (Capacitor $C_B$ is not part of the frequency determining circuitry. It is a blocking capacitor whose purpose is to prevent a dc path from the potentiometer wiper arm to ground through the inductor. $C_B$ must be chosen to have negligible impedance to *ac* at the frequency of operation.) The control voltage must be very clean (i.e., free from voltage spikes or other disturbances) to prevent erratic changes in tuning. Because you can adjust the varactor's capacitance by means of its bias voltage, you can also create automatic tuning circuits as depicted symbolically in (c). In this scheme, the tuning voltage is developed electronically from elsewhere in the circuit. This is a commonly used scheme.

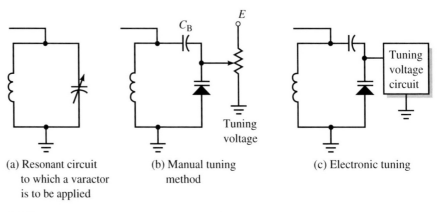

(a) Resonant circuit to which a varactor is to be applied

(b) Manual tuning method

(c) Electronic tuning

**FIGURE 25–30**   Using a varactor in a tuning circuit.

1. Using the second diode approximation, determine currents $I_D$ and $I_T$ (Figure 25–31).

2. A circuit consists of a source $E$, a 2-k$\Omega$ resistor and a forward biased diode with the characteristic of Figure 25–9. At what value of $E$ will $I_D = 8$ mA?

3. A diode has the curve of Figure 25–13. How much current can this diode handle at 50° C? At 100° C?

4. Assuming nominal ratings for the 1N4737A zener, at what current does $V_z = 7.5$ V? At what current does $V_z = 7.54$ V?

5. Using a diode from Figure 25–19, you have designed a circuit where $P_z$ does not exceed 750 mW. What is the maximum temperature at which you can operate this circuit?

6. You want to change the load voltage of Figure 25–18 to 18 V. What diode from Figure 25–19 should you choose? If $E = 30$ V and $R = 68$ $\Omega$, over what range of load current can your circuit operate, assuming the ideal model?

7. For Question 6, if the load current is 50 mA, what is the permissible range of input voltage variation?

IN-PROCESS
LEARNING CHECK 1

*(Answers are at the end of the chapter.)*

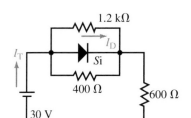

**FIGURE 25–31**

An important application of diodes is in power supply circuits. Here, they are used to convert ac to dc through a process called **rectification.** Following rectification, the dc voltage is filtered, then regulated to produce a constant voltage that is used to power electronic equipment such as computers, DVD players, and so on.

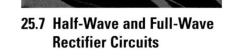

## 25.7 Half-Wave and Full-Wave Rectifier Circuits

### Half-Wave Rectification

To begin, consider **half-wave rectification** in Figure 25–32. During the positive half-cycle the diode is forward-biased and conducts, but during the negative half cycle it is reverse-biased and does not. The result is a pulsating waveform (b) whose peak value $V_m$ is one diode drop below the peak of the applied voltage. The average value (also called the dc value) of the rectified waveform is (as you learned in Chapter 15),

$$V_{dc} = \frac{V_m}{\pi} = 0.318\ V_m \qquad (25\text{–}7)$$

For current,

$$I_{dc} = \frac{I_m}{\pi} = 0.318\ I_m \qquad (25\text{–}8)$$

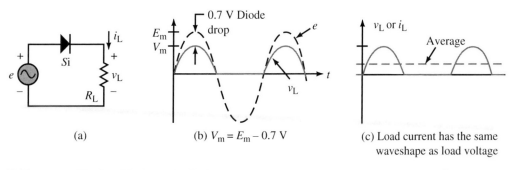

(a)

(b) $V_m = E_m - 0.7$ V

(c) Load current has the same waveshape as load voltage

**FIGURE 25–32**   Half-wave rectification. Maximum load voltage is one diode drop below maximum source voltage.

**Required PIV**

In practice, you need a diode that can withstand the maximum reverse voltage to which it is subjected. To determine this voltage, note that during the negative half cycle, current is zero and thus, the voltage across $R_L$ is zero. Since there is no drop across $R_L$, full source voltage appears across the diode. You must therefore choose a diode with a PIV that can safely withstand $E_m$ volts. To be on the safe side, allow a safety margin—see Practical Note 4, Section 25.3.

**EXAMPLE 25–7**

Determine the average load voltage and current and the peak voltage seen by the diode (Figure 25–33).

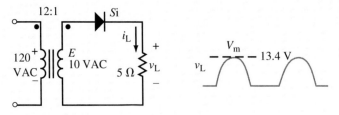

**FIGURE 25–33**

**Solution**    The 10 V rms secondary has a peak value of $E_m = \sqrt{2} \times 10\ V = 14.1\ V$. Subtracting one diode drop yields $V_m = 14.1 - 0.7 = 13.4\ V$. From Ohm's law, $I_m = 13.4\ V/5\ \Omega = 2.68\ A$. From Equations 25–7 and 25–8, $V_{dc} = 0.318\ (13.4\ V) = 4.26\ V$ and $I_{dc} = 0.318(2.68\ A) = 0.852\ A$. The peak reverse voltage seen by the diode is $E_m = 14.1\ V$.

---

**PRACTICE PROBLEMS 7**

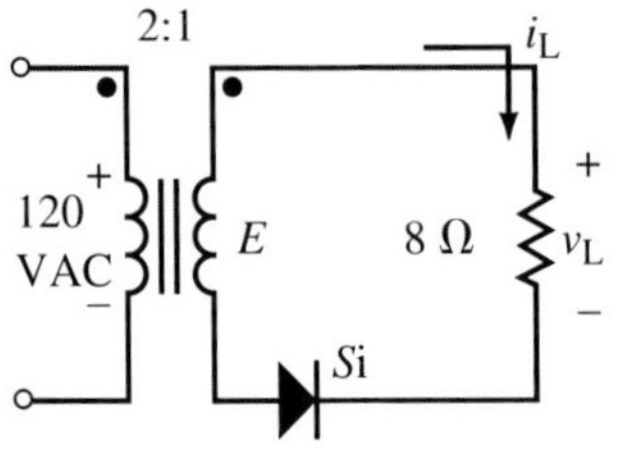

**FIGURE 25–34**

For Figure 25–34, determine $V_{dc}$, $I_{dc}$ and the minimum required PIV for the diode. Sketch the load voltage waveform.

*Answers*
$-26.8\ V$,  $-3.35\ A$,  $84.9\ V$        Same shape as Figure 25–33 except inverted.

**Full-Wave Rectification**

Usually **full-wave rectification** is used instead of half-wave rectification because it provides a smoother dc output with twice the average voltage and current. There are two basic schemes, the center-tapped transformer type and the bridge type.

**Center-Tapped Transformer Type Rectifier**

Two diodes are needed as in Figure 25–35. During the positive half-cycle (a), transformer polarities are as shown and diode $D_1$ conducts while $D_2$ (which is reverse-biased) does not. During the negative half cycle (b), the situation is reversed and diode $D_2$ conducts—thus, load current is in the same direction for both half cycles. Since there is only one diode in the conduction path for each case, the peak value of the rectified waveform $V_m$ is one diode drop below the peak of the applied waveform. Average (dc) values for these waveforms are

$$V_{dc} = \frac{2V_m}{\pi} = 0.637\ V_m \qquad (25\text{--}9)$$

and

$$I_{dc} = \frac{2I_m}{\pi} = 0.637\, I_m \qquad \textbf{(25–10)}$$

To find the maximum reverse voltage that the off diode is subjected to, write KVL around the transformer secondary/$D_1$/$D_2$ loop. After some rearranging, this yields

$$\text{PIV}_{required} = 2\,E_m - 0.7\text{ V} \approx 2\,E_m \qquad \textbf{(25–11)}$$

◀ MULTISIM

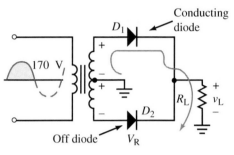

(a) Positive half-cycle

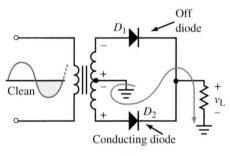

(b) Negative half-cycle

**FIGURE 25–35**    Full-wave rectification.

**EXAMPLE 25–8**

Assume the transformer of Figure 25–35 has a ratio of 5 and that a peak primary voltage of 170 V is applied. Draw the transformer secondary and load voltage waveforms and find the average load voltage and the peak reverse voltage seen by the diodes.

**Solution**    Peak secondary voltage is 170 V/5 = 34 V, yielding $E_m$ = 17 V on each side of the center tap. Subtracting a diode drop of 0.7 V yields $V_m = E_m - 0.7$ V = 16.3 V. Waveforms are shown in Figure 25–36. Average load voltage is $V_{dc} = 0.637\,(16.3\text{ V}) = 10.4$ V and peak inverse voltage seen by the diodes (Equation 25–11) is $2 \times 17 - 0.7 = 33.3$ V.

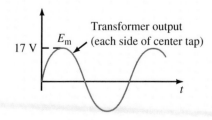
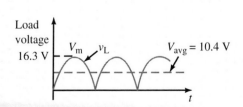

**FIGURE 25–36**

For Example 25–8, assume $R_L = 25\ \Omega$. Sketch the current waveform and determine $I_m$ and $I_{dc}$.

*Answer*
The waveform looks like $v_L$ in Figure 25–36, 652 mA, 415 mA

### Full-Wave Bridge Rectifier

This configuration, shown in Figure 25–37, does not need a center-tapped transformer. Operation is depicted in Figure 25–38. (The transformer has been replaced by an equivalent voltage source for simplicity.) With input polarity as in (a), forward-biased diodes $D_2$ and $D_3$ conduct, while reverse-biased diodes $D_1$ and $D_4$ do not. This yields the current path indicated. When the polarity is reversed, diodes $D_4$ and $D_1$ conduct, yielding the path shown in (b). In both cases, current through $R_L$ is in the same direction, resulting in the familiar waveform of (c). Since there are two diodes in each conduction path, $V_m$ is two diode drops below the applied voltage $E_m$. The required peak inverse voltage (see end of chapter Problem 30) is

$$\text{PIV}_{required} \approx E_m \qquad\qquad (25\text{–}12)$$

(a) A typical bridge rectifier. All 4 diodes are encapsulated in a single package, and only 4 leads are brought out.

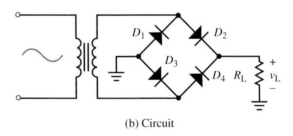

(b) Circuit

**FIGURE 25–37**   Bridge rectifier. Either a bridge as in (a) or 4 individual diodes may be used.

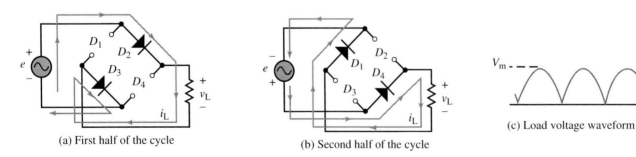

(a) First half of the cycle

(b) Second half of the cycle

(c) Load voltage waveform

**FIGURE 25–38**   Since there are two diode drops in each path, $V_m = E_m - 1.4$ V.

PRACTICE PROBLEMS 9

For Figure 25–37 supply voltage is 120 V (rms), the transformer ratio is 8 and $R_L = 12\ \Omega$. Determine average load voltage and current.

*Answers*
12.6 V;  1.05 A

## 25.8 Power Supply Filtering

Waveforms produced by rectification are unsuited for most applications and must be *filtered*. The simplest filter consists of a large value capacitor placed across the load. Consider Figure 25–39. Assume that the capacitor is initially uncharged (and thus looks like a short). During the first quarter cycle (a), the diode is forward-biased and the capacitor charges to $V_m$ volts. As the input voltage passes its peak and drops below that of the charged capacitor, the diode becomes reverse-biased and looks like an open circuit as in (b). The capacitor, which is now isolated from the supply, discharges through the load until the input voltage is again high enough to forward-bias the diode. If you make $C$ large enough so that the time constant $R_L C$ is considerably larger than the period of the waveform, the capacitor will not discharge appreciably between charging intervals. The final steady-state waveform is shown in (c). Since $C$ charges through the small resistance of the diode circuit, but discharges through the much larger resistance of the load, the charging interval is much shorter than the discharging interval. A similar analysis for the full-wave case yields Figure 25–40.

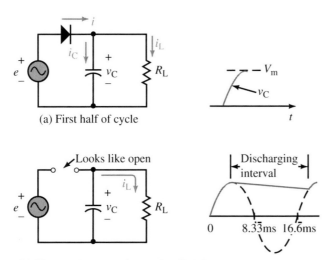

(a) First half of cycle

(b) Since $v_C$ is greater than $e$, the diode is reverse-biased.
The capacitor discharges through $R_L$ until $e$ again exceeds $v_C$.

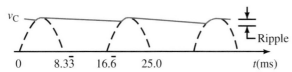

(c) Steady-state capacitor voltage. Times shown are for
a 60 Hz input.

**FIGURE 25–39**  Evolving the capacitor-filtered waveform, half-wave case. Source = 60 Hz.

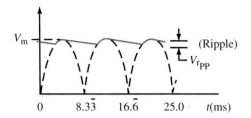

**FIGURE 25–40** Steady state waveform for full-wave, 60 Hz case.

The small variation in output voltage is termed **ripple.** The size of the capacitor (for a given load) determines the size of this ripple. Ripple may be expressed as peak-to-peak volts or as rms volts. We will start with peak-to-peak.

**Analysis of Filter Circuits**

We will follow the usual practice of using an approximate analysis for filter circuits (since it is considerably simpler than a rigorous analysis and yields good results for small to moderate ripple). Let us begin with the full-wave case. First, note that $v_C = \dfrac{q}{C}$. Differentiating both sides yields $\dfrac{dv_C}{dt} = \dfrac{1}{C}\dfrac{dq}{dt}$. Now approximate the waveform of Figure 25–40 by straight lines as shown in Figure 25–41. For this waveform, we can write the above equation as $\dfrac{\Delta v_C}{\Delta t} = \dfrac{1}{C}\dfrac{\Delta q}{\Delta t}$. From Figure 25–41, we see that $\Delta v_C = -V_{r_{pp}}$ (since the slope of $v_C$ is negative during discharge) and $\Delta t = T_2 \approx T$ (since $T_1 << T_2$). Furthermore, $\Delta q/\Delta t$ is the average capacitor discharge current $I_C$. Thus, $\dfrac{\Delta v_C}{\Delta t} = \dfrac{1}{C}\dfrac{\Delta q}{\Delta t}$ reduces to $\dfrac{-V_{r_{pp}}}{T} = \dfrac{I_C}{C}$. From Figure 25–42, we see that load current is the negative of the capacitor current—that is, $I_C = -I_L$. However, average load current is just its dc value—that is, $I_L = I_{dc}$. Substituting and canceling the minus signs yields $\dfrac{V_{r_{pp}}}{T} = \dfrac{I_{dc}}{C}$. Finally,

$$V_{r_{pp}} = \frac{I_{dc}T}{C} \tag{25–13}$$

or

$$V_{r_{pp}} = \frac{V_{dc}T}{R_L C} \tag{25–14}$$

since $I_{dc} = V_{dc}/R_L$. For light loads, you can use $I_m$ instead of $I_{dc}$ in Equation 25–13 with negligible error where $I_m = V_m/R_L$.

DC load voltage is the average of capacitor voltage $v_C$. As indicated in Figure 25–41 the average lies half way between the min and max of the ripple. Thus,

$$V_{dc} = V_m - \frac{V_{r_{pp}}}{2} \tag{25–15}$$

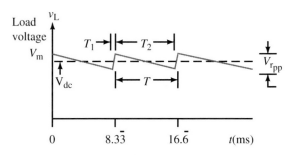

**FIGURE 25–41**  Approximating the filtered waveform. $V_{dc}$ (the average value of the waveform) lies half way between the min and max of the ripple.

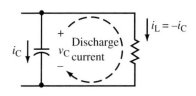

**FIGURE 25–42**  Discharge interval. From this, we can deduce that $I_L = -I_C$.

While Equations 25–13 and 25–14 permit you to determine ripple from load conditions, you sometimes need ripple in terms of input voltage. Combining Equations 25–14 and 25–15 yields

$$V_{r_{pp}} = \frac{V_{dc}T}{R_L C} = \left( V_m - \frac{V_{r_{pp}}}{2} \right)\left( \frac{T}{R_L C} \right)$$

Solving for ripple we get,

$$V_{r_{pp}} = \frac{2V_m}{1 + \dfrac{2R_L C}{T}} \qquad\qquad (25\text{–}16)$$

You can also combine Equations 25–15 and 25–16 (see end of chapter Problem 32) to get

$$V_{dc} = \frac{V_m}{1 + \dfrac{T}{2R_L C}} \qquad\qquad (25\text{–}17)$$

Note that all equations developed above apply to both full-wave and half-wave rectification by appropriate choice of $T$—see Notes.

**NOTES . . .**

1. For the half-wave case, $T$ is the period of the supply voltage waveform and is thus equal to $1/f$. However, for the full-wave case (since the rectified waveform consists of two half sine waves), $T$ is half the period of the supply voltage waveform. Thus, when using these equations at 60 Hz, set $T = 16.66$ ms for the half-wave case and $T = 8.33$ ms for the full-wave case.

2. Various authors use various approximate approaches to filter analysis. However, they ultimately all come down to the same thing. To illustrate, consider dc load voltage Equation 25–17. Noting that $\dfrac{1}{1 + x} \approx 1 - x$ for small $x$, we see that $V_{dc} = \dfrac{V_m}{1 + \dfrac{T}{2R_L C}} \approx V_m(1 - \dfrac{T}{2R_L C})$, which is the equation (or some variation of it) that you sometimes encounter in other works.

**EXAMPLE 25–9**

If $C = 330$ μF, what are the dc load voltage and load current for the circuit of Figure 25–43.

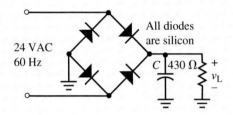

24 VAC
60 Hz

All diodes are silicon

$C$ 430 Ω

$+$
$v_L$
$-$

**FIGURE 25–43**

**Solution**  Peak input voltage is $\sqrt{2}(24) = 33.94$ V. Subtracting two diode drops yields $V_m = 32.54$ V. From Equation 25–16 (using $T = 8.33$ ms since this is full-wave),

$$V_{r_{pp}} = \frac{2(32.54\ V)}{1 + \dfrac{2(430\Omega)(330\mu F)}{8.33\ ms}} = 1.86\ V$$

Load voltage (from Equation 25–15) is

$$V_{dc} = 32.54 - \frac{1.86}{2} = 31.6\ V$$

Load current is

$$I_{dc} = \frac{V_{dc}}{R_L} = \frac{31.6\ V}{430\ \Omega} = 73.5\ mA$$

Since there are a number of approximations in the above equations, just how good are they? Table 25–1 compares the results of Example 25–9 to computer solutions plus a more rigorous analysis (see end of chapter problem 42). Note that agreement is quite good. In fact, other sources contribute more uncertainty in practice than these approximations do. For example, filter capacitors typically have tolerances of ±20%.

**TABLE 25–1**

|  | Approximate Solution | "Exact" Solution | PSpice | MultiSIM |
|---|---|---|---|---|
| $V_{r_{pp}}$ | 1.86 V | 1.67 V | 1.60 V | 1.79 V |
| $V_{dc}$ | 31.6 V | 31.7 V | 31.7 V | 31.8 V |
| $I_{dc}$ | 73.5 mA | 73.7 mA | 73.7 mA | 74.0 mA |

PRACTICE PROBLEMS 10

1. For Figure 25–43, determine the minimum value for $C$ if $V_{r_{pp}}$ is to be no more than 1.2 V.

2. For Figure 25–39, $e = 18 \sin 377\ t$ volts, $C = 1000$ μF, and $R_L = 680\ \Omega$. Determine ripple, $V_{dc}$ and $I_{dc}$.

3. Consider Example 25–9. Assuming light loading, use Equations 25–13 and 25–15 to compute ripple and load voltage $V_{dc}$. Compare your answers to those obtained in Example 25–9.

4. Show that $V_{dc} = V_m - \dfrac{4.17I_{dc}}{C}$ for full-wave by combining Equations 25–13

and 25–15 with $f = 60$ Hz and $I_{dc}$ expressed in mA and $C$ in μF.

*Answers*
1. 516 μF; 2. 0.419 V, 17.1 V, 25.1 mA; 3. 1.91 V, 31.6 V

## Ripple Factor

**Ripple** is sometimes expressed in rms volts or as a ripple factor. Consider again Figure 25–41. Load voltage is approximately a triangular wave with a dc off-set. Using the techniques of Chapter 15, it can be shown that the rms value of

the triangular part is $V_{r(rms)} = \dfrac{V_{r_{pp}}}{2\sqrt{3}}$. The rms **ripple factor** is defined as

$$r = \text{ripple factor} = \frac{\text{rms ripple voltage}}{\text{dc voltage}} \qquad \textbf{(25–18)}$$

Combining Equations 25–16, 25–17 and 25–18, yields

$$r = \frac{T}{2\sqrt{3}R_L C} \qquad \textbf{(25–19)}$$

This formula applies to both the full-wave and half-wave cases. However (as usual), ripple for the half-wave case is double that for the full-wave case, since $T$ is twice as large.

If $R_L = 180$ Ω for the circuit of Figure 25–44, determine the minimum capacitance needed if the rms ripple factor is not to exceed 2.5%. Determine load voltage, peak-to-peak ripple and rms ripple.

**EXAMPLE 25–10**

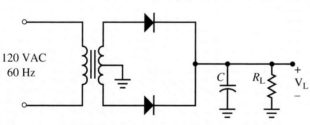

**FIGURE 25–44**        36 VAC, c.t.

**Solution**  From Equation 25–19, $C = \dfrac{T}{2\sqrt{3}rR_L} = \dfrac{8.33 \text{ ms}}{2\sqrt{3}(0.025)(180\Omega)} = 535$ μF

Since the transformer is center-tapped, the peak voltage applied to the diode circuit is $E_m = (\sqrt{2})(18 \text{ V}) = 25.46$ V. Subtracting a diode drop yields $V_m = 25.46 - 0.7 = 24.76$ V. From Equation 25–16 we get

$$V_{r_{pp}} = \frac{2V_m}{1 + \dfrac{2R_L C}{T}} = \frac{2(24.76)}{1 + \dfrac{2(180\Omega)(535 \text{ μF})}{8.33 \text{ ms}}} = 2.06 \text{ V}$$

$$V_{dc} = V_m - \frac{V_{r_{p\text{-}p}}}{2} = 24.76 \text{ V} - \frac{2.06 \text{ V}}{2} = 23.7 \text{ V}$$

RMS ripple is 2.5% of $V_{dc}$. Thus, rms ripple $= (0.025)(23.7 \text{ V}) = 0.59$ V.

---

PRACTICAL NOTES . . .

1. As you can see from Example 25–10, ripple expressed in volts rms is considerably smaller than ripple expressed in volts peak-to-peak. Knowing this is important when you purchase a power supply. When looking at specs, be consistent—that is, compare rms ripple to rms ripple or peak-to-peak ripple to peak-to-peak ripple.

2. When choosing a filter capacitor, there are two competing requirements, keeping the ripple voltage low versus keeping the charging current spikes (considered next) from getting too large. The problem is that for low ripple, you need large filter capacitors, but large capacitors result in large spikes. Thus, a compromise may be needed. In practice, filter capacitors typically range in size from a few hundred μF to a few thousand μF.

---

### Diode Forward Current

Diode conduction occurs only for a brief interval each cycle (during the time that the output voltage decays below the voltage input to the rectifier), resulting in a stream of current pulses as illustrated in Figure 25–45(a). This current is called **diode repetitive forward current.**

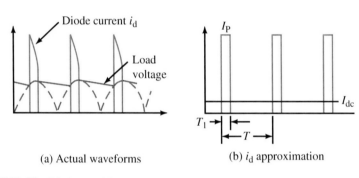

(a) Actual waveforms      (b) $i_d$ approximation

**FIGURE 25–45** Diode repetitive surge currents.

It is customary to approximate this current as a series of rectangular pulses as in (b). To estimate $I_p$, note that during charging, diode current must replenish the charge transferred from the capacitor to the load during discharging. But charge is equal to the area under the current curve (since $q = \int i_c \, dt$). Noting that $I_p \gg I_{dc}$, we see $Q_{charge} \approx I_p \times T_1$, while $Q_{Load} \approx I_{dc} \times T$. Thus, $I_p \times T_1 \approx I_{dc} \times T$. Solving for $I_p$ yields,

$$I_p \approx I_{dc} \frac{T}{T_1} \tag{25–20}$$

From this, you can see that since $T_1 \ll T$, the diode is subjected to quite severe current spikes that are many times larger than the average load current, and that the shorter the charging interval, the larger will be these spikes. Many rectifier data sheets list the maximum permitted value for peak repetitive forward current as $I_{FRM}$ (although unfortunately, the 1N400X family does not show it).

### Effect of Filter on PIV

A filter capacitor doubles the diode PIV requirement for the half-wave circuit, but has no effect on the full-wave circuits. To illustrate, consider the half-wave case (Figures 25–39(b)). Capacitor voltage decays only slightly, so that $v_C \approx E_m$ when the source reaches its peak negative value of $-E_m$ volts. If you write KVL around the source/diode/capacitor loop at this instant of time, you find the voltage across the reverse-biased diode is approximately $2\,E_m$. Thus, you need a minimum PIV of 2 $E_m$ here compared to $E_m$ with no capacitor. A similar analysis for the full-wave case shows that the maximum reverse voltage is approximately $E_m$, the same as without the capacitor as we found in Equation 25–12.

**Looking Ahead**

The power supplies that we have described here are *unregulated supplies*—i.e., supplies whose output voltages vary if the input voltage or the load current varies. However, most power supplies used today are *regulated supplies.* In these, the unregulated dc output that we have described is fed to a regulator whose job it is to hold the output voltage constant. The simplest regulator is a zener diode, Figure 25–46. For some applications, it is adequate. Zener regulators are inefficient, however, because they waste a lot of power, and a more efficient scheme is considered in Chapter 29.

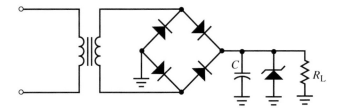

**FIGURE 25–46** Simple regulated supply.

MultiSIM and PSpice may be used to study filter waveforms. Since the only time domain analysis they provide is a transient analysis, and since we are interested only in steady state analysis, we need some way to force the transient component of the solution to zero so that we arrive at the steady state immediately. We can do this by appropriately choosing the capacitor initial condition—see Operational Notes 4 and 5. Let us illustrate using Example 25–9.

## 25.9 Computer Analysis

**Operational Notes for PSpice and MultiSIM**

1. Rotate $C$ (3 times for PSpice, once for MultiSIM) so that its "1" end is up as described in Appendix A. (This is critical for setting initial conditions.) For PSpice, rotate $R$ three times as well.

2. Since our objective here is to study capacitive filtering, we have simplified the circuits by replacing the transformers with equivalent voltage sources.

3. To permit comparison of the various solutions and, hence, to verify how good the approximate answers are, you need $V_m$ to be the same for all cases. (For the computer solutions, suitable values for $E_m$ had to be determined experimentally to achieve this since PSpice and MultiSIM use different values for diode-forward drops.)

4. To eliminate the transient part of the solution, set the initial condition on the capacitor equal to the voltage it would have in steady state at $t = 0$. From Figure 25–39, you can see that this is approximately $V_{dc}$. Thus, set $V_0 \approx V_{dc}$. (If you don't know $V_{dc}$, set $V_0$ to about 10% below $V_m$. For PSpice, don't set $V_0$ too high since it seems to fail if you set $V_0$ higher than its actual initial voltage.)

5. If some transient is still evident, make a closer estimate of $V_0$ from the plot then run the simulation again. Alternatively, if the first few ripples have some transient on them, step past it to where the waveform has stabilized then measure with your cursor.

## MultiSIM

Bridge rectifiers are found in the bin marked by the diode icon. Select the MDA 2501, then build Figure 25–47(a) on the screen. Use a virtual capacitor so that you can easily set $V_0$. Double click $C$ and set the Initial Condition to 31.5 V (the dc value that we determined earlier). Set the source to 60 Hz with Voltage RMS set to 24.

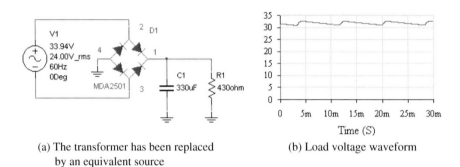

(a) The transformer has been replaced   (b) Load voltage waveform
   by an equivalent source

**FIGURE 25–47**   Waveform analysis using MultiSIM.

Next,

- Click _Options/Preferences/Show Node Names_ to display node numbers. Determine the node number for the top end of the capacitor.

- Select the Analysis icon, choose Transient Analysis and in the dialog box under _Initial Conditions,_ select _User Defined._ Increase the _Minimum Number of Time Points_ to at least 1000 (to get a smooth plot). Set the transient run time (TSTOP) to 0.030. Click the _Output Variable_ tab and specify the node number determined in the previous step.

- Click _Simulate._ When analysis is complete, the waveform of (b) should appear.

- Use the cursors to determine min and max voltages and hence, ripple.

- To find $V_{dc}$, connect a dc voltmeter (from the _Indicators_ tool bin) across $R_L$. Click the simulation switch to _ON_ to run the simulation. Read the meter when it stabilizes.

Results are summarized in Table 25–1. As noted earlier, these reaffirm our contention that the approximate analysis yields quite good results.

## PSpice

- Build the circuit on the screen as in Figure 25–48(a) using 1N4002 diodes and source VSIN.

- Double click the capacitor and set its initial voltage (IC) to 31.4 V. (When you run the simulation, if you get a dialog box that says "There are no data in section number 1", you have probably set IC too high. Try lowering it and run the simulation again.)

- Double click the source and set VAMPL to 34.1V (see Note 3), FREQ to 60 Hz and VOFF to 0.

- Click the _New Simulation Profile_ icon and select _Time Domain (Transient)_ analysis. Set _Run to time_ to 30ms.

- Click the _Run_ icon. You should get the voltage waveform shown in green (Figure 25–48(b)). (Your voltage scale may be different as the axis here has been re-scaled.) Using the cursor, measure the min and max voltage and, from this, compute ripple.

- Add a new Y-axis, then add the diode $D_1$ and $D_2$ current traces. Compare to Figure 25–45(a).

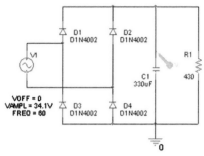

(a) The transformer had been
replaced by an equivalent source

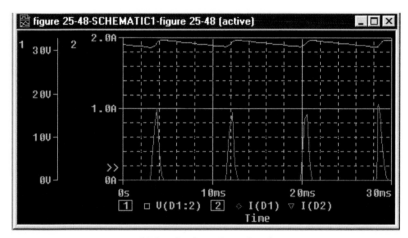

(b) Load voltage (green) and
diode current (red)

**FIGURE 25–48**   Waveform analysis using PSpice.

Results are summarized in Table 25–1. As noted earlier, these reaffirm our contention that the approximate analysis yields quite good results.

PRACTICE PROBLEMS 11

Determine $V_{dc}$. Hints: Delete the voltage probe shown. Use a run time of about 120ms. When the empty display graph appears, use *Add Trace* to plot AVG(V1(R1)). PSpice computes and plots a running average of the waveform. However, you need to wait until the waveform stabilizes to determine its average—thus, measure with the cursor after the waveform has stabilized. Repeat for the load current.

*Answer*
About 31.7 V;  73.7 mA

**PUTTING IT INTO PRACTICE**

Some power supplies that you designed have experienced failures after several years of operation. Ultimately, the trouble was traced to inadequate ripple current rating of the filter capacitor. (You remember an experienced designer once telling you, "Ignore capacitor ripple currents at your peril.") Your design required a minimum of 4100 μF and you chose the next highest valued capacitor, which was 4700 μF. A suggested solution to your problem is to use two 2200 μF capacitors in parallel instead of the single 4700 μF unit. To investigate this suggestion, research ripple current ratings for capacitors, including the effects of excessive ripple current. Document your findings. (You will probably have to go to the Internet for this information.)

**PROBLEMS**

### 25.1  Diode Models

1. Assuming ideal diodes Figure 25–49, determine diode currents and voltages.

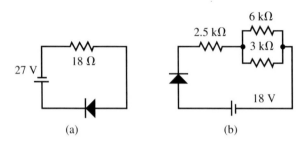

**FIGURE 25–49**

2. The circuit of Figure 25–50(a) has the waveform of (b) applied. Assume an ideal diode and sketch waveform $v_R$. Repeat if the diode is flipped to face the opposite direction.

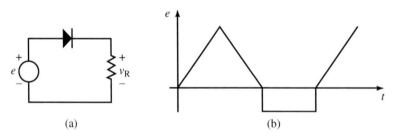

**FIGURE 25–50**

3. You have designed a control circuit with an electronic switch that turns current on and off to an inductor (Figure 25–51). However when the circuit turns the coil current off, a large voltage spike (recall Chapter 14, Section 14.3) occurs that "blows" your circuit. Show how you can connect a diode across the coil to protect your circuit. Sketch the coil voltage before and after adding the diode.

◀ MULTISIM

4. Box 1 of Figure 25–52 contains a rotary switch, while boxes 2 and 3 each contain a lamp. Each box also includes diodes. With the switch in position 1, Lamp 1 alone comes on; in position 2, Lamp 2 alone comes on; in position 3, both lamps come on. Sketch the circuit.

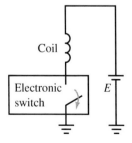

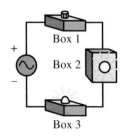

**FIGURE 25–51**

**FIGURE 25–52**  Only a single wire runs from box to box.

5. Using the second approximation, repeat Problem 1 assuming silicon diodes.

6. A second diode (in series with and pointed the same way as the existing diode) is added in Figure 25–49(b). If both are silicon, what is source current?

7. The diodes of Figure 25–53 are silicon. Using the second approximation, find diode currents. Hint: Use Thévenin's theorem.

8. Repeat Problem 7 if the diodes are germanium.

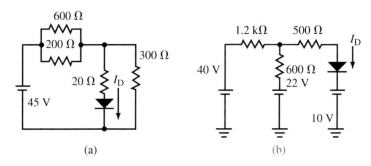

(a)                                    (b)

**FIGURE 25–53**

## 25.2 to 25.4    Diode Characteristic Curve, Data Sheet, Etc.

9. The diode of Figure 25–54 has the characteristic of Figure 25–9. If circuit current is 12 mA, what is $V_D$? What is $E$?

10. Repeat Problem 9 if circuit current is 4 mA.

11. For the circuit of Figure 25–55, average load current is 400 mA. You have a choice of a 1N4001 or a 1N4004. Which would you choose and why?

**FIGURE 25–54**                        **FIGURE 25–55**

12. If you use a 1N4004 in Figure 25–55 and you want a safety margin of 20%, what is the maximum rms value sine wave that you can apply?

13. A 1 amp diode can deliver 1 A up to 75° C, but must be derated by 8.5 mA/° C above that. How much current can you draw at 110° C?

14. A circuit containing a diode with the derating curve of Figure 25–13 draws 0.6 A. What is the maximum ambient temperature in which you can operate the circuit?

15. A diode has a barrier potential of $V_B = 0.73$ V at 25° C. At approximately what temperature will $V_B$ equal 0.76 V?

16. A diode has a reverse current of 420 nA at 45° C. What will be its reverse current at 25° C?

17. A diode has a reverse current of 125 nA at 25° C. At what temperature will it be 1 μA?

## 25.5    The Zener Diode

18. Over what range of current $I_Z$ will the 1N4744A regulate? What is its maximum power rating at 40° C? At 60° C?

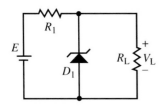

**FIGURE 25–56**

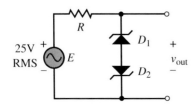

**FIGURE 25–57**

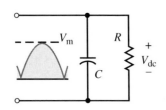

**FIGURE 25–58**    For all problems except #34, assume full-wave input.

19. If the diode in Figure 25–56 is a 1N4746A, $E = 24$ V, $R_1 = 82\ \Omega$ and $R_L = 600\ \Omega$, use the ideal model to determine $I_Z$, $P_D$ and load current $I_L$.

20. For Figure 25–56, $E = 30$ V, $R_1 = 150\ \Omega$, load current is 37.5 mA and the zener is 1N4746A. Use the ideal model and determine $I_Z$ and $P_D$.

21. Using the component values of Problem 20 and the ideal model, determine the acceptable range for $E$.

22. For Figure 25–56, $E = 20$ V, $R_1 = 91\ \Omega$ and the zener is 1N4742A. Using the ideal model, determine the range of load resistance that this circuit can handle while keeping operation within the limits specified by the data sheet.

23. For Figure 25–56, both load current and source voltage vary. If $R_1 = 120\ \Omega$, the zener is an ideal 1N4740A and load current varies from 20 mA to 50 mA, what are the min and max $E$?

24. For Figure 25–56, if $R_1 = 120\ \Omega$, the zener is an ideal 1N4740A and $R_L$ varies from 150 to 800 $\Omega$, what is the min and max $E$?

25. For the 1N4744A, what is $V_Z$ at $I_Z = 17$ mA? Using the model of Figure 25–22(c), determine zener voltage at $I_Z = 1$ mA and at $I_Z = 55$ mA.

26. The voltage of a certain zener is 12.8 V at $I_{ZK} = 0.2$ mA and 13.4 V at $I_Z = 80$ mA. Using the model of Figure 25–22(c), determine its voltage at 22 mA.

27. In Figure 25–57, $D_1$ is a 1N4731A zener and $D_2$ is a 1N4740A.

    a. Assuming $v_F = 0$V for the each zener when forward-biased, sketch waveform $v_{out}$.

    b. Assuming $v_F = 0.7$ V for the each zener when forward-biased, sketch waveform $v_{out}$.

28. Redo Example 25–4 using the model of Figure 25–22(c). Hints: To find $V_Z$, solve iteratively using the results of Example 25–4 as a starting point. See also Example 25–3 for ideas.

### 25.7   Half-Wave and Full-Wave Rectifier Circuits

29. If the transformer of Figure 25–33 has a turns ratio of 5 and $R_L = 7\ \Omega$, determine average load current and the maximum reverse diode voltage.

30. Confirm Equation 25–12. Hint: Write KVL around the source, $D_2$, $D_4$ loop Figure 25–38(a).

### 25.8   Power Supply Filtering

31. For Example 25–9, solve for load voltage using Equation 25–17.

32. Show that Equations 25–15 and 16 yield Equation 25–17.

33. For Figure 25–58, $V_m = 20$ V, $C = 330$ μF and $R_L = 650\ \Omega$. What is peak-to-peak ripple?

34. Repeat Problem 33 assuming the waveform is half-wave and $C = 390$ μF.

35. If $C = 220$ μF, $I_{dc} = 20$ mA and $V_m = 20$ V for Figure 25–58, what are $V_{r_{pp}}$ and $V_{dc}$?

36. If $R_L = 1000\ \Omega$ and $V_m = 20$ V for Figure 25–58 and ripple is not to exceed 0.6 V peak-to-peak, what is minimum required capacitance?

37. A 19.0 V dc load has current 500 mA dc. The load is supplied from a full-wave rectifier with $V_m = 20$ V. What is the peak-to-peak ripple and what is $C$?

38. For Figure 25–58, if $R_L = 300\ \Omega$, $V_m = 24$ V and $C = 470$ μF, what is the percent ripple factor?

39. For Figure 25–58, $R_L = 400\ \Omega$, $V_m = 20$ V and the ripple factor is not to exceed 3%. Determine peak-to-peak ripple, $V_{dc}$ and the rms ripple voltage.

40. For Figure 25–58, $V_{r_{pp}} = 1.22$ V, $R_L = 600\ \Omega$ and $C = 220\ \mu F$. Find ripple factor and $V_{dc}$.

41. A dual voltage power supply with one side positive with respect to ground and the other negative can be created using a tapped transformer and a bridge rectifier. Add components (two resistors and two capacitors) to Figure 25–59 to create such a supply.

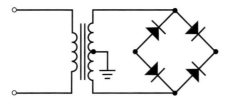

**FIGURE 25–59**

42. A more rigorous ("exact") analysis of the filtered waveform problem may be achieved using an iterative technique. To illustrate, consider Example 25–9. Capacitor discharge voltage is given by $V_m e^{-t/R_L C}$ where $t$ is the discharge time. Discharge time to $v_{C(min)}$ Figure 25–40 looks to be about 90% of half a period, i.e, about 7.5 ms.

   a. Using this guess, compute $v_{C(min)}$.

   b. Using the technique of Chapter 15, Section 15.6, compute a new estimate for discharge time $t$. Repeat a. and b. until $v_{C(min)}$ does not change from trial-to-trial. Finally, determine $V_{r_{pp}} = V_m - V_{C(min)}$. Results are tabulated in Table 25–1.

### 25.9  Computer Analysis (MultiSIM and PSpice)

43. For Figure 25–60, $C_1 = C_2 = 470\ \mu F$.

   a. Estimate $V_0$ and set initial conditions for both capacitors. Run a simulation and refine your estimation of $V_0$ if necessary. When you have a satisfactory waveform, determine ripple and $V_{dc}$.

   b. Compute ripple and $V_{dc}$ using the formulas of this chapter. (Use a value of 0.74 V for the diode drop in your analysis. This is fairly close to what the software packages use.) Compare your computed and computer results.

44. Replace both capacitors with $220\ \mu F$ units, then repeat Problem 43 a and b.

45. Using a full-wave bridge rectifier, repeat Problem 43 a and b.

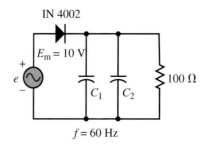

**FIGURE 25–60**

### ✓  ANSWERS TO IN-PROCESS LEARNING CHECKS

**In-Process Learning Check 1**

1. 46.5 mA,  48.8 mA

2. 16.82 V

3. 1 A,  0.7A

4. 34 mA,  44 mA

5. 87.5° C

6. 1N4746A,  126.5 mA to 176.25 mA

7. 21.4 V to 24.8 V

## OBJECTIVES

On completion of this chapter, you will be able to

- identify the three terminals of a junction transistor and explain the biasing of these terminals,

- use the transistor $\beta$ and $\alpha$ to calculate the relationship between emitter, collector, and base currents,

- use manufacturers' specification sheets to determine the limits of operation of a transistor,

- calculate the power dissipation of a transistor,

- predict the *saturation* and *cutoff* points of a transistor circuit,

- sketch a dc load line on a graph of transistor collector characteristic curves and determine the operating point of the transistor circuit,

- analyze the operation of several bias arrangements,

- examine the operation of a transistor used as an electronic switch,

- use a multimeter to determine the pin allocation of pnp and npn transistors and measure the operating point of a transistor in a given amplifier circuit,

- analyze JFET amplifier circuits using Shockley's equation and the JFET transfer curve,

- analyze D-MOSFET and E-MOSFET amplifier circuits,

- use computer programs to predict the bias points of transistor circuits,

- properly handle static sensitive components.

# Basic Transistor Theory

# 26

Since its invention in 1947, the transistor has revolutionized electrical, electronics, and computer engineering. From its crude beginning, the transistor has been miniaturized, modified, and combined with many other components onto complex integrated circuits that have revolutionized communications, travel, medicine, and most other industries.

Miniaturization of the transistor has permitted us to use cell phones and to directly receive television-transmitted signals from satellites. Without the transistor, flying the space shuttle or any other modern aircraft would be impossible. CT scanners and MRI (magnetic resonance imaging) scanners would not function without the circuitry that relies on transistors to process the signals. Even land surveying, which has for many decades used optical and mechanical methods, has been modernized by using GPS (global positioning systems) satellites and receivers.

This chapter examines the structure and basic operation of the transistor. Although the use of discrete transistors is disappearing, it is important to have a rudimentary understanding of transistor operation to appreciate the operation of more complex circuitry using hundreds (or perhaps thousands) of transistors. Students will be introduced to transistor biasing, the use of load lines, and troubleshooting techniques. ∎

## PUTTING IT IN PERSPECTIVE

AS SO MANY OTHER THINGS that we take for granted, modern electronics began with Thomas Edison, who in 1883 discovered that when an electric current is applied to a conductor in a vacuum, electrons are given off in a process called *thermionic emission* (or Edison Effect).

In 1904, an Englishman by the name of John Fleming produced an "electronic valve" by heating a cathode with a small electric current. The heat of the cathode released a small cloud of electrons. Next, he connected a dc voltage between another terminal called the "plate" (anode) and the cathode. Since the plate was positive with respect to the cathode, the electrons were repelled from the cathode and attracted by the positive charge on the plate, resulting in current in one direction. This created the first diode.

In 1906, Lee De Forest inserted a fine metal grid between the plate and the cathode. By applying a small grid current, it was possible to control the current between the cathode and the plate. The triode (which De Forest called the "audion") revolutionized radio transmission, since it was now possible to amplify small electrical signals so that they could be easily transmitted over great distances.

The vacuum tube went through numerous changes between 1906 and 1960, with the introduction of various control grids resulting in tetrodes and pentodes. Miniature vacuum tubes were used in consumer electronics, while enormous vacuum tubes were used to power the radio and television stations that were transmitting the nation's AM, FM, and television stations.

In 1947, three American physicists working for Bell Laboratories made a discovery that would ultimately see the demise of the vacuum tube. William Shockley, John Bardeen, and Walter Brattain invented the transistor. ■

## 26.1 Transistor Construction

The transistor is the basic building block used in complex integrated circuits. We will begin by examining the structure of the **bipolar junction transistor** (BJT), which is constructed of three layers of doped semiconductor material with two p-n junctions. The term *bipolar* refers to the fact that both holes and electrons are used as carriers in the device. Figure 26–1 shows the structure of a BJT, which is built on a substrate of pure silicon. The transistor is manufactured by progressively building and etching each layer over the previous layer. Very thin connections of aluminum are deposited onto the emitter, base, and collector regions. Finally, the entire transistor is covered with a very thin layer of silicon dioxide ($SiO_2$), which acts as a good insulator.

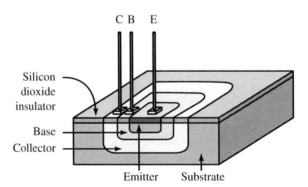

**FIGURE 26–1** Construction of a bipolar junction transistor.

The three layers of the BJT are the emitter, the base, and the collector which can be constructed as either pnp or npn transistors as shown in Figure 26–2. Notice that the emitter and collector are always constructed of the same type of material (n-type material in the npn transistor) and are heavily doped to result in semiconductor material that has a low resistivity. The arrow of the BJT is always between the emitter and base, pointing from the p-type material towards the n-type material just like a diode. The base is constructed of the other type of material (p-type in the npn transistor) and is very lightly doped, resulting in a higher resistivity.

Each BJT shown in Figure 26–2 has two p-n junctions, the B-E (base-emitter) junction and the C-E (collector-emitter) junction. These junctions determine the operation of the transistor.

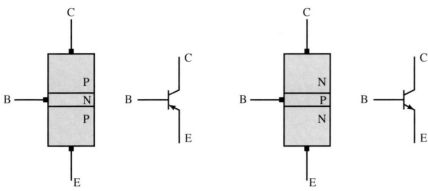

(a) Structure and electronic symbol of a
    pnp transistor

(b) Structure and electronic symbol of an
    npn transistor

**FIGURE 26–2**

## 26.2 Transistor Operation

In order for a transistor to operate as an amplifier, two conditions must be met:

- the B-E junction must be forward-biased, and
- the C-B junction must be reverse-biased.

Figure 26–3 shows that the forward-biased base-emitter junction results in a large majority carrier current from the heavily doped p-type material of the emitter into the lightly doped n-type base region.

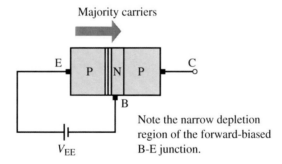

**FIGURE 26–3**   The B-E junction is forward-biased in a transistor amplifier circuit.

Figure 26–4 shows that the reverse-biased collector-base junction results in only a very small minority carrier current from the lightly doped n-type material of the base into the heavily doped collector region. The minority carrier current illustrated is often included in many specification sheets as $I_{CBO}$, which means that this is the leakage current between the base and the collector with

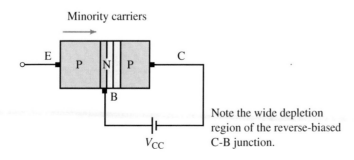

**FIGURE 26–4**   The C-B junction is reverse-biased in a transistor amplifier circuit.

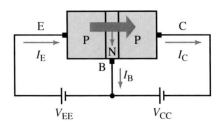

**FIGURE 26–5**    Biasing a pnp transistor.

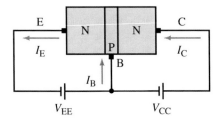

**FIGURE 26–6**    Biasing an npn transistor.

the emitter open. (The manufacturer will also provide the test voltage $V_{CB}$ for which the specification is provided.) In most cases, $I_{CBO}$ can be ignored since its effect is small.

When both junctions are correctly biased, the transistor operation is profoundly different than the simple operation that one expects from the diode-like behavior of the individual junctions.

Figure 26–5 shows that when the majority hole current from the emitter, $I_E$, enters the base region, there are few electrons in the thin base region to combine with the large injection of holes. Consequently, the base current, $I_B$ is very small, typically in the order of microamps. The large number of holes in the narrow base region is able to drift to the reverse-biased C-B junction where the positive-charged holes are attracted to the negative terminal of the bias voltage, $V_{CC}$. This large movement of charge results in a correspondingly large collector current, $I_C$. Figure 26–5 illustrates another very important characteristic of the bipolar junction transistor, namely that the emitter current, collector current, and base current of the transistor are related by the expression.

$$I_E = I_C + I_B \qquad\qquad (26–1)$$

The above equation follows Kirchhoff's current law and is true regardless of whether the transistor is pnp as shown in Figure 26–5 or npn as illustrated in Figure 26–6.

Although Figures 26–5 and 26–6 show voltage sources connected directly to transistors, such an arrangement would never be used in an operational circuit. Rather, any transistor circuit will always contain resistors to limit the amount of current to prevent damaging the device. Another important characteristic of any properly biased BJT amplifier circuit is that, since the base-emitter junction is forward biased, the voltage across this p-n junction will be approximately 0.7 V (for a silicon transistor). Figure 26–7 shows properly biased pnp and npn transistor amplifier circuits. We will examine these and other circuits in greater detail later in the chapter.

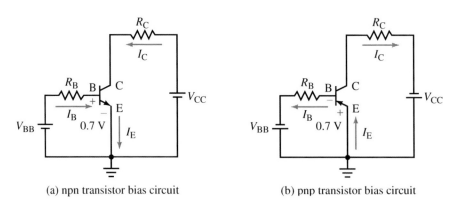

(a) npn transistor bias circuit          (b) pnp transistor bias circuit

**FIGURE 26–7**

Notice that for the npn transistor, the base-emitter voltage, $V_{BE} = +0.7$ V, while for the pnp transistor $V_{BE} = -0.7$ V. It is not surprising that these properties are exactly the same as for a forward-biased diode. Remember that the p-type material of a forward-biased junction will always be positive (p) with respect to the n-type material, which will be negative (n). Just as was the case with the diode, the arrow of the emitter points in the direction of conventional current (when the transistor is "on").

## dc Beta ($\beta_{dc}$)

We have already determined that due to the very light doping of the base material of any transistor, the base current, $I_B$ will be very small when compared to both the emitter current, $I_E$ and the collector current, $I_C$. Although small, the base current will not be zero. We define the **dc beta,** which is also called the **dc current gain,** $\beta_{dc}$ (or $h_{FE}$ in specification sheets) of a transistor as the ratio of collector current to base current.

$$\beta_{dc} = \frac{I_C}{I_B} \qquad (26\text{--}2)$$

Typical values of $\beta_{dc}$ for a transistor range from about 40 for power transistors to about 400 for small-signal transistors. Even for a particular transistor type, the value of $\beta_{dc}$ can range quite drastically. For example, the specification for the 2N3904 transistor (commonly used npn transistor) shows that $\beta_{dc}$ ranges from 100 to 300. Although we often treat it as one, $\beta_{dc}$ is not a constant for a given transistor. The value depends on the operating point and on the ambient temperature.

## dc Alpha ($\alpha_{dc}$)

A less commonly used specification that is used to analyze transistor circuits is the dc alpha, $\alpha_{dc}$, which is specified as the ratio of collector current to emitter current.

$$\alpha_{dc} = \frac{I_C}{I_E} \qquad (26\text{--}3)$$

Since $I_C$ is always smaller than $I_E$, we see that $\alpha$ will always be less than 1, with typical values between 0.95 and 0.99.

A transistor circuit is measured to have $I_C = 2.00$ mA and $I_E = 2.05$ mA. Determine $I_B$, $\alpha$, and $\beta$.

**EXAMPLE 26–1**

**Solution**
By applying Equations 26–1, 26–2, and 26–3, we have

$$I_B = I_E - I_C = 2.05 \text{ mA} - 2.00 \text{ mA} = 0.05 \text{ mA} = 50 \text{ }\mu\text{A}$$

$$\alpha_{dc} = \frac{I_C}{I_E} = \frac{2.00 \text{ mA}}{2.05 \text{ mA}} = 0.976$$

$$\beta_{dc} = \frac{I_C}{I_B} = \frac{2.00 \text{ mA}}{0.05 \text{ mA}} = 40$$

A transistor circuit is measured to have $\beta = 100$ and $I_C = 4.00$ mA. Determine $I_B$, $I_E$, and $\alpha$.

PRACTICE PROBLEMS 1

*Answers*
40 $\mu$A,  4.04 mA,  0.9901

By manipulating Equations 26–1 and 26–2, it is possible to determine a relationship between $I_E$, $\beta$, and $I_B$, namely

$$I_E = (\beta + 1)I_B \qquad (26\text{--}4)$$

Now, by applying algebraic manipulation to Equations 26–2, 26–3, and 26–4 we arrive at two other expressions for $\alpha$ and $\beta$.

$$\alpha = \frac{\beta}{\beta + 1} \qquad (26\text{–}5)$$

$$\beta = \frac{\alpha}{1 - \alpha} \qquad (26\text{–}6)$$

It is left as end-of-chapter problems for the student to derive Equations 26–4 through 26–6.

---

PRACTICE PROBLEMS 2

A transistor has $\beta = 150$ and $I_B = 30\ \mu A$. Determine $\alpha$, $I_C$, and $I_E$.

*Answers*
0.9934, 4.50 mA, 4.53 mA

---

## 26.3 Transistor Specifications

All semiconductor manufacturers publish comprehensive specifications for each component that is manufactured. These specifications provide the technologist or engineer with a complete guide to the performance of the particular component, allowing us to analyze and design electronic circuits. While a typical specification contains many pages of data, it is often necessary to consider only a few of the important characteristics. It is extremely important that the first-time user not be intimidated by the large amount of information that is contained in a manufacturer's specification.

Consider the specification for the 2N3904 npn transistor that is provided in Figure 26–8. Notice that the specification corresponds to three different packages, each with a different part number. The TO-92 case is a fairly large package that can be easily handled in the lab. The SOT-23 and SOT-223 are surface mount packages that are much smaller, requiring a much smaller "footprint" on a printed surface board. The disadvantage of the smaller cases is that they are more difficult to handle and are not practical for most lab measurements by students.

### Absolute Maximum Ratings and Thermal Characteristics

$V_{CEO} = 40\ V$ is the maximum voltage (V) that can be applied between the collector and emitter (CE) with the base terminal left open (O). For the 2N3904 this value is 40 V, which means that this is the maximum supply voltage that would be used for any circuit. If this voltage is exceeded, there is a very good likelihood that the transistor would be permanently damaged.

$V_{CBO} = 60V$ is the maximum voltage that can be applied to the reverse-biased collector-base junction (with the emitter terminal left open). If the supply voltage is kept less than 40 V, we see that this rating will not be exceeded.

$V_{EBO} = 6.0V$ is the maximum voltage that can be applied to the reverse-biased emitter-base junction. (In this case the collector terminal is left open.) Recall that this junction will not normally be reverse-biased. However, you can see that it is extremely important to ensure that the B-E junction is not inadvertently connected to a supply with the wrong polarity.

$I_C = 200\ mA$ is the largest continuous collector current that can be handled by the transistor.

$P_D = 625\ mW$ is the maximum power that the transistor can safely dissipate at an ambient temperature, $T_A = 25°$. For any transistor, the power dissipation is determined as the product of collector current, $I_C$ and the collector-emitter voltage, $V_{CE}$, namely

$$P_D = I_C V_{CE} \qquad (26\text{–}7)$$

We will examine an application of the power calculation later in the chapter.

## NPN General Purpose Amplifier (continued)

### Electrical Characteristics    $T_A$ = 25°C unless otherwise noted

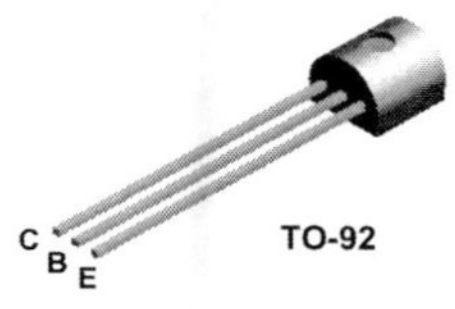

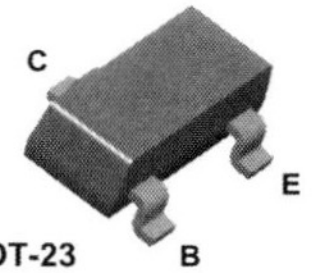

| Symbol | Parameter | Test Conditions | Min | Max | Units |
|---|---|---|---|---|---|
| **OFF CHARACTERISTICS** | | | | | |
| $V_{(BR)CEO}$ | Collector-Emitter Breakdown Voltage | $I_C$ = 1.0 mA, $I_B$ = 0 | 40 | | V |
| $V_{(BR)CBO}$ | Collector-Base Breakdown Voltage | $I_C$ = 10 µA, $I_E$ = 0 | 60 | | V |
| $V_{(BR)EBO}$ | Emitter-Base Breakdown Voltage | $I_E$ = 10 µA, $I_C$ = 0 | 6.0 | | V |
| $I_{BL}$ | Base Cutoff Current | $V_{CE}$ = 30 V, $V_{EB}$ = 3V | | 50 | nA |
| $I_{CEX}$ | Collector Cutoff Current | $V_{CE}$ = 30 V, $V_{EB}$ = 3V | | 50 | nA |
| **ON CHARACTERISTICS*** | | | | | |
| $h_{FE}$ | DC Current Gain | $I_C$ = 0.1 mA, $V_{CE}$ = 1.0 V | 40 | | |
| | | $I_C$ = 1.0 mA, $V_{CE}$ = 1.0 V | 70 | | |
| | | $I_C$ = 10 mA, $V_{CE}$ = 1.0 V | 100 | | |
| | | $I_C$ = 50 mA, $V_{CE}$ = 1.0 V | 60 | | |
| | | $I_C$ = 100 mA, $V_{CE}$ = 1.0 V | 30 | | |
| $V_{CE(sat)}$ | Collector-Emitter Saturation Voltage | $I_C$ = 10 mA, $I_B$ = 1.0 mA | | 0.2 | V |
| | | $I_C$ = 50 mA, $I_B$ = 5.0 mA | | 0.3 | V |
| $V_{BE(sat)}$ | Base-Emitter Saturation Voltage | $I_C$ = 10 mA, $I_B$ = 1.0 mA | 0.65 | 0.85 | V |
| | | $I_C$ = 50 mA, $I_B$ = 5.0 mA | | 0.95 | V |
| **SMALL SIGNAL CHARACTERISTICS** | | | | | |
| $f_T$ | Current Gain - Bandwidth Product | $I_C$ = 10 mA, $V_{CE}$ = 20 V, f = 100 MHz | 300 | | MHz |
| $C_{obo}$ | Output Capacitance | $V_{CB}$ = 5.0 V, $I_E$ = 0, f = 1.0 MHz | | 4.0 | pF |
| $C_{ibo}$ | Input Capacitance | $V_{EB}$ = 0.5 V, $I_C$ = 0, f = 1.0 MHz | | 8.0 | pF |
| NF | Noise Figure | $I_C$ = 100 µA, $V_{CE}$ = 5.0 V, $R_S$ =1.0kΩ, f=10 Hz to 15.7kHz | | 5.0 | dB |
| **SWITCHING CHARACTERISTICS** | | | | | |
| $t_d$ | Delay Time | $V_{CC}$ = 3.0 V, $V_{BE}$ = 0.5 V, | | 35 | ns |
| $t_r$ | Rise Time | $I_C$ = 10 mA, $I_{B1}$ = 1.0 mA | | 35 | ns |
| $t_s$ | Storage Time | $V_{CC}$ = 3.0 V, $I_C$ = 10mA | | 200 | ns |
| $t_f$ | Fall Time | $I_{B1}$ = $I_{B2}$ = 1.0 mA | | 50 | ns |

*Pulse Test: Pulse Width ≤ 300 µs, Duty Cycle ≤ 2.0%

### Spice Model

NPN (Is=6.734f Xti=3 Eg=1.11 Vaf=74.03 Bf=416.4 Ne=1.259 Ise=6.734 Ikf=66.78m Xtb=1.5 Br=.7371 Nc=2 Isc=0 Ikr=0 Rc=1 Cjc=3.638p Mjc=.3085 Vjc=.75 Fc=.5 Cje=4.493p Mje=.2593 Vje=.75 Tr=239.5n Tf=301.2p Itf=.4 Vtf=4 Xtf=2 Rb=10)

---

**2N3904 / MMBT3904 / PZT3904**

**FAIRCHILD** SEMICONDUCTOR™

**2N3904**  TO-92

**MMBT3904**  SOT-23  Mark: 1A

**PZT3904**  SOT-223

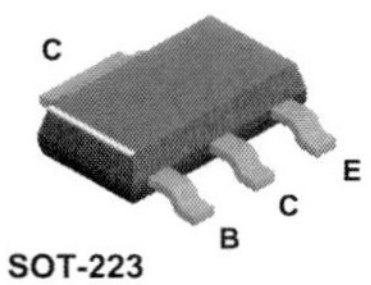

## NPN General Purpose Amplifier

This device is designed as a general purpose amplifier and switch. The useful dynamic range extends to 100 mA as a switch and to 100 MHz as an amplifier.

### Absolute Maximum Ratings*    $T_A$ = 25°C unless otherwise noted

| Symbol | Parameter | Value | Units |
|---|---|---|---|
| $V_{CEO}$ | Collector-Emitter Voltage | 40 | V |
| $V_{CBO}$ | Collector-Base Voltage | 60 | V |
| $V_{EBO}$ | Emitter-Base Voltage | 6.0 | V |
| $I_C$ | Collector Current - Continuous | 200 | mA |
| $T_J$, $T_{stg}$ | Operating and Storage Junction Temperature Range | -55 to +150 | °C |

*These ratings are limiting values above which the serviceability of any semiconductor device may be impaired.

NOTES:
1) These ratings are based on a maximum junction temperature of 150 degrees C.
2) These are steady state limits. The factory should be consulted on applications involving pulsed or low duty cycle operations.

### Thermal Characteristics    $T_A$ = 25°C unless otherwise noted

| Symbol | Characteristic | Max 2N3904 | Max *MMBT3904 | Max **PZT3904 | Units |
|---|---|---|---|---|---|
| $P_D$ | Total Device Dissipation | 625 | 350 | 1,000 | mW |
| | Derate above 25°C | 5.0 | 2.8 | 8.0 | mW/°C |
| $R_{\theta JC}$ | Thermal Resistance, Junction to Case | 83.3 | | | °C/W |
| $R_{\theta JA}$ | Thermal Resistance, Junction to Ambient | 200 | 357 | 125 | °C/W |

*Device mounted on FR-4 PCB 1.6" X 1.6" X 0.06."
**Device mounted on FR-4 PCB 36 mm X 18 mm X 1.5 mm; mounting pad for the collector lead min. 6 cm².

© 2001 Fairchild Semiconductor Corporation

2N3904/MMBT3904/PZT3904  Rev. A

**FIGURE 26–8**    Data sheets of a 2N3904 transistor. (*Courtesy of Fairchild Semiconductor Corporation*)

### Electrical Characteristics

All electrical characteristics of transistors are specified for certain test conditions. In many instances, the manufacturer provides both minimum and maximum values that one can expect to measure in a lab.

At this point, we will examine only two additional characteristics. It is left as an exercise for the student to examine some of the other specifications.

$V_{(BR)CEO} = 40$ V implies that this is the minimum collector-emitter voltage at which one can expect the transistor to breakdown. As expected, this is precisely the same value that was specified under the heading **Absolute Maximum Ratings.** However, this specification also provides the test conditions, namely that $I_C = 1.0$ mA and $I_B = 0$.

$h_{FE}$ is the dc current gain (or beta) of the transistor. As seen in the specification, this value is not constant, but rather is very dependent on the operating conditions of the transistor. As an illustration, we see that the transistor beta varies between 100 and 300 for a collector current of 10 mA. This illustrates clearly that two circuits having the same component values and device numbers can easily have different operating conditions.

## 26.4 Collector Characteristic Curves

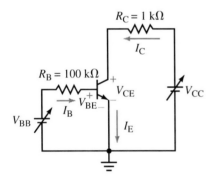

**FIGURE 26–9**

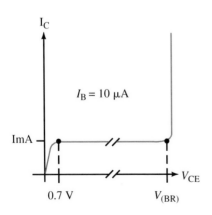

**FIGURE 26–10**

Consider the circuit shown in Figure 26–9. By changing the values of the supply voltages, it is possible to change the operating conditions of the transistor. The supply voltage, $V_{BB}$, determines the value of $I_B$, while the supply voltage, $V_{CC}$, determines both $I_C$ and $V_{CE}$.

Imagine that we let $V_{CC} = 0$ and vary only $V_{BB}$. Once $V_{BB}$ is greater than the barrier potential of the forward-biased B-E junction (0.7 V for silicon), base current results. For instance, if we were to set $V_{BB} = 1.7$ V, we can determine that the base current would remain constant at a value determined as

$$I_B = \frac{1.7 \text{ V} - 0.7 \text{ V}}{100 \text{ k}\Omega} = 10 \text{ }\mu\text{A}$$

With $V_{CC} = 0$, the collector will be at zero volts, which means that both the B-E and the C-B junctions are forward biased. Now, if we were to increase $V_{CC}$, collector current will increase linearly until the bias potential on the C-B junction is returned to 0 V. At this point, the voltage across the collector-emitter terminals can be determined from Kirchhoff's voltage law as $V_{CE} = 0.7$ V. Further increases in $V_{CC}$ will simply increase the voltage across the now reverse-biased C-B junction, resulting in an increase of $V_{CE}$. Collector current will remain constant until the collector-emitter breakdown voltage, $V_{(BR)CEO}$, is exceeded. Figure 26–10 shows how of $I_C$ varies as a function of $V_{CE}$.

If we were to plot the collector current as a function of the collector-emitter voltage, for numerous values of base current, we would arrive at a family of curves similar to those shown in Figure 26–11.

The collector characteristic curves of Figure 26–11 show several important points. The **cutoff region** is the portion of the graph that occurs below the line corresponding to $I_B = 0$. If no base current were applied to the transistor, one would expect that there would not be any collector current. This, however, is not true since there will always be a small leakage current (generally in the order of nanoamps) through the reverse-biased C-B junction. In the cutoff region, the transistor behaves very much like an open switch; current is very small and the voltage across the collector-emitter of the transis-

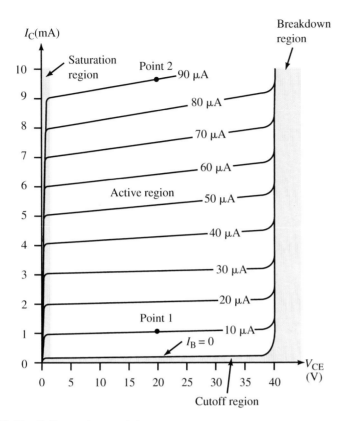

**FIGURE 26–11** Collector characteristic curves.

tor is large. In the cutoff region, both the B-E and the C-B junctions are reverse-biased.

The **saturation region** is that portion of the graph where collector current increases rapidly for very small values of $V_{CE}$. In the saturation region, the transistor behaves very much like a closed switch; current is large and the voltage across the collector-emitter of the transistor is very small. In the saturation region, both the B-E and the C-B junctions are forward-biased. When transistors are used as switching devices, they will operate in either saturation (ON) or cutoff (OFF). We will examine the operation of the transistor switch in Section 26.7.

If the voltage across the collector-emitter of the transistor exceeds $V_{(BR)CE}$ of the transistor, a large amount of collector current will result in probable destruction of the device.

Finally, the **active region** is that portion of the collector characteristic curves in which the transistor can be used as an amplifier. Recall that in this region, the B-E junction is forward biased and the C-B junction is reverse-biased.

By examining the curves of Figure 26–11, we may conclude that the $\beta_{dc}$ of a particular transistor is not constant, but rather is dependent on the **operating point.** The operating point (also called the quiescent point or simply the Q-point) of a transistor is a collection of dc bias conditions, which include $I_B$, $I_C$, and $V_{CE}$. The following example shows how we may use the collector characteristic curves to determine the $\beta$ of a transistor at a given operating point.

**EXAMPLE 26–2**

Determine $\beta_{dc}$ for the transistor having characteristic curves shown in Figure 26–11,

a. if the operating point of the transistor is $V_{CE} = 20$ V and $I_C = 1.0$ mA (point 1)

b. if the operating point of the transistor is $V_{CE} = 20$ V and $I_B = 90$ μA (point 2)

**Solution**

a. From the graph, we see that when $V_{CE} = 20$ V and $I_C = 1.0$ mA, the base current is $I_B = 10$ μA. Therefore,

$$\beta_1 = \frac{I_C}{I_B} = \frac{1.0 \text{ mA}}{0.01 \text{ mA}} = 100$$

b. At point 2, when $V_{CE} = 20$ V and $I_B = 90$ μA, the collector current is $I_C = 9.7$ mA, and so

$$\beta_2 = \frac{I_C}{I_B} = \frac{9.7 \text{ mA}}{0.09 \text{ mA}} = 108$$

Although Figure 26–11 does not illustrate it, the active region of a transistor is restricted by two other conditions that were mentioned previously; the maximum forward current $I_{C(MAX)}$ and the total device power dissipation, $P_D$. Figure 26–12 shows that the active region for the 2N3904 transistor is limited by $I_{C(MAX)} = 200$ mA, $V_{(BR)CEO} = 40$ V, and $P_D = 625$ mW.

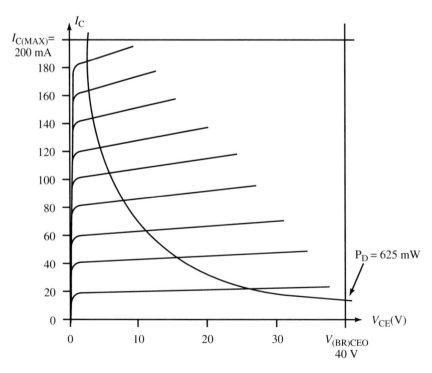

**FIGURE 26–12** Limits of transistor operation.

Consider the transistor circuit shown in Figure 26–13.

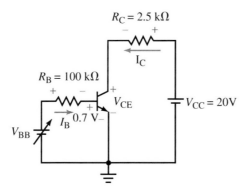

**FIGURE 26–13**

For any given set of component values, the transistor operation will occur somewhere between two extreme limits: *saturation* and *cutoff.* The components contained in the collector-emitter circuit determine these two points. When in saturation, the transistor behaves as a closed switch, resulting in maximum $I_C$ through the transistor and a $V_{CE}$ that is essentially zero. Conversely, when in cutoff the transistor behaves as an open switch where $I_C$ is essentially zero and $V_{CE}$ is at a maximum. Figure 26–14 shows equivalent circuits of the transistor in each of the two conditions described above.

By examining the circuit models that are shown in Figure 26–14, we see that the saturation current for the transistor is

$$I_{C(SAT)} = \frac{V_{CC}}{R_C} = \frac{20 \text{ V}}{2.5 \text{ k}\Omega} = 8.0 \text{ mA}$$

and the cutoff voltage is

$$V_{CE(OFF)} = V_{CC} = 20 \text{ V}$$

The cutoff and saturation points form the limits of the dc load line for a transistor as illustrated in Figure 26–15.

## 26.5  dc Load Line

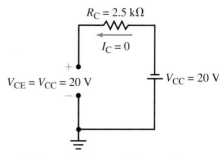

(a) A transistor in saturation behaves like a closed switch

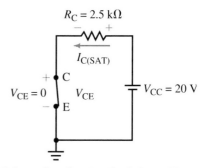

(b) A transistor in cutoff behaves like an open switch

**FIGURE 26–14**

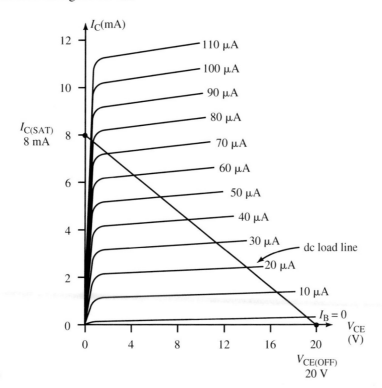

**FIGURE 26–15**

When the transistor is used as a linear amplifier, the actual operating point of the transistor should generally lie near the midpoint between cutoff and saturation and is determined by the base circuit. This important concept becomes evident if we vary $V_{BB}$ in the circuit of Figure 26–13. For example, if we let $V_{BB} = 4.7$ V, we determine the base current to be

$$I_B = \frac{4.7 \text{ V} - 0.7 \text{ V}}{100 \text{ k}\Omega} = 40 \text{ }\mu\text{A}$$

The operating point for this base current is illustrated as $Q_1$ on the dc load line of Figure 26–16. Although a transistor operating point will generally be near the midpoint of the load line, this will not always be the case. Consider the condition where we let $V_{BB} = 1.7$ V, the base current would be determined as

$$I_B = \frac{1.7 \text{ V} - 0.7 \text{ V}}{100 \text{ k}\Omega} = 10 \text{ }\mu\text{A}$$

This operating point is illustrated as $Q_2$ on the dc load line, clearly indicating that by reducing the base current, we can move a transistor operating point towards cutoff. Alternatively if we let the base voltage, $V_{BB} = 8.7$ V, the base current is

$$I_B = \frac{8.7 \text{ V} - 0.7 \text{ V}}{100 \text{ k}\Omega} = 80 \text{ }\mu\text{A}$$

This last condition shows that by increasing the base current of the transistor circuit, we will cause the operating point to move towards saturation as shown by $Q_3$ in Figure 26–16. We may conclude, therefore, that for a given load line, the operating point is determined by the components in the base circuit.

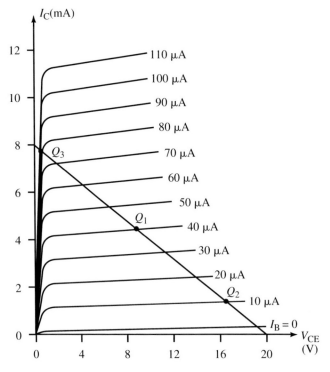

**FIGURE 26–16**

Refer to the circuit of Figure 26–13. Sketch the corresponding dc load lines for each of the following conditions.

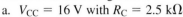 

a. $V_{CC} = 16$ V with $R_C = 2.5$ k$\Omega$

b. $V_{CC} = 24$ V with $R_C = 2.5$ k$\Omega$

c. $V_{CC} = 20$ V with $R_C = 2$ k$\Omega$

d. $V_{CC} = 20$ V with $R_C = 4$ k$\Omega$

*Answers*

a. $V_{CE(OFF)} = 16$ V, $I_{C(SAT)} = 6.4$ mA

b. $V_{CE(OFF)} = 24$ V, $I_{C(SAT)} = 9.6$ mA

c. $V_{CE(OFF)} = 20$ V, $I_{C(SAT)} = 10$ mA

d. $V_{CE(OFF)} = 20$ V $I_{C(SAT)} = 5$ mA

To this point, we have examined only the dc operation of a transistor. Although we will examine the ac operation in much greater detail in the next chapter, it is useful to see how a transistor can be used to amplify an ac signal. Consider the circuit shown in Figure 26–17.

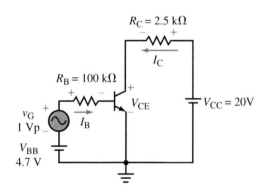

**FIGURE 26–17**

In Figure 26–17, we see that the ac voltage source is in series with the dc base bias voltage $V_{BB} = 4.7$ V. As in the previous illustration, we see that the dc load line has end points determined by $I_{SAT} = 8.0$ mA and $V_{CE(OFF)} = 20$ V. The operating point, which is determined by the base bias voltage, will be at the Q-point shown in Figure 26–18. ($I_{CQ} = 4.4$ mA and $V_{CEQ} = 9.0$ V).

As the alternating voltage source goes up, so too will the base current. When the generator voltage is at its maximum $v_G = +1$ V, the resulting base current will be

$$I_B = \frac{4.7 \text{ V} + 1 \text{ V} - 0.7 \text{ V}}{100 \text{ k}\Omega} = 50 \text{ }\mu\text{A}$$

At this point the collector-emitter voltage will be approximately $V_{CE} = 6.5$ V. Similarly, when the generator voltage is at its peak negative voltage, $v_G = -1$ V, the resulting base current will be

$$I_B = \frac{4.7 \text{ V} - 1 \text{ V} - 0.7 \text{ V}}{100 \text{ k}\Omega} = 30 \text{ }\mu\text{A}$$

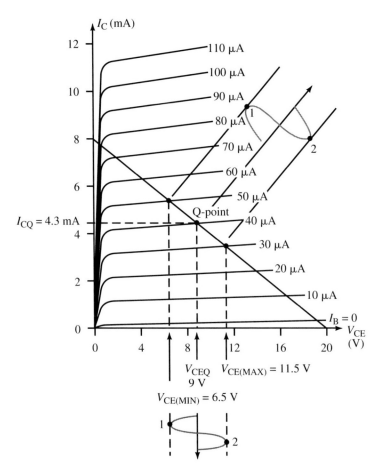

**FIGURE 26-18**

At this point on the dc load line we see that $V_{CE} = 11.5$ V. This illustrates that if the input voltage goes between $+1$ V and $-1$ V (total voltage swing of 2 $V_{p-p}$), the output voltage swings between 6.5 V and 11.5 V (5.0 $V_{p-p}$). We say that this circuit has a *voltage gain* of 2.5, since the output voltage, $V_{CE}$, is 2.5 times larger than the applied input ac voltage. We will examine the ac operation of transistor circuits in much greater detail in the following chapter.

## 26.6 Transistor Biasing

Although two separate voltage supplies may be used to bias a circuit as shown in Figure 26–13, it is generally not done. Rather, it is much more efficient to use a single supply to bias both the base bias and the collector. We will now examine several different types of biasing to determine how each type of circuit may be analyzed. You will also find that by making slight changes to the circuit, the circuits become increasingly less dependent on the transistor beta. This is particularly important when you consider that for a given transistor type, the beta may vary a large amount. Consider the specification for the 2N3904, which shows that $h_{FE}$ (dc beta) can have values between 100 and 300. Clearly this can present quite a problem when designing a circuit for a given operating point.

### The Fixed-Bias Circuit

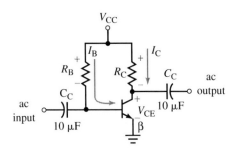

**FIGURE 26-19**

The fixed-bias circuit of Figure 26–19 operates exactly the same as the dual-supply circuits examined previously. As in previous circuits, we determine the operating point of this circuit by starting at the input loop (the loop containing the base-emitter junction) and then transferring to the output loop (the loop containing the collector-emitter voltage).

Although the circuit of Figure 26–19 does not initially look the same as the previous fixed-bias circuit, you will find that by redrawing the circuit, we do indeed have the same circuit. The circuit of Figure 26–19 shows capacitors, which are needed in the circuit to permit ac signals to pass. At this point, you simply need to remember that a capacitor operating at dc is effectively an open circuit and so may simply be removed when we are calculating the dc operating point. Figure 26–20 shows the equivalent redrawn circuit, with capacitors removed and the voltage supply, $V_{CC}$, shown as part of both the input loop and the output loop.

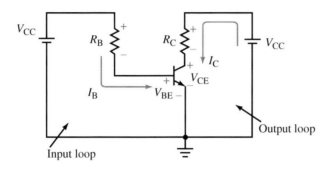

**FIGURE 26–20**

By examining the input loop, we see that we may easily determine the base current for the circuit as

$$I_B = \frac{V_{CC} - V_{BE}}{R_B} \qquad \textbf{(26–8)}$$

The base current allows us to transfer into the output loop by using the transistor beta, hence

$$I_C = \beta I_B \qquad \textbf{(26–9)}$$

Finally we use Kirchhoff's voltage law to write the output loop equation.

$$V_{CC} = I_C R_C + V_{CE}$$

and so we solve the collector-emitter voltage as

$$V_{CE} = V_{CC} - I_C R_C \qquad \textbf{(26–10)}$$

Determine $I_B$, $I_C$, and $V_{CE}$ for the circuit of Figure 26–21 if the transistor has $\beta = 200$.

**EXAMPLE 26–3**

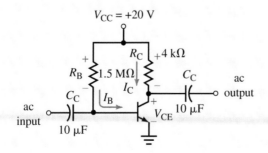

**FIGURE 26–21**

**Solution**

Writing the Kirchhoff Voltage Law equation for the input loop, we have

$$20 \text{ V} = 1.5 \text{ M}\Omega \, I_B + 0.7 \text{ V}$$

which allows us to calculate $I_B$ as

$$I_B = \frac{20 \text{ V} - 0.7 \text{ V}}{1.5 \text{ M}\Omega} = 12.87 \text{ } \mu\text{A}$$

Now, transferring into the output circuit, we have

$$I_C = \beta I_B = (200)(12.87 \text{ } \mu\text{A}) = 2.57 \text{ mA}$$

and writing the Kirchhoff Voltage Law equation for the output loop, we have

$$20 \text{ V} = 4 \text{ k}\Omega \, I_C + V_{CE}$$
$$= (4 \text{ k}\Omega) (2.57 \text{ mA}) + V_{CE}$$

and so

$$V_{CE} = 20 \text{ V} - 10.29 \text{ V} = 9.71 \text{ V}$$

---

**PRACTICE PROBLEMS 4**

Determine $I_B$, $I_C$, and $V_{CE}$ for the circuit of Figure 26–21 if the transistor has
a.  $\beta = 100$
b.  $\beta = 300$

*Answers*
a.  $I_B = 12.87 \text{ } \mu\text{A}$, $I_C = 1.287 \text{ mA}$, $V_{CE} = 14.85 \text{ V}$
b.  $I_B = 12.87 \text{ } \mu\text{A}$, $I_C = 3.86 \text{ mA}$, $V_{CE} = 4.56 \text{ V}$

## Emitter-Stabilized Bias Circuit

While the circuit of Figure 26–21 is relatively simple to analyze, the operating point is highly dependent upon the beta of the transistor. Introducing a "feedback resistor" into the emitter circuit of the transistor will stabilize the effects of changing beta. Figure 26–22 shows the schematic of an emitter-stabilized amplifier.

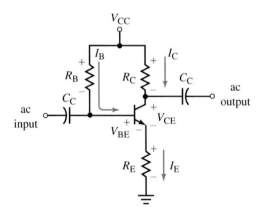

**FIGURE 26–22**

In the circuit of Figure 26–22, we see that the emitter resistor, $R_E$ appears in both the input loop and the output loop. This resistor results in a feedback effect, which will reduce $I_B$ as $\beta$ is increased. By applying Kirchhoff's Voltage Law to the input loop, we have

$$V_{CC} = R_B I_B + V_{BE} + R_E I_E$$

However, from Equation 26–4 we have $I_E = (\beta + 1)I_B$ and so we have

$$V_{CC} = R_B I_B + V_{BE} + R_E (\beta + 1)I_B$$

which allows us to determine $I_B$ as

$$I_B = \frac{V_{CC} - V_{BE}}{R_B + R_E(\beta + 1)} \qquad \textbf{(26–11)}$$

As before, $I_C = \beta I_B$. Writing the Kirchhoff Voltage Law equation for the output loop gives us

$$V_{CC} = R_C I_C + V_{CE} + R_E I_E$$

and since $I_C \cong I_E$, we may solve for $V_{CE}$ as

$$V_{CE} \cong V_{CC} - (R_C + R_E)I_C \qquad \textbf{(26–12)}$$

The following example shows how the stabilizing resistor, $R_E$ affects a transistor circuit.

Determine $I_B$, $I_C$, and $V_{CE}$ for the circuit of Figure 26–23 if the transistor has $\beta = 200$.

**EXAMPLE 26–4**

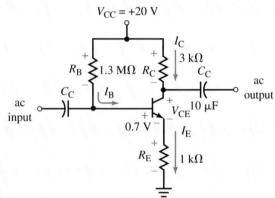

**FIGURE 26–23**

**Solution**
Using Kirchhoff's Voltage Law to write the loop equation for the input loop, we have

$$20\ V = (1.3\ M\Omega)I_B + 0.7\ V + (1\ k\Omega)I_E$$
$$= (1300\ k\Omega)I_B + 0.7\ V + (1\ k\Omega)(201 I_B)$$

Solving for $I_B$ we get

$$I_B = \frac{20\ V - 0.7\ V}{1300\ k\Omega + 201\ k\Omega} = 12.86\ \mu A$$

Next, we transfer into the output loop to solve for the $I_C$ as

$$I_C = \beta I_B = (200)(12.86\ \mu A) = 2.57\ mA$$

Writing the output loop equation, we have

$$20\ V = 3\ k\Omega\ I_C + V_{CE} + 1\ k\Omega\ I_E$$
$$\cong (4\ k\Omega)(2.57\ mA) + V_{CE}$$

and so

$$V_{CE} \cong 20\ V - 10.29\ V = 9.71\ V$$

---

**PRACTICE PROBLEMS 5**

Determine $I_B$, $I_C$, and $V_{CE}$ for the circuit of Figure 26–23 if the transistor has
a. $\beta = 100$
b. $\beta = 300$

*Answers*
a.  $I_B = 13.78$ μA, $I_C = 1.38$ mA, $V_{CE} = 14.49$ V
b.  $I_B = 12.05$ μA, $I_C = 3.62$ mA, $V_{CE} = 5.53$ V

Notice that the operating point for the circuit of Figure 26–23 does not change as dramatically with changes in beta as did the circuit of Figure 26–21. This effect is the result of the emitter-stabilizing resistor.

## The Universal-Bias Circuit

Although the emitter-stabilized transistor circuit has an improved stability, it does not provide sufficient stability. The Universal-Bias circuit show in Figure 26–24 is a much-improved design over other bias arrangements.

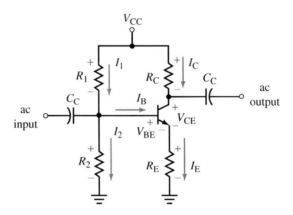

**FIGURE 26–24**   The universal-bias circuit.

The analysis of this design is complicated somewhat by adding the extra bias resistor into the circuit. We will discover that there are two methods that may be used to solve for the operating point of the transistor; the *exact method,* which always works, and the *approximate method,* which provides good results for most conditions.

**Exact Method**

First let's simplify the circuit by removing the two coupling capacitors that have no effect on the dc operation of the transistor. Next, we separate the circuit into two clearly identifiable circuits consisting of the input loop and the output loop as shown in Figure 26–25.

In Figure 26–25, we then further simplify the input loop by finding the Thévenin equivalent circuit as seen between the base and the reference point (ground). The Thévenin voltage is determined as

$$V_{BB} = E_{Th} = \frac{R_2}{R_1 + R_2} V_{CC} \qquad (26–13)$$

and the Thévenin resistance is

$$R_{BB} = R_{Th} = R_1 \| R_2 = \frac{R_1 R_2}{R_1 + R_2} \qquad (26–14)$$

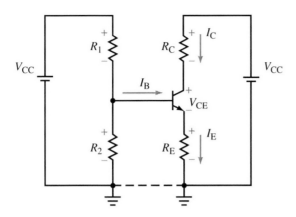

**FIGURE 26–25**

The resultant circuit is shown in Figure 26–26. It is now an easy matter to write the input loop equation

$$V_{BB} = R_{BB} I_B + V_{BE} + R_E I_E$$
$$= R_{BB} I_B + V_{BE} + R_E (\beta + 1)I_B$$

and solving for $I_B$, we have

$$I_B = \frac{V_{BB} - V_{BE}}{R_{BB} + (\beta + 1)R_E} \qquad (26\text{–}15)$$

Now, transferring into the output loop, we have the same results as those for the emitter stabilized bias circuit.

$$I_C = \beta I_B \qquad (26\text{–}16)$$

and

$$V_{CE} \cong V_{CC} - (R_C + R_E)I_C \qquad (26\text{–}17)$$

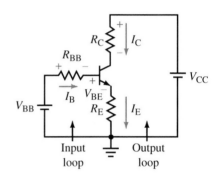

**FIGURE 26–26**

**EXAMPLE 26–5**

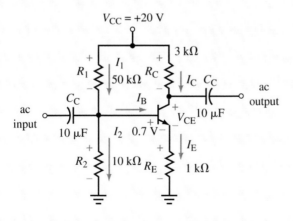

**FIGURE 26–27**

a. Determine $I_B$, $I_C$, and $V_{CE}$ for the circuit of Figure 26–27 if the transistor has $\beta = 200$.

b. Use the above results to determine the current through each of the bias resistors, $R_1$ and $R_2$.

**Solution**

a. After removing the coupling capacitors, $C_C$, which have no effect on the dc operation of the circuit, we determine the Thévenin equivalent circuit of the input circuit as follows:

$$V_{BB} = \left( \frac{10 \text{ k}\Omega}{50 \text{ k}\Omega + 10 \text{ k}\Omega} \right) 20 \text{ V} = 3.33 \text{ V}$$

and

$$R_{BB} = \frac{(10 \text{ k}\Omega)(50 \text{ k}\Omega)}{10 \text{ k}\Omega + 50 \text{ k}\Omega} = 8.33 \text{ k}\Omega$$

Now, by substituting the Thévenin equivalent of the input circuit, we have the equivalent amplifier shown in Figure 26–28.

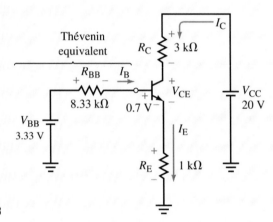

**FIGURE 26–28**

The loop equation of the input loop is

$$3.33 \text{ V} = (8.33 \text{ k}\Omega)I_B + 0.7 \text{ V} + (1 \text{ k}\Omega)I_E$$
$$= (8.33 \text{ k}\Omega)I_B + 0.7 \text{ V} + (1 \text{ k}\Omega)(\beta + 1)I_B$$
$$= (8.33 \text{ k}\Omega)I_B + 0.7 \text{ V} + (1 \text{ k}\Omega)(201I_B)$$

which gives

$$I_B = \frac{3.33 \text{ V} - 0.7 \text{ V}}{8.33 \text{ k}\Omega + 201 \text{ k}\Omega} = 12.58 \text{ μA}$$

Now, transferring into the output loop, we have

$$I_C = \beta I_B = (200)12.58 \text{ μA} = 2.52 \text{ mA} \cong I_E$$

Finally, we write the loop equation for the output loop.

$$20 \text{ V} = (3 \text{ k}\Omega)I_C + V_{CE} + (1 \text{ k}\Omega)I_E$$
$$\cong (4 \text{ k}\Omega)(2.52 \text{ mA}) + V_{CE}$$

Now we solve for $V_{CE}$ as

$$V_{CE} \cong 20 \text{ V} - 10.06 \text{ V} = 9.94 \text{ V}$$

b. If we examine the circuit of Figure 26–28, we see that we can calculate the voltage at the base of the transistor as

$$V_B = 0.7 \text{ V} + R_E I_E$$
$$= 0.7 \text{ V} + (1 \text{ k}\Omega)(2.52 \text{ mA})$$
$$= 3.22 \text{ V}$$

Now, if we go back to the original circuit shown in Figure 26–27, we see that this is the same voltage that must appear across $R_2$. Therefore, we can calculate the current $I_2$ as

$$I_2 = \frac{3.22 \text{ V}}{10 \text{ k}\Omega} = 322 \text{ }\mu\text{A}$$

Applying Kirchhoff's Voltage Law, we determine the voltage across $R_1$ as

$$V_{R1} = 20 \text{ V} - 3.22 \text{ V} = 16.78 \text{ V}$$

which allows us to determine the current $I_1$ as

$$I_1 = \frac{16.78 \text{ V}}{50 \text{ k}\Omega} = 336 \text{ }\mu\text{A}$$

---

Determine $I_B$, $I_C$, and $V_{CE}$ for the circuit of Figure 26–27 if the transistor has

a.  $\beta = 100$

b.  $\beta = 300$

 PRACTICE PROBLEMS 6

*Answers*

a.  $I_B = 24.09 \text{ }\mu\text{A}$,  $I_C = 2.41 \text{ mA}$,  $V_{CE} = 10.37 \text{ V}$

b.  $I_B = 8.51 \text{ }\mu\text{A}$,  $I_C = 2.55 \text{ mA}$,  $V_{CE} = 9.78 \text{ V}$

Notice that although the value of beta ranges from 100 to 300, the corresponding operating point ($I_{CQ}$ and $V_{CEQ}$) changed only slightly. For this reason, the universal bias circuit is considered to be the most stable bias arrangement.

## Approximate Method

In the previous example, $I_B$ is very small in comparison to both $I_1$ and $I_2$. We may therefore assume that the base current is negligible in comparison to the current through the bias resistors, $R_1$ and $R_2$. However, this assumption is only valid if the bias current is relatively large. As a general rule of thumb, we say that the base current is negligible if

$$R_2 \leq \frac{1}{10} \beta R_E \qquad\qquad \textbf{(26–18)}$$

If the condition of Equation 26–18 is not met, it is necessary to analyze the circuit using the exact method that was shown previously.

Now, this assumption allows us to further conclude that the base voltage, $V_B$ can be determined by applying the voltage divider rule. Therefore,

$$V_B = \left(\frac{R_2}{R_1 + R_2}\right) V_{CC} \qquad\qquad \textbf{(26–19)}$$

We can easily determine the voltage at the emitter (with respect to ground) as

$$V_E = V_B - V_{BE} \qquad\qquad \textbf{(26–20)}$$

Next, we determine the emitter current from Ohm's Law. Since $I_E \cong I_C$, we have the following expression.

$$I_E = \frac{V_E}{R_E} \cong I_C \qquad (26\text{-}21)$$

And finally

$$V_{CE} \cong V_{CC} - (R_C + R_E)I_C \qquad (26\text{-}22)$$

The following example shows how the approximate analysis method can be applied to the universal bias circuit.

**EXAMPLE 26–6**

Use the approximate method to solve for $I_C$ and $V_{CE}$ for the circuit of Figure 26–27 if the transistor has $\beta = 200$.

**Solution**
First, we must test to determine whether we are entitled to use the approximate method to analyze the circuit. In other words, is the condition of Equation 26–19 met? By inserting values into Equation 26–19, we have the following

$$10 \text{ k}\Omega \le \frac{1}{10}(200)(1\text{k}\Omega) \text{ as required for the approximate method}$$

$$\le 20\text{k}\Omega$$

$$V_B = \left(\frac{10 \text{ k}\Omega}{10 \text{ k}\Omega + 50 \text{ k}\Omega}\right)20 \text{ V} = 3.33 \text{ V}$$

$$V_E = 3.33 \text{ V} - 0.7 \text{ V} = 2.63 \text{ V}$$

$$I_E = \frac{2.63 \text{ V}}{1 \text{ k}\Omega} = 2.63 \text{ mA} \cong I_C$$

and finally

$$V_{CE} \cong V_{CC} - (R_C + R_E)I_C$$
$$= 20 \text{ V} - (3 \text{ k}\Omega + 1 \text{ k}\Omega)(2.63 \text{ mA})$$
$$= 9.47 \text{ V}$$

The above results are consistent with those found using the exact method, where we had $I_C = 2.52$ mA and $V_{CE} = 9.94$ V. The variation using the approximate method is less than 5% and certainly is a much easier approach than using the exact method.

## The Common Collector Circuit

As the name implies, the common collector circuit is connected so that the collector of the transistor is connected to ground (rather than the emitter, as in previous circuits). Although the circuit may appear differently, the analysis follows the same technique as previous circuits. As before, we begin our analysis by examining the input loop, which contains the forward-biased base-emitter junction. Then we use beta to transfer into the output loop, which contains the collector-emitter of the transistor. The following example shows that the method is not dramatically different from that used previously.

Determine $I_B$, $I_C$, and $V_{CE}$ for the circuit of Figure 26–29 if the transistor has $\beta = 200$.

EXAMPLE 26–7

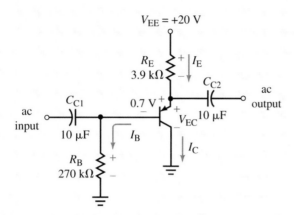

**FIGURE 26–29**

**Solution**
Notice that the transistor in the circuit of Figure 26–19 is a pnp transistor. Although this does not change the method of analysis, there are a few precautions. As one might expect, the voltage $V_{BE}$ for the pnp transistor is $-0.7$ V rather than $+0.7$ V as in the npn transistor. The input loop equation begins at the supply voltage $V_{EE}$ and is written as

$$V_{EE} = R_E I_E + V_{EB} + R_B I_B$$
$$20 \text{ V} = (3.9 \text{ k}\Omega)I_E + 0.7 \text{ V} + (270 \text{ k}\Omega)I_B$$
$$= (3.9 \text{ k}\Omega)(\beta + 1)I_B + 0.7 \text{ V} + (270 \text{ k}\Omega)I_B$$

and so we have

$$I_B = \frac{20 \text{ V} - 0.7 \text{ V}}{(3.9 \text{ k}\Omega)(201) + 270 \text{ k}\Omega}$$
$$= 18.3 \text{ } \mu\text{A}$$

Now, transferring into the output loop, we have

$$I_C = \beta I_B = (200)18.3 \text{ } \mu\text{A} = 3.66 \text{ mA} \cong I_E$$

Writing the output loop, we have

$$V_{EE} = R_E I_E + V_{EC}$$
$$20 \text{ V} = (3.9 \text{ k}\Omega)(3.66 \text{ mA}) + V_{EC}$$

We calculate $V_{EC}$ as

$$V_{EC} = 20 \text{ V} - (3.9 \text{ k}\Omega)(3.66 \text{ mA}) = 5.72 \text{ V}$$

This results in a collector-emitter voltage of $V_{CE} = -5.72$ V, which is precisely the polarity that one expects in a transistor amplifier having a pnp transistor.

**The Common Base Circuit**

The common base amplifier is typically used for high-frequency applications and so is not a circuit that is as common as the common emitter or the common collector circuit. The following example shows the techniques used in determining the operating point of a common base amplifier.

**EXAMPLE 26–8**

Determine the $V_{CE}$ and $I_C$ of the common base amplifier circuit shown in Figure 26–30.

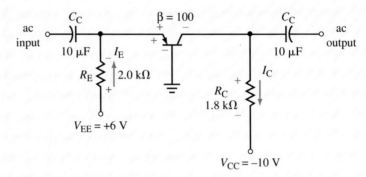

**FIGURE 26–30**

**Solution**

As always, we begin our analysis by examining the "input loop"—the loop containing the forward-biased base-emitter junction. The input loop equation is written as

$$R_E I_E + V_{EB} = +6 \text{ V}$$
$$(2.0 \text{ k}\Omega)I_E + 0.7 \text{ V} = +6 \text{ V}$$

which gives an emitter current (and the approximate value of collector current) as

$$I_E = \frac{6.0 \text{ V} - 0.7 \text{ V}}{2.0 \text{ k}\Omega} = 2.65 \text{ mA} \cong I_C$$

Now, we examine the output loop to arrive at the following equation:

$$6 \text{ V} + 10 \text{ V} = (2.0 \text{ k}\Omega)I_E + V_{EC} + (1.8 \text{ k}\Omega)I_C$$
$$= (3.8 \text{ k}\Omega)(2.65 \text{ mA}) + V_{EC}$$

which gives

$$V_{EC} = 16 \text{ V} - 10.07 \text{ V}$$
$$= 5.93 \text{ V}$$

and so the collector-emitter voltage is $V_{CE} = -5.93$ V.

## 26.7 The Transistor Switch

Although the transistor was once primarily used as an amplifier, its main application in modern electronic circuits is as a switch or as an inverter. In both cases, the operation of the transistor is either at saturation (analogous to a closed switch) or at cutoff (corresponding to an open switch). A low current signal applied at the base is translated into a high collector current that is capable of providing sufficient current to turn on LEDs (light emitting diodes) or operating relays. If a power transistor is used, the collector current may be sufficient to operate small motors.

When used as an inverter, a logic "1" ($\equiv$ 5 V) applied at the base input will result in a logic "0" ($\equiv$ 0 V) at the collector output. Conversely, a logic "0" applied at the base will result in a logic "1" at the collector.

The following example shows how a small base current can be translated into a fairly large collector current that can be used to operate an LED. A logic gate typically does not provide enough current to turn on an LED. In order to boost the current, a transistor circuit can be used as *buffer*.

EXAMPLE 26–9

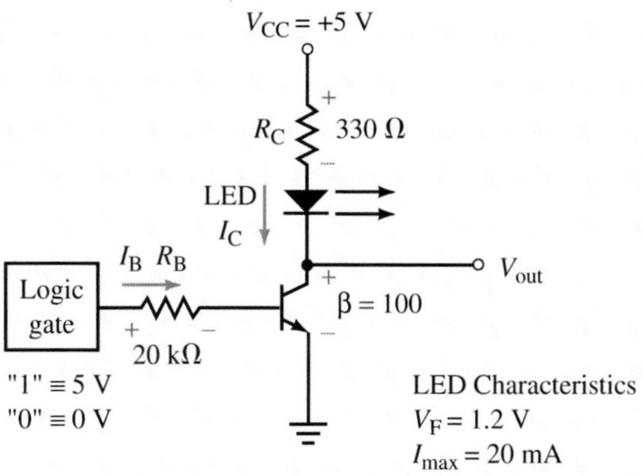

FIGURE 26–31

The transistor shown in Figure 26–31 is used as a buffer, providing sufficient current to turn on an LED when the output of the logic gate is "1".

a. Find the saturation current for the transistor.

b. Calculate the current through the LED when the output of the logic gate is "1".

c. Determine the output voltage at the collector (with respect to ground) for part a.

d. Calculate the current through the LED when the output of the logic gate is "0".

e. Determine the output voltage at the collector for part d.

**Solution**

a. In this example, the saturation current must take into account the forward voltage of the LED. Suppose $V_F$ is the forward voltage drop across the LED when "on". Also recall that $V_{CE} = 0$ when the transistor is in saturation. Then

$$I_{C(SAT)} = \frac{V_{CC} - V_F}{R_C} = \frac{5\ V - 1.2\ V}{330\ \Omega} = 11.51\ mA$$

b. When the output of the logic gate is a logic "1," the base current for the transistor is determined as

$$I_B = \frac{5\ V - 0.7\ V}{20\ k\Omega} = 0.215\ mA$$

Now, using the transistor beta, we evaluate the collector current as

$$I_C = \beta I_B = (100)(0.215\ mA) = 21.5\ mA$$

However, since the collector current cannot exceed the saturation current, we conclude that the collector current for the transistor is 11.5 mA.

c. With the transistor in saturation, the output voltage must be

$$V_{out} = 0\ V$$

d. If the logic gate produces a logic "0" at its output, the transistor must go into cutoff since there can be no base current. Consequently, there can also be no collector current and so we have

$$I_C = 0$$

e. With the transistor in cutoff, the output voltage must be

$$V_{out} = 5\ V$$

The results of part c. and e. illustrate that the transistor in this circuit behaves as both a buffer and a logic inverter. A logic "1" applied at the input results in a logic "0" at the output, while a logic "0" applied at the input results in a logic "1" at the output.

a. If the logic gate shown in Figure 26–31 is capable of providing a maximum "source" current of 50 μA, determine the minimum size of the current-limiting resistor, $R_B$.

b. If you were given an LED having $V_F = 1.8$ V and $I_{max} = 20$ mA calculate the range of resistance, $R_C$ that would provide for a minimum current of 10 mA to the LED when the logic gate produces a "1."

*Answers*
a.  86 kΩ; b. $R_C = 160$ Ω → 320 Ω

## 26.8 Testing a Transistor with a Multimeter

Transistors and transistor circuits can be easily tested using a multimeter. Indeed, many inexpensive multimeters such as the one shown in Figure 26–32 include a provision for testing of both pnp and npn transistors. This type of multimeter allows us to determine the approximate dc beta of the transistor by simply inserting the transistor into the appropriate plugins. In this section you will find that there are several other methods that can be used to determine whether a transistor is operating correctly.

**FIGURE 26–32**    Multimeter with built-in transistor tester.

Since a transistor is essentially constructed as two back-to-back diodes, we may use an ohmmeter to measure the resistance of each of the p-n junctions. Recall that a forward-biased p-n junction has a small resistance, while a reverse-biased junction will essentially be an open circuit. By correctly using an ohmmeter, it is possible to determine whether an unknown transistor is pnp or npn and also to determine the correct pin configuration. If a transistor fails an ohmmeter test, we know that the transistor will not work properly when used in a circuit. Unfortunately, it is possible for a transistor to pass a simple ohmmeter test and yet fail in an operational circuit. We will examine this condition in the next chapter.

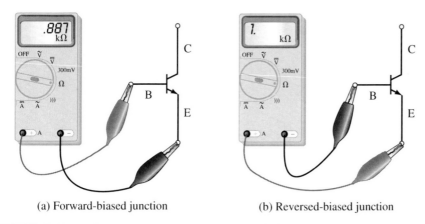

(a) Forward-biased junction               (b) Reversed-biased junction

**FIGURE 26–33**    Typical ohmmeter measurements of the BE junction of an npn transistor.

Consider the npn transistor shown in Figure 26–33. If we were to connect an ohmmeter with the positive (red) terminal at the base and the negative (black) terminal at the emitter, the BE junction would be forward-biased and we would expect to measure a relatively low resistance. Although the actual value is not important, here we see that we are measuring 0.887 kΩ. Remember that the ohmmeter uses a dc voltage source to generate a small current through the component under test. Now if we were to reverse the ohmmeter terminals and connect the negative terminal to the base and the positive terminal to the emitter, the BE junction would be reverse-biased. This time there would be no current through the junction, and the ohmmeter would indicate infinite resistance.

Figure 26–34 shows that a similar effect would occur if the ohmmeter were placed between the collector and base terminals. In this instance, we see that the forward-biased CB junction gives a reading of 0.849 kΩ with the ohmmeter in the same range as the first measurement.

> **PRACTICAL NOTES . . .**
>
> When using a digital ohmmeter to measure resistance of semiconductors, it is generally necessary to change the range of the meter to a location showing a diode symbol.
>
>

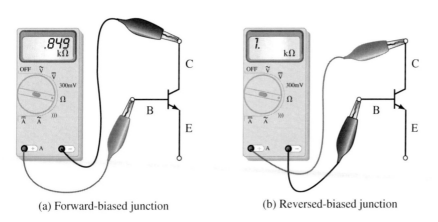

(a) Forward-biased junction               (b) Reversed-biased junction

**FIGURE 26–34**    Typical ohmmeter measurements of the CB junction of an npn transistor.

Finally, with the ohmmeen connected between the collector and emitter as shown in Figure 26–35, we see that both connections will indicate an open circuit. This is because each measurement results in one reverse-biased junction.

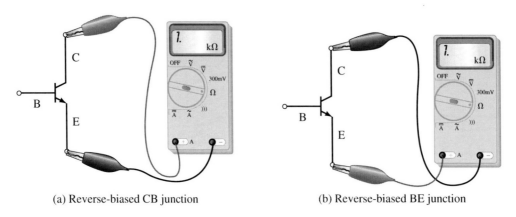

(a) Reverse-biased CB junction          (b) Reverse-biased BE junction

**FIGURE 26–35**   Typical ohmmeter measurements between the collector and emitter of an npn transistor.

Although the illustrations were for an npn transistor, we would notice similar effects for the pnp transistor. For all transistors, there will be two low resistance readings, and in all such cases, the terminal connected to the positive (red) terminal of the ohmmeter will be connected to p-type material, while the terminal connected to the negative (black) terminal of the ohmmeter will be connected to n-type material. Also, for all transistors (npn or pnp), the lower resistance reading will indicate that the measurement involves the collector of the transistor. The following steps may determine the type of transistor and the pin allocations.

1. Six different measurements must always be made.
2. If you measure an open circuit between any two terminals regardless of how the ohmmeter is connected, you may conclude that the remaining terminal is the base.
3. With any transistor, you will have exactly two low measurements if the transistor is functioning correctly. If you have a low reading when the positive terminal of the ohmmeter is connected to the base you have an npn transistor. Conversely, if the reading is low when the negative terminal is connected to the base, you have a pnp transistor.
4. The lower of the two low-resistance readings corresponds to the collector of the transistor, since the collector is the most heavily doped region. This, of course, means that the remaining terminal must be the emitter.

The following example shows how an ohmmeter can be used to determine the transistor type and pin configuration.

**EXAMPLE 26–10**

**FIGURE 26–36**

You are given the unknown transistor shown in Figure 26–36 and use an ohmmeter to take resistance measurements as tabulated. As always, the ohmmeter has two terminals; the positive $(+$ , red) terminal and the negative $(-$ , black) terminal.

| Pins 1 & 2 | | Pins 2 & 3 | | Pins 1 & 3 | |
|---|---|---|---|---|---|
| Pin 1 $(+)$ Pin 2 $(-)$ | ∞ | Pin 2 $(+)$ Pin 3 $(-)$ | ∞ | Pin 1 $(+)$ Pin 3 $(-)$ | ∞ |
| Pin 2 $(+)$ Pin 1 $(-)$ | 0.457 kΩ | Pin 3 $(+)$ Pin 2 $(-)$ | ∞ | Pin 3 $(+)$ Pin 1 $(-)$ | 0.482 kΩ |

a. What type of transistor were you given—pnp or npn?

b. What are the pin designations?

**Solution**

a. After examining the given results, we determine that pin 1 must be the base, since both measurements between pins 2 and 3 indicate open circuits. Since the base (pin 1) is connected to the negative terminal of the ohmmeter, we know that the base must be constructed of n-type material. Hence, your transistor must be pnp.

b. Finally, since the resistance measurement between pins 1 and 2 is smaller than the measurement between pins 1 and 3, we conclude that pin 2 must be the collector. Therefore, we have the following pin designations:

Pin 1: Base

Pin 2: Collector

Pin 3: Emitter

You are given the unknown transistor shown in Figure 26–36 and use an ohmmeter to take resistance measurements as tabulated below.

PRACTICE PROBLEMS 8

| Pins 1 & 2 | | Pins 2 & 3 | | Pins 1 & 3 | |
|---|---|---|---|---|---|
| Pin 1 $(+)$ Pin 2 $(-)$ | ∞ | Pin 2 $(+)$ Pin 3 $(-)$ | 0.780 kΩ | Pin 1 $(+)$ Pin 3 $(-)$ | ∞ |
| Pin 2 $(+)$ Pin 1 $(-)$ | 0.745 kΩ | Pin 3 $(+)$ Pin 2 | ∞ | Pin 3 $(+)$ Pin 1 $(-)$ | ∞ |

a. What type of transistor were you given—pnp or npn?

b. What are the pin designations?

*Answers*

a. npn; b. pin 1 = collector, pin 2 = base, pin 3 = emitter

**NOTES . . .**

When determining current in an operating circuit, we first measure voltage across a known resistance, and then calculate current as $I = \dfrac{V_R}{R}$ .

A multimeter can be used not only to test isolated transistors, but is extremely useful for assessing whether a transistor in a working circuit is operating as expected. Remember, when a transistor is used as an amplifier, the BE junction will always be forward-biased and one would expect to measure $V_{BE} \approx$ 0.7 V (for a silicon transistor). This means that the first test that one should perform on an amplifier is to determine whether this junction is biased correctly.

If the BE junction is forward-biased, we may then determine whether an amplifier is operating in its active region by measuring the operating point ($V_{CEQ}$ and $I_{CQ}$). The voltage is very easy to measure since we would simply connect the voltmeter directly at the collector and emitter terminals of the transistor. In order to directly measure the current, we would need to break the circuit at the collector and insert the ammeter directly between collector resistor and the collector of the transistor. **This is not a practical method!** A much easier and preferred method for measuring current is to measure the voltage across a known resistance and then simply calculate the current using Ohm's Law.

Figure 26–37 illustrates typical measurements for an operational transistor circuit. The illustration shows that an additional voltage measurement can be taken to provide the current through the base bias resistor, $R_B$. This additional measurement allows us to calculate β for this transistor.

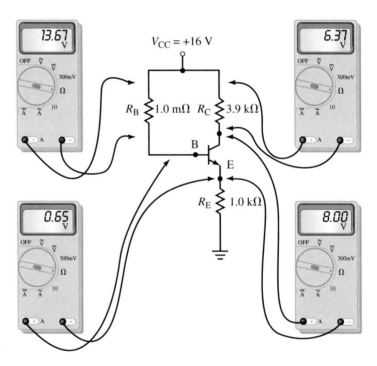

**FIGURE 26–37**

**NOTES . . .**

Notice that our calculation results do not show more than two significant figures. This reflects the uncertainty shown by the resistor color codes (two significant figures). Although we could obtain better results by breaking the circuit and measuring the currents, the improved precision would not justify the extra time. The purpose of these measurements is to determine whether the circuit is operating correctly.

The measurements of Figure 26–37 provide much useful information on the operating point of the circuit. The BE voltage, $V_{BE} = 0.65$ V indicates that the base-emitter junction of the transistor is correctly biased. We solve for the collector current at the operating point as

$$I_{CQ} = \frac{6.37 \text{ V}}{3.9 \text{ k}\Omega} = 1.6 \text{ mA}$$

The collector-emitter voltage at the operating point is determined as $V_{CEQ} = 8.00$ V. The base current for the circuit is determined as

$$I_{BQ} = \frac{13.67 \text{ V}}{1.0 \text{ M}\Omega} = 14 \text{ }\mu\text{A}$$

which allows us to approximate β as

$$\beta_Q = \frac{1.6 \text{ mA}}{14 \text{ }\mu\text{A}} \approx 110$$

Given the circuit of Figure 26–38:

**EXAMPLE 26–11**

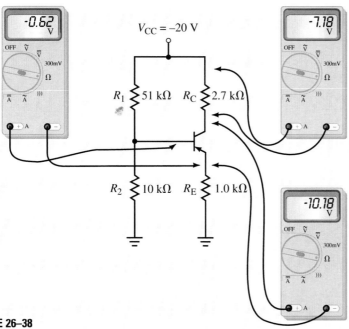

**FIGURE 26–38**

a. Is the BE junction biased correctly? Explain your answer.

b. What is the operating point of the transistor?

c. For the given information, can you calculate β of the circuit? If so, what is its value? If not, explain your answer.

**Solution**

a. The BE junction is biased correctly, since for a pnp transistor the base will be more negative than the emitter by a value of around 0.7 V. (In this case, a voltage $V_{BE} = -0.62$ V is within acceptable values.)

b. The collector current at the operating point is

$$I_{CQ} = \frac{-7.18 \text{ V}}{2.7 \text{ k}\Omega} = 2.7 \text{ mA}$$

(The negative in the above calculation is simply due to the voltage measurement being taken with the positive terminal of the voltmeter at the top of $R_C$.)

The collector-emitter voltage at the operating point is determined as $V_{CEQ} = -10.18$ V. As expected, for a pnp transistor, the collector-emitter voltage is negative.

c. β of the circuit cannot be found, since we are unable to calculate for base current by measuring across a known resistor. (A common mistake that is made is to measure the voltage across $R_1$ and then say that the base current is the same as the current through this resistor. It is not! The current entering the base is much smaller.)

## 26.9 Junction Field Effect Transistor Construction and Operation

### Construction of the JFET

The JFET (**junction field effect transistor**) is similar to the BJT in that it has three terminals and can be used to amplify small ac signals. By embedding a p-type material around an n-type channel, as shown in Figure 26–39, we have an n-channel JFET. Notice that the arrow on the gate of the transistor points away from the p-type material towards the n-type material in the channel.

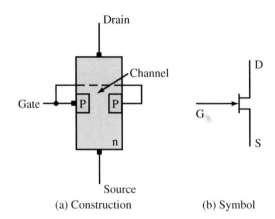

(a) Construction          (b) Symbol

**FIGURE 26–39**   n-channel JFET

We will find that the biasing of the n-channel JFET is similar to the npn BJT. Indeed, it will become evident that the gate(G), drain(D), and source(S) terminals of the JFET are very much like the base, collector, and emitter of the BJT. Just as the pnp transistor is the complement of the npn, the p-channel JFET is the complement to the n-channel. Operationally, the two FETs are the same, except that the n-channel is biased with a positive supply, while the p-channel is biased with a negative supply. Figure 26–40 shows both the structure and the symbol of the p-channel JFET. Once again notice that the arrow in the symbol points from the p-type material (channel) towards the n-type material (of the gate).

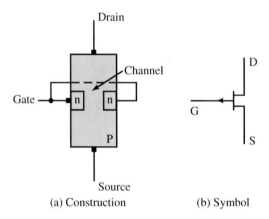

(a) Construction          (b) Symbol

**FIGURE 26–40**   p-channel JFET

While there are some similarities between the BJT and the JFET, there are several characteristics of the JFET that are quite different than the BJT. Whereas the BJT is a semiconductor device that provides current amplification, the JFET provides voltage amplification. The base-emitter junction of the BJT amplifier is always forward-biased, while in the JFET circuit, the gate-source is always reverse-biased. These conditions will become more evident as we examine the operation of the JFET. Other characteristics of the JFET are:

1. The input impedance of the device approaches infinity due to the reverse-biased gate-source junction.

2. The JFET amplifier is less sensitive to changes in input voltage than a junction transistor, since the JFET amplifier typically has a lower voltage gain (as we will find in the next chapter.)

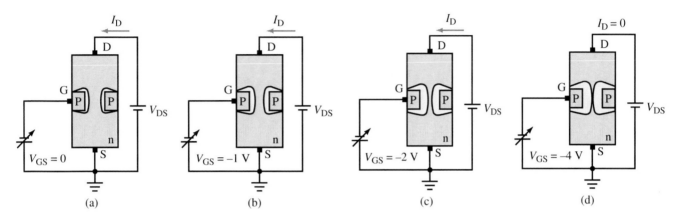

**FIGURE 26–41**   Channel width of a JFET decreases as the gate-source is reverse-biased.

## Operation of the JFET

Although we will examine the operation of the n-channel JFET, the operation of the p-channel is precisely the same, except that currents and voltages will be the opposite directions and polarities. In some respects, the operation of the JFET is easier to understand than the operation of the BJT. The JFET has an operation that is similar to how a water hose works. Examine the structure and circuit of Figure 26–41.

If there is no control voltage applied at the gate ($V_{GS} = 0$) as shown in Figure 26–41(a), charge moves freely through the JFET, impeded only by the bulk resistance of the semiconductor material. The drain current, $I_D$, is relatively large. Figures 26–41(b) and (c) show that as the negative bias on the gate is increased, a depletion region is established in the channel region, effectively reducing the cross-sectional area of the channel. This is similar to squeezing a water hose that has water moving through. With light pressure, the flow will decrease somewhat; with increased pressure, the flow will reduce even further. Since the p-n junction in the channel region is reverse-biased, the gate current $I_G = 0$. Applying Kirchhoff's current law, we have a very important equation for FETs:

$$I_S = I_D \qquad (26\text{–}23)$$

In Figure 26–41(d), we see that when $V_{GS} = -4$ V, the depletion region is so large that there is effectively no channel between the drain and the source. Using the water hose analogy, this is the same as tightly pinching the hose. The value of the gate-source voltage at which the drain current just becomes zero (is $I_D = 0$) is expressed as $V_{GS(OFF)}$. Typical values for n-channel JFETs are between $V_{GS(OFF)} = -3$ V and $V_{GS(OFF)} = -8$ V. Making $V_{GS}$ more negative than $V_{GS(OFF)}$ has no further effect. This is analogous to applying further pressure to a water hose that is already squeezed hard enough to stop flow.

Figure 26–42 shows that the depletion region can be increased even without applying an external bias voltage between the gate and the source. By

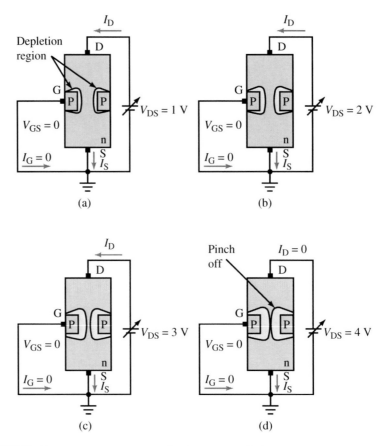

**FIGURE 26–42**   Channel width of a JFET decreases as $V_{DS}$ increases.

increasing the drain-source voltage, the internal bulk resistance of the JFET sets up a voltage divider. Consequently, the channel in the region of the gate is at a higher potential than the gate (which is at ground). This results in the reverse-biased p-n junction at the gate and the corresponding depletion region. As $V_{DS}$ is increased, $I_D$ increases linearly and the depletion region at the gate becomes larger. Eventually, the depletion region becomes so large that additional drain current is no longer possible. At this point, $I_D = 0$ and the gate-source voltage at which the JFET is off is called the pinch-off voltage and is designated as $V_P$. For JFET transistors, the pinch-off voltage, $V_P$, and the gate shut-off voltage, $V_{GS(OFF)}$, are essentially the same magnitude and so we have

$$|V_P| = |V_{GS(OFF)}| \qquad\qquad \textbf{(26–24)}$$

The drain characteristics of the JFET are shown in Figure 26–43. Notice the similarity between these curves and the collector characteristic curves for a BJT. The notable difference is that each line corresponds to a different gate-to-source voltage, with the maximum drain current, $I_{DSS}$, occurring when $V_{GS} = 0$ V. When the forward breakdown voltage for the JFET is exceeded, the current through the device will generally destroy the component.

The output characteristic curves are used to generate the **transfer curve,** which relates the operation of the output portion of the circuit to the input. This curve is useful for determining the dc operating point (Q-point) of the JFET and will be used in the next chapter to determine the ac operation of a JFET amplifier. In all cases the transfer curve of any JFET is a parabolic segment between $V_{GS(OFF)}$ and $I_{DSS}$ that provides the relationship between $I_D$ and $V_{GS}$.

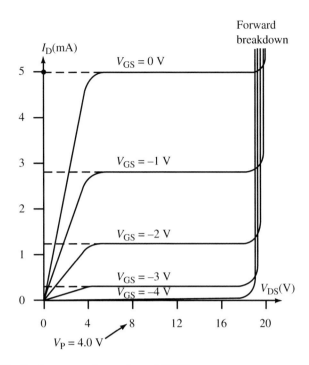

**FIGURE 26–43**   Drain curves of an n-channel JFET.

The equation that follows is called **Shockley's equation** after the Bell scientist who explained the *field-effect* theory for FETs.

$$I_D = I_{DSS}\left(1 - \frac{V_{GS}}{V_{GS(OFF)}}\right)^2$$    **Shockley's equation (26–25)**

The values for $I_{DSS}$ and $V_{GS(OFF)}$ are constants that are generally found experimentally for a given transistor. Figure 26–44 shows the transfer curve as well as the drain curves that generate the transfer curve.

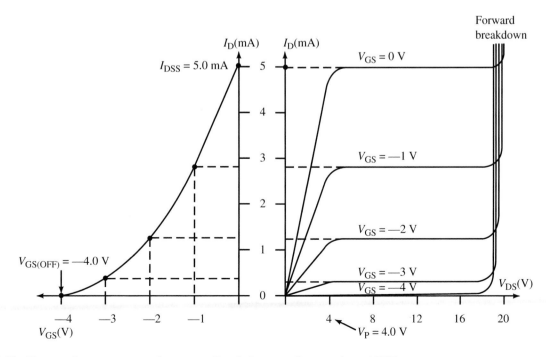

**FIGURE 26–44**   Transconductance curve and corresponding drain curves for an n-channel FET.

The transfer curve of Figure 26–44 shows that the drain current for values of $V_{GS}$ less (more negative for an n-channel JFET) than $V_{GS(OFF)}$ is zero and the drain current can never exceed $I_{DSS}$. In the next section, we will use the transfer curve for a transistor to determine the operating point.

## 26.10 JFET Biasing

Just as was the case with the junction transistor, the JFET has several bias configurations. In analyzing a JFET circuit, there are only three considerations that we must remember. The first is that the gate-source junction of the JFET is always reverse-biased. This means that we can expect $V_{GS}$ to be any value between 0 V and $V_{GS(OFF)}$. The second point that must be remembered is that $I_S = I_D$, and the third is that the operating point must occur on the transfer curve (namely between $I_{DSS}$ and $V_{GS(OFF)}$) for the given transistor. Although we could solve for the $I_{DQ}$ and $V_{GSQ}$ using algebra, a much simpler approach is to use graphical means. When solving for the operating point of a JFET using graphical method, we will use the normalized transfer curve illustrated in Figure 26–45. This diagram can be modified for any JFET transistor by simply inserting the correct values for $I_{DSS}$ and $V_{GS(OFF)}$ and then re-scaling the divisions accordingly.

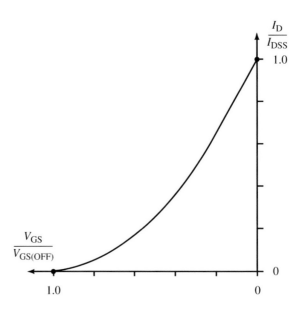

**FIGURE 26–45**   Normalized transconductance curve for an n-channel JFET.

In order to determine the operating point of the JFET, we use the output loop of the circuit (containing the drain and source terminals) to sketch the dc load line. The operating point of the transistor will occur at the intersection of the dc load line and the transfer curve. The following examples show how the transfer curve is used to solve for the operating point for any JFET circuit. You will notice that capacitors have been included in each of the circuits to more accurately represent working circuits. However, just as was the case for BJT circuits, we will ignore the effects of the capacitors when calculating the dc operating points since they behave as open circuits for dc.

The self-bias circuit shown in Figure 26–46 has a JFET with $I_{DSS} = 8.0$ mA and $V_{GS(OFF)} = -4.0$ V.

**EXAMPLE 26–12**

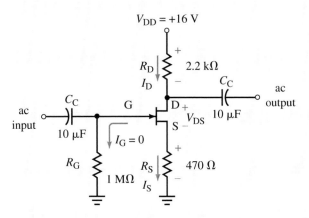

**FIGURE 26–46**

a. Find $I_{DQ}$ and $V_{GSQ}$.

b. Solve for $V_{DSQ}$.

**Solution**

a. In order to determine the operating point we first sketch the dc load line on the transfer curve. To sketch this line, we need to arbitrarily select two points that will occur on the graph and yet be far enough apart to allow us to draw a suitable straight line.

Let $I_S = I_D = 0$ mA:

Examining the input loop shown in Figure 26–47, we write the input loop equation for the JFET as follows:

$$I_G R_G - V_{GS} - I_S R_S = 0$$

Now, since $I_G = 0$ due to the reverse-biased gate-source junction, we simplify the above expression for this circuit as

$$V_{GS} = -I_S R_S \qquad \textbf{(26–26)}$$

Now, because $I_S = I_D = 0$ mA, we have

$$V_{GS} = 0$$

For the second point on the dc load line, we again select a drain current value and use Equation 26–26 to solve for the corresponding value of $V_{GS}$.

Let $I_S = I_D = 8$ mA:

$$
\begin{aligned}
V_{GS} &= -I_D R_S \\
&= -(8 \text{ mA})(0.470 \text{ k}\Omega) \\
&= -3.76 \text{ V}
\end{aligned}
$$

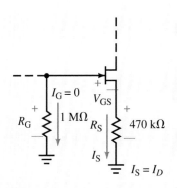

**FIGURE 26–47**

The resulting straight line is found by connecting the two points and is shown in Figure 26–48. Finally, we approximate the intersection of the dc load line and the transfer curve as $I_{DQ} \approx 3.1$ mA and $V_{GSQ} \approx -1.5$ V. Clearly, the graphical method will not give precise results, since it is open to interpretation. However, it is a much simpler approach than

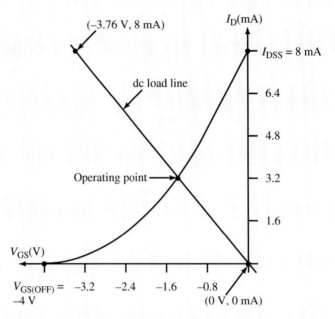

**FIGURE 26–48**

using the algebraic method, which involves the solution of two simultaneous equations, one being a quadratic equation. It is left as an exercise for the enthusiastic student to solve for the Q-point determined by the following two equations.

$$I_{DQ} = -\frac{V_{GSQ}}{0.47 \text{ k}\Omega}$$

$$I_{DQ} = 8 \text{ mA}\left(1 - \frac{V_{GSQ}}{-4 \text{ V}}\right)^2$$

(The algebraic results yield $I_{DQ} = 3.161$ mA and $V_{GSQ} = -1.486$ V.)

b. By examining the output loop of Figure 26–46, we write the output loop equation as

$$V_{DD} = I_D R_D + V_{DS} + I_S R_S \tag{26–27}$$

Since $I_S = I_D$, we rewrite the above expression as

$$V_{DS} = V_{DD} - I_D (R_D + R_S) \tag{26–28}$$

which gives

$$V_{DS} = 16 \text{ V} - 3.1 \text{ mA} (2.2 \text{ k}\Omega + 0.47 \text{ k}\Omega)$$
$$= 7.7 \text{ V}$$

Another bias arrangement uses a voltage divider similar to that used when working with the universal bias junction transistor. Just as in the previous example, we must again sketch the dc load line in order to determine the operating point on the transfer curve.

The circuit shown in Figure 26–49 has a p-channel JFET with $I_{DSS} = 10.0$ mA and $V_{GS(OFF)} = 5.0$ V.

**EXAMPLE 26–13**

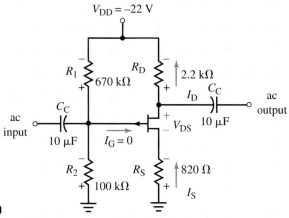

**FIGURE 26–49**

a. Find $I_{DQ}$ and $V_{GSQ}$.

b. Solve for $V_{DSQ}$.

**Solution**

a. Due to the voltage divider of the resistors in the gate circuit, we see that the gate voltage will remain at a constant value determined as

$$V_G = \left( \frac{R_2}{R_1 + R_2} \right) V_{DD} \qquad (26\text{--}29)$$

and so we have

$$V_G = \left( \frac{100 \text{ k}\Omega}{670 \text{ k}\Omega + 100 \text{ k}\Omega} \right)(-22 \text{ V}) = -2.86 \text{ V}$$

Now, we examine the input loop of the JFET as shown in Figure 26–50.

Here we see that the input loop equation gives the following linear equation.

$$V_G = V_{GS} - I_S R_S \qquad (26\text{--}30)$$

Substituting the known values into the above expression we have

$$V_{GS} = -2.86 \text{ V} + (0.82 \text{ k}\Omega)I_D$$

In order to sketch the dc load line, we once again need to arbitrarily select two points. Remember that for the p-channel JFET, the operating point must occur between 0 and $V_{GS} = +5.0$ V.

Let $I_S = I_D = 4$ mA:

$$V_{GS} = -2.86 \text{ V} + (0.82 \text{ k}\Omega)(4 \text{ mA})$$

$$= 0.42 \text{ V}$$

and

Let $I_S = I_D = 8$ mA:

$$V_{GS} = -2.86 \text{ V} + (0.82 \text{ k}\Omega)(8 \text{ mA})$$

$$= 3.70 \text{ V}$$

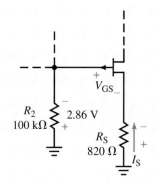

**FIGURE 26–50**

Now connecting the two points, we have the dc load line shown in Figure 26–51. At the intersection of the dc load line and the transfer curve, we obtain the operating point as $I_{DQ} \approx 5.2$ mA and $V_{GSQ} \approx 1.4$ V.

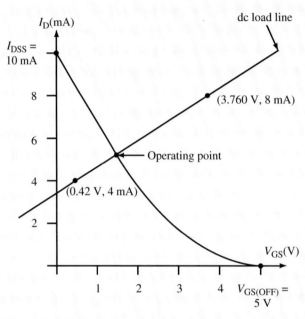

**FIGURE 26–51**

b. The output loop equation for the p-channel JFET of Figure 26–49 is written as

$$V_{DD} = -I_D R_D + V_{DS} - I_S R_S \qquad (26–31)$$

and so using the drain current found in part a., we find $V_{DS}$ at the operating point as

$$
\begin{aligned}
V_{DSQ} &= V_{DD} + I_D R_D + I_S R_S \\
&= -22 \text{ V} + 5.2 \text{ mA}(2.2 \text{ k}\Omega + 0.82 \text{ k}\Omega) \\
&= -6.30 \text{ V}
\end{aligned}
$$

## 26.11 MOSFETs

Most integrated circuits today use metal oxide semiconductor field effect transistors to meet the size constraints and low power consumption requirements of modern electronic circuits. Although JFETs must be reverse-biased and are therefore restricted to working in the depletion region, you will discover that MOSFETs have no such restriction. Consequently, MOSFETs are typically able to handle more current than corresponding JFETs and are able to handle a broader operating range. There are two basic types of MOSFETs; depletion (or D-MOSFETs) and enhancement (or E-MOSFETs). Depletion MOSFETs can be reverse-biased to operate in the depletion region or they can be forward-biased to operate in the enhancement region. Figure 26–52 illustrates the structure and symbol of the n-channel depletion MOSFET, while Figure 26–53 shows the structure and symbol of the n-channel enhancement MOSFET.

Notice that for both the depletion and the enhancement MOSFET, the gate is isolated from the transistor by a layer of silicon dioxide insulator. Indeed, MOSFETs are often referred to as isolated gate FETs (or IGFETs). The origin of

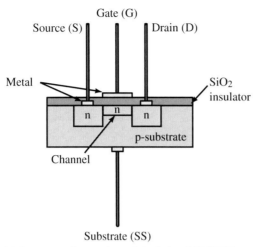

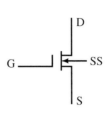

(a) Structure of an n-channel depletion MOSFET

(b) Symbol of an n-channel depletion MOSFET

**FIGURE 26–52**

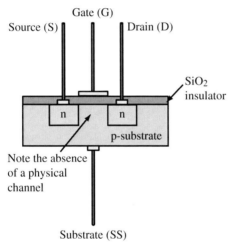

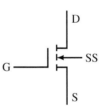

(a) Structure of an n-channel enhancement MOSFET

(b) Symbol of an n-channel enhancement MOSFET

**FIGURE 26–53**

the name MOSFETs for the devices shown in the previous figures is now fairly obvious. **Metal** is derived from the contacts at the drain, source, and particularly the gate. **Oxide** relates to the insertion of silicon dioxide insulator between the gate and the channel. The term **semiconductor** is due to the semiconductor materials that are used to construct the device and finally, the term **field effect** relates to the electric field that is generated by the gate to control the channel.

Since the gate of the MOSFET is isolated from the rest of the circuit, the input impedance of the MOSFET is much larger than the JFET (which already has an input impedance of many megohms). For this reason, the gate circuit of a MOSFET requires very little current (in the order of pA).

The principle difference between the D-MOSFET and the E-MOSFET is that for the former, there is a physical channel between the drain and the source, while for the latter a physical channel does not exist between the drain and the source. This means that an external voltage must be applied to the gate terminal to electrically generate a channel. In all circuits using MOSFETS, the substrate will be connected to a fixed potential, usually ground or the power supply. In many circuits, the source terminal will also be at ground. Therefore, a MOSFET will have either three or four terminals.

We will now examine the operation and biasing of both types of transistors in greater detail.

### Depletion MOSFETs (D-MOSFETs)

When the gate to source of a D-MOSFET is made negative as shown in Figure 26–54, the majority carriers (electrons) of the channel are repelled into the p-substrate, effectively depleting the number of carriers available for the drain to source current. In this illustration we see that the MOSFET is very similar to a JFET operating in its **depletion region.**

As was the case with the JFET, if the magnitude of $V_{GS}$ exceeds the $|V_{GS(OFF)}|$, there will be no available majority carriers available in the channel, and $I_D = 0$.

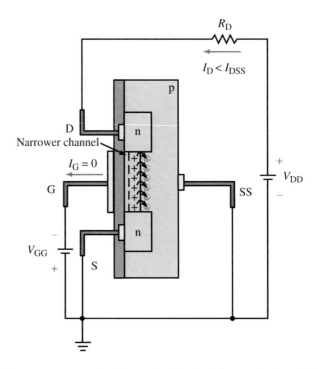

**FIGURE 26–54**   n-channel D-MOSFET operates in its depletion mode when $V_{GS}$ is negative.

However, unlike the JFET, if the gate to source voltage of the D-MOSFET is made positive as shown in Figure 26–55, the majority carriers (holes) in the substrate will be repelled, effectively increasing (or enhancing) the channel width between the drain and the source. When the gate of an n-channel MOSFET is positive with respect to the source, we say that it is operating in its **enhancement region.**

With an increase in the size of the channel, additional current is now possible. The transfer curve for the n-channel D-MOSFET is illustrated in Figure 26–56.

Notice that the output current is no longer limited to a maximum value of $I_{DSS}$. However, the equation of the transfer curve for a D-MOSFET is precisely the same as that of a JFET, namely

$$I_D = I_{DSS}\left(1 - \frac{V_{GS}}{V_{GS(OFF)}}\right)^2 \qquad \textbf{(26–32)}$$

The operating point of a D-MOSFET amplifier circuit is found by determining the intersection of the dc load line and the transfer curve, exactly the same way as for a JFET. The following example illustrates the method.

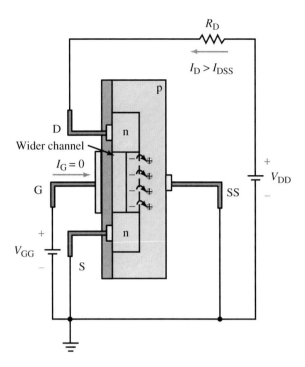

**FIGURE 26–55**   n-channel D-MOSFET operates in its enhancement mode when $V_{GS}$ is positive.

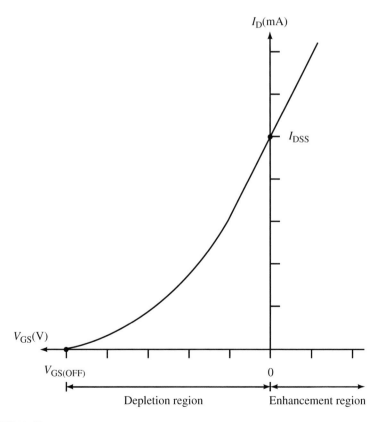

**FIGURE 26–56**   Transconductance curve of an n-channel D-MOSFET

**EXAMPLE 26–14**

The circuit shown in Figure 26–57 uses an n-channel D-MOSFET with $I_{DSS} = 10.0$ mA and $V_{GS(OFF)} = -5.0$ V.

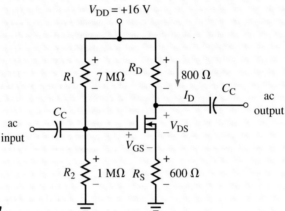

**FIGURE 26–57**

a. Find $I_{DQ}$ and $V_{GSQ}$.

b. Is the MOSFET operating in its depletion mode or enhancement mode?

c. Solve for $V_{DSQ}$.

**Solution**

a. The gate voltage (with respect to ground) will remain constant due to the voltage divider and is calculated to be

$$V_G = \left( \frac{1 \text{ M}\Omega}{1 \text{ M}\Omega + 7 \text{ M}\Omega} \right)(16 \text{ V}) = 2.00 \text{ V}$$

As in previous examples, we arbitrarily select two points to help sketch the dc load line on the transfer curve shown in Figure 26–58.

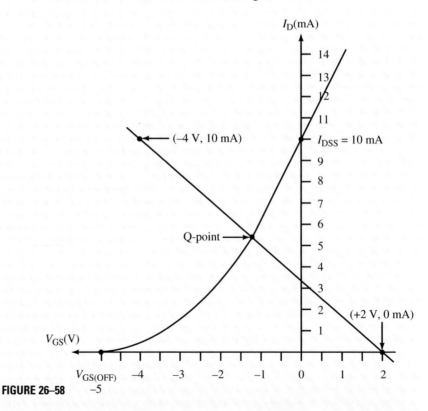

**FIGURE 26–58**

Let $I_S = I_D = 0$ mA:

$$V_{GS} = +2 \text{ V} - (0.6 \text{ k}\Omega)(0 \text{ mA})$$
$$= +2.00 \text{ V}$$

and

Let $I_S = I_D = 10$ mA:

$$V_{GS} = +2 \text{ V} - (0.6 \text{ k}\Omega)(10 \text{ mA})$$
$$= -4.00 \text{ V}$$

At the operating point, $I_{DQ} \approx 5.5$ mA and $V_{GSQ} \approx -1.28$ V.

b. Since $I_{DQ}$ is less than $I_{DSS}$, the transistor is operating in its depletion region.

c. We find $V_{DS}$ at the operating point as

$$V_{DSQ} = V_{DD} - I_D R_D - I_S R_S$$
$$= 16 \text{ V} - 5.5 \text{ mA}(0.8 \text{ k}\Omega + 0.6 \text{ k}\Omega)$$
$$= 8.3 \text{ V}$$

---

Repeat the work of Example 26–14, if the value of $R_S = 120$ Ω.

PRACTICE PROBLEMS 9

*Answers*

a.  $I_{DQ} \approx 12.2$ mA,  $V_{GSQ} \approx +0.52$ V; b. Enhancement; c. $V_{DSQ} = 4.78$ V

## Enhancement MOSFETs (E-MOSFETs)

Since E-MOSFETs do not have a channel, there can be no drain current until a channel is established by applying a positive gate to source voltage (for an n-channel E-MOSFET). This transistor can only operate in its enhancement mode, since the depletion mode is not possible. Although the transfer curve for an E-MOSFET is a parabolic curve, this curve is significantly different than for JFETs and D-MOSFETs. Refer to Figure 26–59.

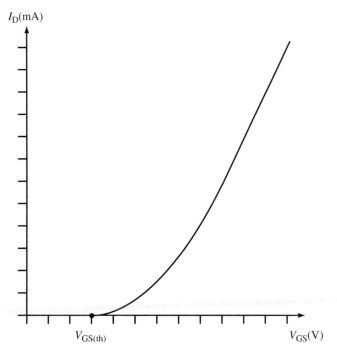

**FIGURE 26–59**  Transconductance curve of an n-channel E-MOSFET

There can be no current through the transistor until a minimum threshold voltage, $V_{GS(th)}$ is applied between the gate and the source. For the E-MOSFET, there is no value for $I_{DSS}$. Lastly, the relationship between the $I_D$ and $V_{GS}$ is given by the following expression.

$$I_D = k(V_{GS} - V_{GS(th)})^2 \qquad \text{(26–33)}$$

In the above expression, the value of the constant, $k$ is dependent on the particular transistor and can be easily calculated from the specification sheets of the transistor. We can solve for $k$ of any E-MOSFET as

$$k = \frac{I_{D(ON)}}{\left(V_{GS(ON)} - V_{GS(th)}\right)^2} \qquad \text{(26–34)}$$

For example, the 3N170 has a specified "ON" characteristic of $I_{D(ON)} = 10\text{ mA}$ for $V_{GS(ON)} = 10\text{ V}$. The threshold voltage is $V_{GS(th)} = 1.5\text{ V}$. Equation 26–33 would be written as

$$I_{D(ON)} = k(V_{GS(ON)} - 1.5\text{ V})^2$$

and so for the given transistor, we have

$$k = \frac{I_{D(ON)}}{\left(V_{GS(ON)} - 1.5\text{ V}\right)^2}$$

$$= \frac{10\text{ mA}}{(10\text{ V} - 1.5\text{ V})^2}$$

$$= 0.138\text{ mA/V}^2$$

The biasing for E-MOSFETs must be such that $V_{GS}$ is positive. The two best methods that provide correct biasing are the voltage divider circuit and the *drain-feedback circuit,* shown in Figure 26–60.

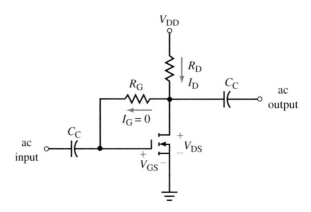

**FIGURE 26–60**

When we examine this circuit, several important characteristics become evident. First, due to the very high input impedance at the gate, we realize that there can be no gate current and so $I_G = 0$. Next, due to the zero gate current, we conclude that the voltage across $R_G$ must also be zero. And finally, applying Kirchhoff's voltage law at both the input and output loops, we see that

$$V_{GS} = V_{DS} \qquad \text{(26–35)}$$

The E-MOSFET shown in Figure 26–61 has the following characteristics:

**EXAMPLE 26–15**

$$V_{GS(th)} = 2.00 \text{ V}$$
$$I_{D(ON)} = 200 \text{ mA}$$
$$V_{GS(ON)} = 4 \text{ V}$$

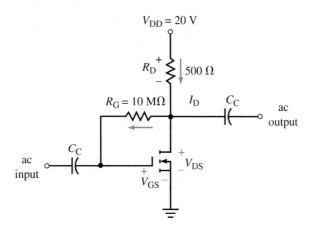

**FIGURE 26–61**

a. Write the expression for the $I_D$ in terms of $V_{GS}$.

b. Solve for $I_{DQ}$, $V_{GSQ}$, $V_{DSQ}$ at the quiescent (operating) point of the circuit.

**Solution**

a. We begin by using the given characteristics and Equation 26–34 to solve for the constant, $k$.

$$k = \frac{200 \text{ mA}}{(4 \text{ V} - 2 \text{ V})^2} = 50 \text{ mA/V}^2$$

Now, substituting this result into Equation 26–33, we get $I_D = (50 \text{ mA} / \text{V}^2)$ $(V_{GS} - 2 \text{ V})^2$. This expression can be plotted on a transfer curve. However, we need additional information to help scale the graph appropriately.

b. Examining the circuit of Figure 26–61, we see that the relationship between $I_D$ and $V_{DS}$ is determined as

$$I_D = \frac{V_{DD} - V_{DS}}{R_D} = \frac{20 \text{ V} - V_{DS}}{0.5 \text{ k}\Omega}$$

and for the drain-follower circuit, $V_{GS} = V_{DS}$. Therefore, the equation for the dc load line can now be written in terms of $I_D$ and $V_{GS}$ as

$$I_D = \frac{20 \text{ V} - V_{GS}}{0.5 \text{ k}\Omega}$$

Now, by inspection we notice that the absolute maximum current for the circuit will be $I_D = 40 \text{ mA}$. We use this value to help scale the graph of the transfer curve with a maximum current of 50 mA as shown in Figure 26–62. (You may use the parabolic equation to show that at this value of $I_D$, $V_{GS} = 3.00 \text{ V}$.) The rest of the graph is scaled accordingly.

Now, in order to sketch the dc load line we need to select suitable points on the graph of Figure 26–62.

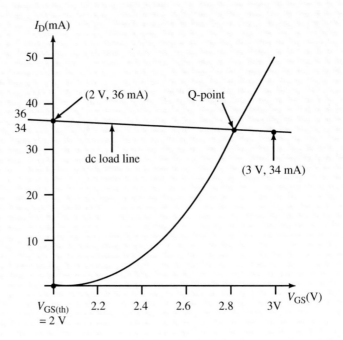

**FIGURE 26–62**

Let $V_{GS} = 2$ V:

And so we have $I_D = \dfrac{20 \text{ V} - 2 \text{ V}}{0.5 \text{ k}\Omega} = 36$ mA

Let $V_{GS} = 3$ V:

And so we have $I_D = \dfrac{20 \text{ V} - 3 \text{ V}}{0.5 \text{ k}\Omega} = 34$ mA

The intersection of the dc load line and the transfer curve reveals the operating point of the E-MOSFET circuit as $I_{DQ} \approx 34.2$ mA, $V_{GSQ} = V_{DSQ} \approx 2.82$ V.

## MOSFET Handling Precautions

Because MOSFETs use very thin insulation between the gate and the channel, they are subject to damage by electrostatic discharge (ESD). Unfortunately, our bodies and many of the materials we use in daily activities generate substantial amounts of static electricity. Very often, the act of simply picking up a MOSFET transistor (or IC containing MOSFETs) will result in permanent damage or destruction of the component. In order to prevent damage to these sensitive components some simple, but effective procedures have been developed. They are outlined as follows:

1. When MOSFETs are shipped from a manufacturer, they will be packaged in static resistive bags or inserted into static conductive foam. Occasionally, a shorting wire is connected between all of the terminals of the MOSFET. Do not remove the components from these protective environments until you are at a workstation that is also protected. Never place a MOSFET circuit into ordinary plastic foam, since materials such as Styrofoam are extremely effective at generating dangerous amounts of static charge.

2. The single most important element when handling MOSFET circuits is to have a static-safe workstation. This means that you must use a wrist strap that is connected between you and ground. When properly connected, this wrist strap will effectively drain any static charge from your body through

a very large (usually 1–MΩ) resistor. All instruments at the workstation will be connected to earth ground through the ac plug. Additionally, in order to provide total protection, a workstation should have a static dissipative mat that is also connected to earth ground.

3. Never insert or remove a MOSFET component into or from an active circuit. Turn off all dc power supplies before working with the component.

4. Never apply an ac signal to MOSFET unless the circuit has been correctly biased.

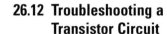

## 26.12 Troubleshooting a Transistor Circuit

Now that you know how transistors are biased, you can use this knowledge to determine whether a given transistor circuit is operating as expected. Although troubleshooting a circuit is often more art than science, there are some basic rules that any successful technician or technologist will follow. If you have just built a circuit and it doesn't work properly, the chances are that you have either used a wrong component or you have made a faulty connection. Unless the components in the circuit were previously used, it is highly unlikely that you started with faulty components. In this case, before you go any further, check your resistor color codes and ensure that you have connected the transistor correctly. You may need to refer to the manufacturer's specifications to determine the correct pin allocations since each transistor type is different. Make sure that you have properly connected the dc voltage source; remember an npn transistor or n-channel FET will normally require a positive voltage supply while a pnp transistor or p-channel FET will need a negative supply. If all connections appear to be correct, you will need to take dc voltage measurements of the circuit.

Since we have not yet worked with transistor circuits using ac sources, it is assumed that your circuit does not use one. However, if there is an ac source, turn it off and remove it from the circuit. It is now a simple matter to use a dc voltmeter to determine whether the circuit is operating.

Consider the amplifier circuit shown in Figure 26–63. The operation of this circuit can be easily analyzed with the following steps:

1. The first step of any troubleshooting procedure is to plan a strategy of attack. Begin with the most obvious and progress to the less likely problems. The important thing is that you must know what to expect. Do the necessary calculations so that you have an idea of typical voltage measurements.

2. Your first measurement should be to measure the dc supply voltage (with respect to ground) to ensure that the correct bias voltage has been provided. Clearly the operation of the circuit is dependent upon the supply having both the correct magnitude and polarity.

3. Measure $V_{BE}$. Because this is an amplifier circuit, we know that the base-emitter junction must be forward-biased and since we have an npn transistor, we expect $V_{BE} \approx 0.7$ V. If the transistor is faulty, or if it is incorrectly connected, this voltage may be incorrect. The possible exception is if the collector and emitter terminals were reversed, since this would still result in a forward-biased junction. In this case however, the following step will generally indicate a problem.

4. Determine the operating point of the transistor under test by determining $V_{CEQ}$ and $I_{CQ}$ at the quiescent point. (Remember that we don't normally measure the current in an operating circuit, but rather measure the voltage across a known resistor—in this case $R_C = 2.2$ kΩ—and then calculating the current using Ohm's law.)

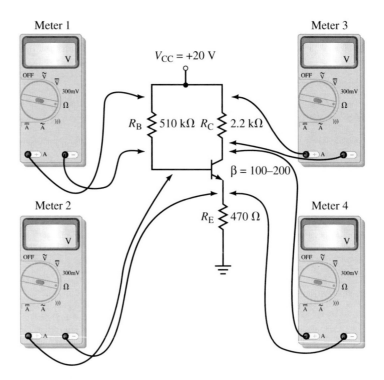

**FIGURE 26–63**

5. The circuit shown in Figure 26–63 is a beta-dependent circuit. If the transistor is not operating in its active region, it is possible that the value of the transistor beta is either much larger or much smaller than expected. The last measurement is to determine $I_{BQ}$ and from this the value, calculate beta. Once again, remember that the preferred method of finding the base current is to measure the voltage across $R_B$ and then solving for the current using Ohm's law.

Whenever you troubleshoot a circuit, it is imperative that you have a clear plan of action. You will not be an effective troubleshooter unless you know what readings to expect at each step of the way. In order to do this, you will need to know how the circuit should work.

PRACTICE PROBLEMS 10

For the circuit of Figure 26–63, the transistor specification sheet shows that the transistor type has $\beta = 100 \rightarrow 200$. What are the typical voltages that you would expect to measure on each of the voltmeters?

*Answers*
Meter 1: 16.3 V → 17.7 V;  Meter 2: 0.7 V;  Meter 3: 7.6 V → 14.1 V;
Meter 4: 3.0 V → 10.8 V

## 26.13 Computer Analysis of Transistor Circuits

MultiSIM and PSpice are extremely useful tools when analyzing the operation of complex circuits. In this section, we will enter several circuits and observe how the software predictions compare to the theoretical calculations. Needless to say, there will be some variation between the theoretical calculations and the values predicted by the software. In fact, you will find that if you were to build the circuits in the lab, you would have a third set of values. Although there will be differences between theoretical and measured values, it is important to observe that all values will normally have a discrepancy of less than 10%. When we take into account variations in the manufacturer's specifications, we find that the discrepancies are generally well within the expected limits.

## MultiSIM

MultiSIM provides numerous semiconductor models and is extremely useful when simulating the operation of transistor circuits. The following example verifies that the theoretical calculations are very good approximations of transistor operation.

a. Use MultiSIM to find $V_B$, $I_{CQ}$, $I_{EQ}$, $V_{CEQ}$, and $V_{BEQ}$ for the circuit of Figure 26–64.

b. Compare the values of $I_{CQ}$ and $V_{CEQ}$ to those predicted in Practice Problems 6.

### Solution

a. Open the MultiSIM program and open a new file. Construct the circuit by selecting components and indicators from the Component toolbar. (You will need to select these components from the *Sources, Basic, Transistors,* and *Indicators* parts bins.) Remember to place ammeters into the circuit and voltmeters across the components to be measured. Change the component values to correspond to those shown in Figure 26–64. Select a 2N3904 transistor as follows: Click on the *Transistors* parts bin, whereupon you will be given a button bar showing a large number of transistor types. There are two buttons, one gray and one green, that allow you to select the npn transistor. The green button corresponds to a generic transistor, while the gray button allows you to select from a large number of actual component types. Click on the gray button. From the *Component Name List* scroll down until you come to the 2N3904. Highlight this transistor and click on *OK* to place the transistor into the circuit. Click on the *Run* button to simulate your design. You should have a display that appears as shown in Figure 26–65. The result of this simulation gives the following values:

$V_B$ = 3.18 V, $I_{CQ}$ = 2.47 mA, $I_{EQ}$ = 2.49 mA, $V_{CEQ}$ = 10.09 V, and $V_{BEQ}$ = 0.687 V

b. In Practice Problems 6, we assumed that the transistor had β = 100 → 300, which is precisely the value specified for the 2N3904 transistor. The values $I_{CQ}$ = 2.47 mA and $V_{CEQ}$ = 10.09 V are well within the expected range of $I_C$ = 2.41 mA → 2.55 mA and $V_{CEQ}$ = 9.78 V → 10.37 V.

**EXAMPLE 26–16**

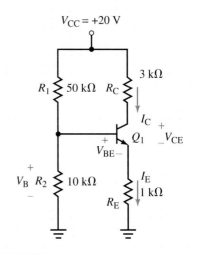

**FIGURE 26–64**

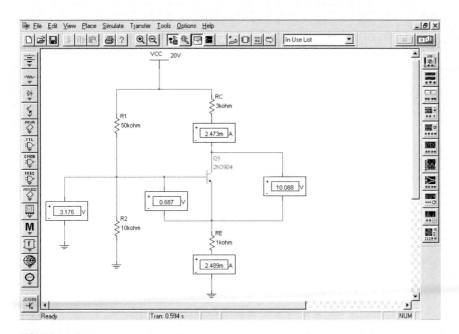

**FIGURE 26–65**

MULTISIM

**PRACTICE PROBLEMS 11**

Remove the 2N3904 transistor and replace it with a 2N3906, its complement pnp transistor and change the supply to $V_{CC} = -20$ V. Simulate the design for the new transistor. What are the new values for $V_B$, $I_{CQ}$, $I_{EQ}$, $V_{CEQ}$, and $V_{BEQ}$?

*Answers*
$V_B = -3.22$ V, $I_{CQ} = -2.49$ mA, $I_{EQ} = -2.50$ mA, $V_{CEQ} = -10.01$ V, and $V_{BEQ} = -0.72$ V (As expected, the main difference between these values and those for the 2N3904 is that all voltages and currents are negative.)

## PSpice

Although the student version of PSpice does not provide a comprehensive list of semiconductor components, there is a good selection allowing us to examine many different circuits. The following example analyzes the E-MOSFET circuit of Example 26–15.

**EXAMPLE 26–17**

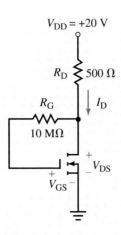

$V_{DD} = +20$ V

$R_D$  500 Ω

$R_G$  ↓ $I_D$

10 MΩ

$+$ $V_{DS}$ $-$

$+$ $V_{GS}$ $-$

**FIGURE 26–66**

a. Use PSpice to find $V_{GSQ}$, $I_{DQ}$, and $V_{DSQ}$ for the circuit of Figure 26–66. (Since we are not applying an ac signal to the circuit, coupling capacitors are not shown.)

b. Compare the values to those found in Example 26–15.

**Solution**

a. Construct the PSpice circuit as illustrated in Figure 26–67. Obtain the MOSFET by holding down **Ctrl-G** (or by selecting the <u>D</u>raw menu item and selecting <u>G</u>et New Part). The semiconductor devices to which we have access are in the *EVAL* library. Once you are in this library, simply scroll down to the device labeled IRF150. In the description of this component, you will notice that this is an n-channel E-MOSFET as required. Place the transistor into the circuit and make all required connections. In order to show the bias voltages and currents, we can enable these features by clicking on the *Enable Bias Voltage Display* and *Enable Bias Current Display*. Save your file as Example 26–17 and click on the *Simulate* button. You should have an output that appears similar to that shown in Figure 26–67.

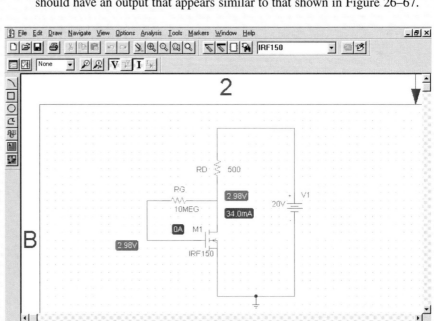

**FIGURE 26–67**

To disable the display of some of the bias voltages and currents, you may do so as follows:

To disable the display of a bias current, click on the part and then click on the button labeled as *Show/Hide Currents on Selected Part(s)*.

To disable the display of a bias voltage, click on the node and then click on the button labeled as *Show/Hide Voltage on Selected Net(s)*. The results of Figure 26–67 indicate that $V_{GSQ} = V_{DSQ} = 2.98$ V and $I_{DQ} = 34.0$ mA.

b. The above results are very close to those found in Example 26–15 where we had $V_{GSQ} = V_{DSQ} = 2.82$ V and $I_{DQ} = 34.2$ mA.

## PROBLEMS

### 26.2   Transistor Operation

1. A transistor circuit is measured to have $I_C = 4.50$ mA and $I_E = 4.55$ mA. Determine $I_B$, $\alpha$, and $\beta$.

2. A power transistor is measured to have $I_C = 24.5$ mA and $I_E = 25.1$ mA. Determine $I_B$, $\alpha$, and $\beta$.

3. A transistor has $\beta = 120$ and $I_C = 5.00$ mA. Calculate the values of $I_B$, $I_E$, and $\alpha$.

4. If a transistor has $\alpha = 0.92$ and $I_E = 3.50$ mA, determine the values of $I_C$, $\beta$, and $I_B$.

5. A transistor has $\beta = 100$ and $I_E = 4.94$ mA. Calculate the values of $\alpha$, $I_C$, and $I_B$.

6. Use Equations 26–1 and 26–2 to derive Equation 26–4, $I_E = (\beta + 1)I_B$.

7. Use Equations 26–2, 26–3, and 26–4 to derive Equation 26–5, $\alpha = \dfrac{\beta}{\beta + 1}$.

8. Use Equations 26–2, 26–3, and 26–4 to derive Equation 26–6, $\beta = \dfrac{\alpha}{1 - \alpha}$.

### 26.3   Transistor Specifications

Refer to the specification sheets for the 2N3904 shown in Figure 26–8 for the problems in this section.

9. One of the electrical characteristics of the 2N3904 transistor is given as $V_{(BR)EBO}$. What is the value of this specification? What does the subscript of the symbol mean? What are the test conditions that are used to measure this characteristic?

10. One of the electrical characteristics of the 2N3904 transistor is given as $V_{(BR)CBO}$. What is the value of this specification? What does the subscript of the symbol mean? What are the test conditions that are used to measure this characteristic?

### 26.4   Collector Characteristic Curves

Refer to the collector characteristic curves shown in Figure 26–68 for the problems of this section.

11. Determine $\beta_{dc}$ for a transistor having an operating point at $V_{CE} = 10$ V and $I_C = 5.5$ mA.

12. Determine $\beta_{dc}$ for a transistor having an operating point at $V_{CE} = 6$ V and $I_C = 10.5$ mA.

13. Determine $\beta_{dc}$ for a transistor having an operating point at $V_{CE} = 10$ V and $I_C = 8.0$ mA.

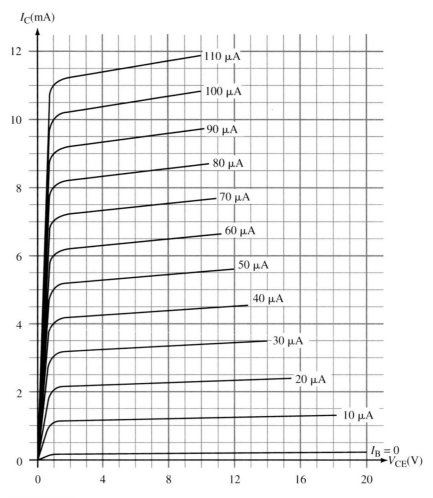

**FIGURE 26–68**

14. Determine $\beta_{dc}$ for a transistor having an operating point at $V_{CE} = 8$ V and $I_C = 4.0$ mA.

15. A transistor is operating at a point having $I_C = 8.0$ mA and $I_B = 100$ μA. This operating point will place the transistor in which of the following regions:

    a. Active                b. Saturation                c. Cutoff

16. A transistor is operating at a point having $V_{CE} = 16$ V and $I_C = 200$ μA. This operating point will place the transistor in which of the following regions:

    a. Active                b. Saturation                c. Cutoff

### 26.5   dc Load Line

The transistors used in this section have the collector characteristics shown in Figure 26–68.

17. The circuit of Figure 26–69 has $V_{BB} = 5$ V, $V_{CC} = 16$ V, and $R_C = 2$ kΩ.

    a. Sketch the dc load line for the circuit.

    b. Determine the operating point and calculate $\beta$ of the circuit if $R_B = 100$ kΩ.

    c. Determine the operating point and calculate $\beta$ of the circuit if $R_B = 200$ kΩ.

d. Determine the operating point and calculate β of the circuit if $R_B = 20$ kΩ.

e. In general, what happens to the operating point as the value of $R_B$ is increased?

18. The circuit of Figure 26–69 has $V_{BB} = 5$ V, $R_B = 100$ kΩ, and $R_C = 2$ kΩ.

a. Sketch the dc load line and indicate the operating point if $V_{CC} = 16$ V.

b. Sketch the dc load line and indicate the operating point if $V_{CC} = 20$ V.

c. Sketch the dc load line and indicate the operating point if $V_{CC} = 12$ V.

d. In general, what happens to the load line as the value of $V_{CC}$ is increased?

19. The circuit of Figure 26–69 has $V_{BB} = 5$ V, $R_B = 100$ kΩ, and $V_{CC} = 16$ V.

a. Sketch the dc load line and indicate the operating point if $R_C = 2$ kΩ.

b. Sketch the dc load line and indicate the operating point if $R_C = 1.6$ kΩ.

c. Sketch the dc load line and indicate the operating point if $R_C = 4$ kΩ.

d. In general, what happens to the load line as the value of $R_C$ is increased?

20. The circuit of Figure 26–69 has $V_{BB} = 5$ V, $V_{CC} = 16$ V, and $R_C = 2$ kΩ.

a. Calculate the value of $R_B$ so that the transistor operates at the midpoint of the dc load line.

b. Determine the value of β at the operating point.

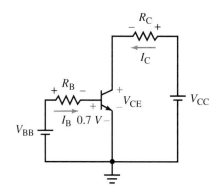

**FIGURE 26–69**

## 26.6  Transistor Biasing

21. For the circuit of Figure 26–70, let $V_{CC} = 16$ V, $R_B = 620$ kΩ, $R_C = 2$ kΩ, and β = 120.

a. Calculate the saturation current, $I_{C(SAT)}$.

b. Determine $I_B$, $I_C$, $I_E$, and $V_{CE}$.

c. Sketch the dc load line showing $I_{C(SAT)}$, $V_{CE(OFF)}$, and the values of the Q-point.

22. a. If the transistor beta of Problem 21 doubles to β = 240, determine the resulting values of $I_B$, $I_C$, $I_E$, and $V_{CE}$.

b. With the 100% increase in β, what is the percentage change in $I_C$?

c. Does the operating point of the transistor move towards saturation or cutoff?

23. For the circuit of Figure 26–70, let $V_{CC} = 24$ V, $R_B = 1.2$ MΩ, $R_C = 3.9$ kΩ, and β = 150.

a. Calculate the saturation current, $I_{C(SAT)}$.

b. Determine $I_B$, $I_C$, $I_E$, and $V_{CE}$.

c. Sketch the dc load line showing $I_{C(SAT)}$, $V_{CE(OFF)}$, and the values of the Q-point.

24. a. If the transistor beta of Problem 23 decreases to β = 240, determine the resulting values of $I_B$, $I_C$, $I_E$, and $V_{CE}$.

b. With the decrease in β, does the operating point of the transistor move towards saturation or cutoff?

25. For the circuit of Figure 26–71, let $V_{CC} = 22$ V, $R_B = 1.5$ MΩ, $R_C = 3.9$ kΩ, $R_E = 1.0$ kΩ, and β = 150.

a. Calculate the saturation current, $I_{C(SAT)}$.

b. Determine $I_B$, $I_C$, $I_E$, and $V_{CE}$.

c. Sketch the dc load line showing $I_{C(SAT)}$, $V_{CE(OFF)}$, and the values of the Q-point.

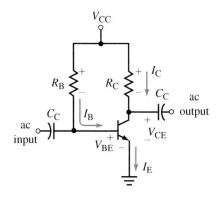

**FIGURE 26–70**        ◀ MULTISIM

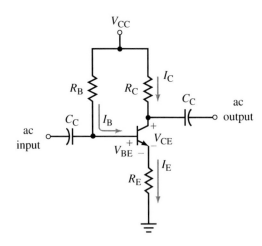

**FIGURE 26–71**

26. a. If the transistor beta of Problem 25 doubles to $\beta = 300$, determine the resulting values of $I_B$, $I_C$, $I_E$, and $V_{CE}$.

  b. With the 100% increase in $\beta$, what is the percentage change in $I_C$?

27. For the collector-feedback circuit of Figure 26–72, let $V_{CC} = 20$ V, $R_B = 270$ k$\Omega$, $R_C = 2.0$ k$\Omega$, and $\beta = 125$.

  a. Calculate the saturation current, $I_{C(SAT)}$.

  b. Determine $I_B$, $I_C$, $I_E$, $I$, and $V_{CE}$.

  c. Sketch the dc load line showing $I_{C(SAT)}$, $V_{CE(OFF)}$, and the values of the Q-point.

28. a. If the transistor beta of Problem 27 doubles to $\beta = 250$, determine the resulting values of $I_B$, $I_C$, $I_E$, $I$, and $V_{CE}$.

  b. With the 100% increase in $\beta$, what is the percentage change in $I_C$?

29. For the circuit of Figure 26–73, let $V_{EE} = 20$ V, $R_B = 1.0$ M$\Omega$, $R_C = 2.0$ k$\Omega$, $R_E = 2.0$ k$\Omega$, and $\beta = 160$.

  a. Calculate the saturation current, $I_{C(SAT)}$.

  b. Determine $I_B$, $I_C$, $I_E$, and $V_{CE}$.

  c. Sketch the dc load line showing $I_{C(SAT)}$, $V_{CE(OFF)}$, and the values of the Q-point.

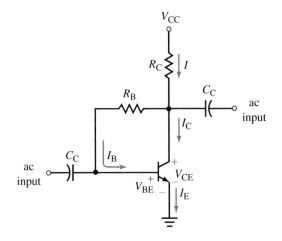

**FIGURE 26–72**   Collector-feedback circuit.

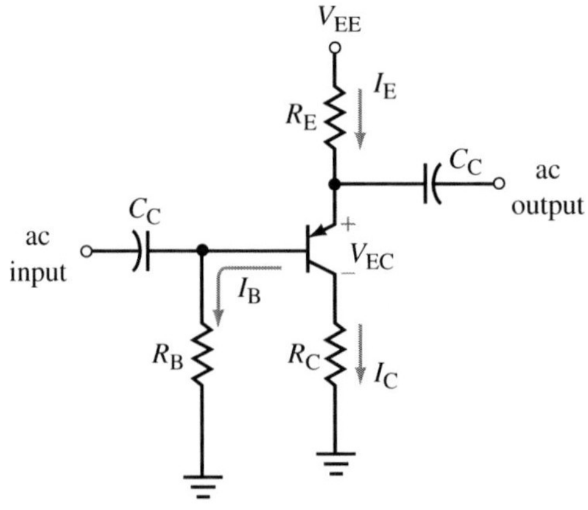

**FIGURE 26–73**

30. For the circuit of Figure 26–73, let $V_{EE} = 24V$, $R_B = 820\ k\Omega$, $R_C = 3.3\ k\Omega$, $R_E = 1.0\ k\Omega$, and $\beta = 120$.

   a. Calculate the saturation current, $I_{C(SAT)}$.

   b. Determine $I_B$, $I_C$, $I_E$, and $V_{CE}$.

   c. Sketch the dc load line showing $I_{C(SAT)}$, $V_{CE(OFF)}$, and the values of the Q-point.

   d. If you wanted a Q-point to have $I_C = 2.0\ mA$, what value of base resistor, $R_B$ would you need?

31. For the circuit of Figure 26–74, let $V_{CC} = 16\ V$, $R_1 = 33\ k\Omega$, $R_2 = 5.1\ k\Omega$, $R_C = 1.5\ k\Omega$, $R_E = 510\ \Omega$, and $\beta = 120$.

   a. Calculate the saturation current, $I_{C(SAT)}$.

   b. Use the exact method to solve for $I_B$, $I_C$, $I_E$, and $V_{CE}$.

   c. Sketch the dc load line showing $I_{C(SAT)}$, $V_{CE(OFF)}$, and the values of the Q-point.

32. a. If the transistor beta of Problem 31 doubles to $\beta = 240$, use the exact method to solve for the new values of $I_B$, $I_C$, $I_E$, and $V_{CE}$.

   b. With the 100% increase in $\beta$, what is the percentage change in $I_C$.

33. For the circuit of Figure 26–74, let $V_{CC} = 16\ V$, $R_1 = 330\ k\Omega$, $R_2 = 51\ k\Omega$, $R_C = 1.5\ k\Omega$, $R_E = 510\ \Omega$, and $\beta = 120$.

   a. Calculate the saturation current, $I_{C(SAT)}$.

   b. Use the exact method to solve for $I_B$, $I_C$, $I_E$, and $V_{CE}$.

   c. Sketch the dc load line showing $I_{C(SAT)}$, $V_{CE(OFF)}$, and the values of the Q-point.

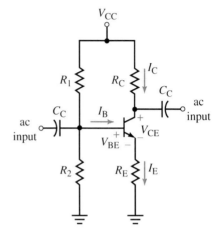

**FIGURE 26–74**

34. a. If the transistor beta of Problem 33 doubles to $\beta = 240$, use the exact method to solve for the new values of $I_B$, $I_C$, $I_E$, and $V_{CE}$.

   b. With the 100% increase in $\beta$, what is the percentage change in $I_C$.

35. a. Use the approximate method and the component values of Problem 31 to solve for $I_C$ and $V_{CE}$.

   b. The approximate method often provides results that are close to the exact solution (using Thévenin's theorem) method. Determine the percent variation between the calculations of $I_C$ and $V_{CE}$ in part a. and those of Problem 31.

36. a. Use the approximate method and the component values of Problem 33 to solve for $I_C$ and $V_{CE}$.

   b. Determine the percent variation between the calculations of $I_C$ and $V_{CE}$ in part a. and those of Problem 33.

37. For the circuit of Figure 26–75, let $V_{CC} = -30\ V$, $R_1 = 62\ k\Omega$, $R_2 = 8.2\ k\Omega$, $R_C = 3.9\ k\Omega$, $R_E = 1.0\ k\Omega$, and $\beta = 100$.

   a. Calculate the saturation current, $I_{C(SAT)}$.

   b. Use the approximate method to solve for $I_C$ and $V_{CE}$.

   c. Sketch the dc load line showing $I_{C(SAT)}$, $V_{CE(OFF)}$, and the values of the Q-point.

38. For the circuit of Figure 26–75, let $V_{CC} = -30\ V$, $R_2 = 8.2\ k\Omega$, $R_C = 3.9\ k\Omega$, $R_E = 1.0\ k\Omega$, and $\beta = 100$. Calculate the value of $R_1$ needed to result in $I_C = 3.0\ mA$.

39. The transistor of Figure 26–74 has $\beta = 100 \rightarrow 300$. Design the circuit for the following conditions:

   $V_{CC} = +20\ V$, $I_{C(SAT)} = 8.0\ mA$, $I_{CQ} = 4.0\ mA$, $R_E = R_C/4$, $R_2 \le 0.1\ \beta\ R_E$ for all $\beta$.

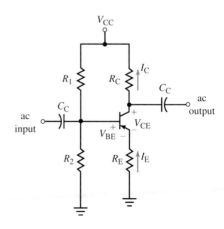

**FIGURE 26–75**

40. The transistor of Figure 26–74 has $\beta = 100 \rightarrow 300$. Design the circuit for the following conditions:

    $V_{CC} = +24$ V, $I_{C(SAT)} = 6.0$ mA, $I_{CQ} = 4.0$ mA, $R_E = R_C/5$, $R_2 \leq 0.1 \, \beta \, R_E$ for all $\beta$.

41. For the circuit of Figure 26–76, let $V_{EE} = +10$ V, $V_{CC} = -20$ V, $R_E = 2.0$ k$\Omega$, $R_C = 2.0$ k$\Omega$, and $\beta = 120$.

    a. Calculate the saturation current, $I_{C(SAT)}$.

    b. Solve for $I_E$, $I_C$, $I_B$, and $V_{CE}$.

    c. Sketch the dc load line showing $I_{C(SAT)}$, $V_{CE(OFF)}$, and the values of the Q-point.

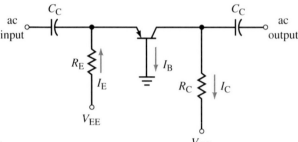

**FIGURE 26–76**

42. For the circuit of Figure 26–76, let $V_{EE} = +8$ V, $V_{CC} = -12$ V, $R_E = 2.2$ k$\Omega$, $R_C = 1.8$ k$\Omega$, and $\beta = 180$.

    a. Calculate the saturation current, $I_{C(SAT)}$.

    b. Solve for $I_E$, $I_C$, $I_B$, and $V_{CE}$.

    c. Sketch the dc load line showing $I_{C(SAT)}$, $V_{CE(OFF)}$, and the values of the Q-point.

## 26.7   The Transistor Switch

43. The transistor shown in Figure 26–77 is used as a buffer, providing sufficient current to turn on an LED when the output of the logic gate is "1." The circuit has $V_{CC} = 8$ V, $R_B = 33$ k$\Omega$, $R_C = 470 \, \Omega$, and $\beta = 120$.

    a. Find the saturation current for the transistor.

    b. Calculate the current through the LED when the output of the logic gate is "1."

    c. Determine the output voltage at the collector (with respect to ground) for part a.

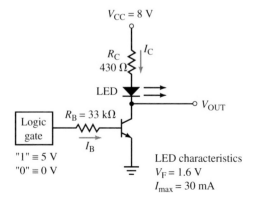

**FIGURE 26–77**

d. Calculate the current through the LED when the output of the logic gate is "0."

e. Determine the output voltage at the collector for part d.

44. For the circuit of Figure 26–77, which single component would you change to obtain a current of 25 mA through the diode? What would be the new value of this component? (Select the nearest commercial value of resistor having a tolerance of ±5%)

### 26.8   Testing a Transistor with a Multimeter

45. You are given the unknown transistor shown in Figure 26–36 and use an ohmmeter to take resistance measurements as tabulated. As always, the ohmmeter has two terminals: the positive (+ , red) terminal and the negative (− , black) terminal.

a. What type of transistor were you given? pnp or npn?

b. What are the pin designations?

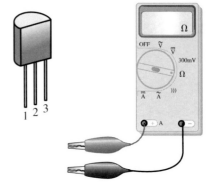

**FIGURE 26–78**

| Pins 1 & 2 | | Pins 2 & 3 | | Pins 1 & 3 | |
|---|---|---|---|---|---|
| Pin 1 (+) Pin 2 (−) | 0.223 kΩ | Pin 2 (+) Pin 3 (−) | ∞ | Pin 1 (+) Pin 3 (−) | ∞ |
| Pin 2 (+) Pin 1 (−) | ∞ | Pin 3 (+) Pin 2 (−) | 0.259 kΩ | Pin 3 (+) Pin 1 (−) | ∞ |

46. Repeat Problem 45 if the measurements are as follows:

| Pins 1 & 2 | | Pins 2 & 3 | | Pins 1 & 3 | |
|---|---|---|---|---|---|
| Pin 1 (+) Pin 2 (−) | ∞ | Pin 2 (+) Pin 3 (−) | ∞ | Pin 1 (+) Pin 3 (−) | ∞ |
| Pin 2 (+) Pin 1 (−) | 0.321 kΩ | Pin 3 (+) Pin 2 (−) | ∞ | Pin 3 (+) Pin 1 (−) | 0.357 kΩ |

47. Repeat Problem 45 if the measurements are as follows:

| Pins 1 & 2 | | Pins 2 & 3 | | Pins 1 & 3 | |
|---|---|---|---|---|---|
| Pin 1 (+) Pin 2 (−) | ∞ | Pin 2 (+) Pin 3 (−) | ∞ | Pin 1 (+) Pin 3 (−) | ∞ |
| Pin 2 (+) Pin 1 (−) | 0.321 kΩ | Pin 3 (+) Pin 2 (−) | ∞ | Pin 3 (+) Pin 1 (−) | 0.357 kΩ |

48. You are given another transistor of the same type as the one in Problem 46. The measurements for this transistor are as follows:

| Pins 1 & 2 | | Pins 2 & 3 | | Pins 1 & 3 | |
|---|---|---|---|---|---|
| Pin 1 (+) Pin 2 (−) | ∞ | Pin 2 (+) Pin 3 (−) | ∞ | Pin 1 (+) Pin 3 (−) | 0.354 kΩ |
| Pin 2 (+) Pin 1 (−) | 0.344 kΩ | Pin 3 (+) Pin 2 (−) | ∞ | Pin 3 (+) Pin 1 (−) | 0.362 kΩ |

What conclusion can you make about this transistor? Explain your answer.

### 26.9   Junction Field Effect Transistor Construction and Operation

49. A JFET transistor has $V_{GS(OFF)} = -5$ V and $I_{DSS} = 8$ mA.

a. What type of JFET is this (n-channel or p-channel)?

b. Use Shockley's equation to solve for $I_D$ when $V_{GS} = -3$ V.

c. Solve for $I_D$ when $V_{GS} = -2$ V.

d. Solve for $I_D$ when $V_{GS} = -6$ V.

50. A JFET transistor has $V_{GS(OFF)} = +4$ V and $I_{DSS} = 10$ mA.

   a. What type of JFET is this (n-channel or p-channel)?

   b. Use Shockley's equation to solve for $I_D$ when $V_{GS} = +2$ V.

   c. Solve for $I_D$ when $V_{GS} = +3$ V.

   d. Solve for $I_D$ when $V_{GS} = +5$ V.

### 26.10  JFET Biasing

Use the following normalized JFET transfer curve to help you solve the problems of this section.

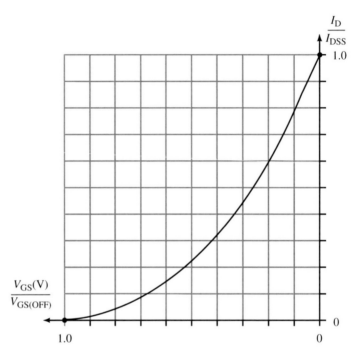

**FIGURE 26–79**  Normalized transconductance curve of an n-channel JFET.

51. For the circuit of Figure 26–80, let $V_{DD} = 16$ V, $R_D = 1.8$ k$\Omega$, $R_S = 910$ $\Omega$, $V_{GS(OFF)} = -4$ V, and $I_{DSS} = 8$ mA. At the operating point determine $V_{GSQ}$, $I_{DQ}$, and $V_{DSQ}$.

52. For the circuit of Figure 26–80, let $V_{DD} = 20$ V, $R_D = 2.4$ k$\Omega$, $R_S = 1.0$ k$\Omega$, $V_{GS(OFF)} = -5$ V, and $I_{DSS} = 10$ mA. At the operating point determine $V_{GSQ}$, $I_{DQ}$, and $V_{DSQ}$.

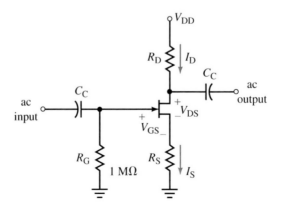

**FIGURE 26–80**

53. For the circuit of Figure 26–81, let $V_{DD} = 16$ V, $R_1 = 6.7$ MΩ, $R_2 = 1.0$ MΩ, $R_D = 3.9$ kΩ, $R_S = 2.0$ kΩ, $V_{GS(OFF)} = -4$ V, and $I_{DSS} = 8$ mA. At the operating point determine $V_{GSQ}$, $I_{DQ}$, and $V_{DSQ}$.

54. For the circuit of Figure 26–81, let $V_{DD} = 20$ V, $R_1 = 6.7$ MΩ, $R_2 = 1.0$ MΩ, $R_D = 3.9$ kΩ, $R_S = 2.0$ kΩ, $V_{GS(OFF)} = -5$ V, and $I_{DSS} = 10$ mA. At the operating point determine $V_{GSQ}$, $I_{DQ}$, and $V_{DSQ}$.

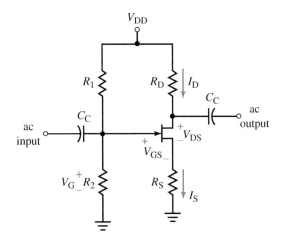

**FIGURE 26–81**

MULTISIM

## 26.11    MOSFETs

55. For the D-MOSFET circuit of Figure 26–82, let $V_{DD} = 20$ V, $R_1 = 1.8$ MΩ, $R_2 = 200$ kΩ, $R_D = 1.5$ kΩ, $R_S = 470$ Ω, $V_{GS(OFF)} = -5$ V, and $I_{DSS} = 10$ mA.

a. Find $I_{DQ}$ and $V_{GSQ}$.

b. Is the MOSFET operating in its depletion mode or enhancement mode?

c. Solve for $V_{DSQ}$.

56. For the D-MOSFET circuit of Figure 26–82, let $V_{DD} = 20$ V, $R_1 = 1.2$ MΩ, $R_2 = 680$ kΩ, $R_D = 680$ Ω, $R_S = 620$ Ω, $V_{GS(OFF)} = -5$ V, and $I_{DSS} = 10$ mA.

a. Find $I_{DQ}$ and $V_{GSQ}$.

b. Is the MOSFET operating in its depletion mode or enhancement mode?

c. Solve for $V_{DSQ}$.

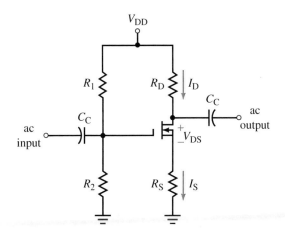

**FIGURE 26–82**

57. An E-MOSFET is specified as having $V_{GS(th)} = 2.0$ V and $I_{D(ON)} = 20$ mA for $V_{GS(ON)} = 12$ V. Determine the value of $k$ for this MOSFET. Write the expression for $I_D$ as a function of $V_{GS}$.

58. An E-MOSFET is specified as having $V_{GS(th)} = 3.0$ V and $I_{D(ON)} = 20$ mA for $V_{GS(ON)} = 15$ V. Determine the value of $k$ for this MOSFET. Write the expression for $I_D$ as a function of $V_{GS}$.

59. For the circuit of Figure 26–83, use the E-MOSFET of Problem 57 and let $V_{DD} = 20$ V. Find $I_{DQ}$, $V_{GSQ}$, and $V_{DSQ}$.

60. For the circuit of Figure 26–83, use the E-MOSFET of Problem 58 and let $V_{DD} = 30$ V. Find $I_{DQ}$, $V_{GSQ}$, and $V_{DSQ}$.

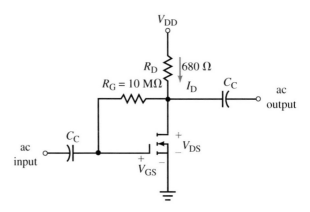

**FIGURE 26–83**

## 26.12 Troubleshooting a Transistor Circuit

61. Refer to the circuit shown in Figure 26–63. You obtain the following voltage readings on the indicated meters:

Meter 1: 0 V      Meter 2: 20.0 V      Meter 3: 0 V      Meter 4: 20.0 V

You have determined that the supply is operating correctly and that all components are the correct values and have been inserted correctly. What could be wrong with the transistor? Briefly explain your answer.

62. Refer to the circuit shown in Figure 26–63. You obtain the following voltage readings on the indicated meters:

Meter 1: 19.2 V      Meter 2: 0.7 V      Meter 3: 0.04 V      Meter 4: 19.94 V

You have determined that the supply is operating correctly and that all components are the correct values. What could be wrong with the transistor? Explain your answer.

## 26.13 Computer Analysis of Transistor Circuits

◀ MULTISIM

63. Use MultiSIM to find $V_B$, $I_{CQ}$, $I_{EQ}$, $V_{CEQ}$, and $V_{BEQ}$ for the circuit of Figure 26–70. Use a 2N3904 transistor and the component values provided in Problem 21. Compare the values of $I_{CQ}$ and $V_{CEQ}$ to those predicted in Problem 21.

◀ MULTISIM

64. Use MultiSIM to find $V_B$, $I_{CQ}$, $I_{EQ}$, $V_{CEQ}$, and $V_{BEQ}$ for the circuit of Figure 26–70. Use a 2N2222A transistor and the same component values of Problem 21. Compare the values of $I_{CQ}$ and $V_{CEQ}$ to those in Problem 63.

◀ MULTISIM

65. Use MultiSIM to find $V_B$, $I_{CQ}$, $I_{EQ}$, $V_{CEQ}$, and $V_{BEQ}$ for the circuit of Figure 26–71. Use a 2N3904 transistor and the component values provided in Problem 25. Compare the values of $I_{CQ}$ and $V_{CEQ}$ to those predicted in Problem 25.

66. Use MultiSIM to find $V_B$, $I_{CQ}$, $I_{EQ}$, $V_{CEQ}$, and $V_{BEQ}$ for the circuit of Figure 26–71. Use a 2N2222A transistor and the same component values of Problem 25. Compare the values of $I_{CQ}$ and $V_{CEQ}$ to those in Problem 65.    ◀ MULTISIM

67. Use MultiSIM to find $V_{GSQ}$, $I_{DQ}$, and $V_{DSQ}$ for the circuit of Figure 26–81. Use a 2N5045 JFET and the same component values of Problem 53. Compare the values of $I_{DQ}$ and $V_{DSQ}$ to those in Problem 53. Why is there a difference between the results?    ◀ MULTISIM

68. Use MultiSIM to find $V_{GSQ}$, $I_{DQ}$, and $V_{DSQ}$ for the circuit of Figure 26–81. Use a 2N5045 JFET and the same component values of Problem 54. Compare the values of $I_{DQ}$ and $V_{DSQ}$ to those in Problem 54. Why is there a difference between the results?    ◀ MULTISIM

69. Use Capture to find $V_B$, $I_{CQ}$, $I_{EQ}$, $V_{CEQ}$, and $V_{BEQ}$ for the circuit of Figure 26–71. Use a 2N3904 transistor and the component values provided in Problem 25. Compare the values of $I_{CQ}$ and $V_{CEQ}$ to those predicted in Problem 25.    ◀ CADENCE

70. Use Capture to find $V_B$, $I_{CQ}$, $I_{EQ}$, $V_{CEQ}$, and $V_{BEQ}$ for the circuit of Figure 26–71. Use a 2N2222A transistor and the same component values of Problem 25. Compare the values of $I_{CQ}$ and $V_{CEQ}$ to those in Problem 69.    ◀ CADENCE

71. Use Capture to find $V_{GSQ}$, $I_{DQ}$, and $V_{DSQ}$ for the circuit of Figure 26–81. Use a 2N3819 JFET and the same component values of Problem 53. Compare the values of $I_{DQ}$ and $V_{DSQ}$ to those in Problem 53. Why is there a difference between the results?    ◀ CADENCE

72. Use Capture to find $V_{GSQ}$, $I_{DQ}$, and $V_{DSQ}$ for the circuit of Figure 26–81. Use a 2N3819 JFET and the same component values of Problem 54. Compare the values of $I_{DQ}$ and $V_{DSQ}$ to those in Problem 54. Why is there a difference between the results?    ◀ CADENCE

## ■ OBJECTIVES

On completion of this chapter, you will be able to

- use the frequency range of an amplifier to determine the size of coupling and bypass capacitors for amplifier circuits,

- determine the correct placement of electrolytic capacitors into a circuit and understand the importance of this placement,

- use the *T*-equivalent model and the *h*-parameter model to sketch the ac equivalent circuit of a BJT amplifier,

- calculate voltage gain, input impedance, output impedance, current gain, and power gain of a BJT amplifier,

- sketch the ac load line for a transistor circuit and use the ac load line to determine the maximum undistorted output signal for a given amplifier,

- determine the small-signal ac equivalent model of a FET transistor amplifier,

- calculate voltage gain, input impedance, and output impedance of JFET and MOSFET amplifiers,

- use troubleshooting skills to analyze ac operation of transistor amplifiers,

- use PSpice and MultiSIM to simulate the operation of amplifier circuits.

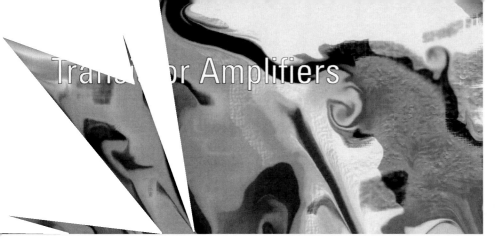

# Transistor Amplifiers

# 27

**CHAPTER PREVIEW**

In the previous chapter, you were introduced to the bipolar junction transistor (BJT) and several types of field effect transistors (FETs). Specifically, you learned that before a transistor can be used as an amplifier, it must be correctly biased so that it is ready to accept an ac signal. In this chapter you will examine how, once the transistor is biased, it is able to process an ac signal. To help understand transistor operation, several models have been developed. Each of these models uses dependent sources (refer to Chapter 19) to help explain how an ac signal at the input is ultimately amplified.

As mentioned previously, the use of discrete transistors in electronic circuits is less common. This chapter uses single transistors to develop concepts such as voltage gain, current gain, input impedance, and output impedance. Although we use a single transistor amplifier to define and analyze these characteristics, you will find that these same principles will be applied to IC amplifiers containing many hundreds or thousands of transistors. Most students of electronics find that it is much easier to start analyzing amplifiers that use a single three-terminal transistor than to immediately work with multi-terminal integrated circuits. ∎

**PUTTING IT IN PERSPECTIVE**

SINCE THE INVENTION OF THE transistor in 1947 by Bell physicists, William Shockley, John Bardeen, and Walter Brattain, the transistor has changed dramatically. The original transistor was a bipolar junction transistor (BJT) that consisted of a sandwich of p- and n-type materials, allowing both positive and negative charge carriers. By applying a small current variation current in the base circuit, a much larger variation in collector current is possible. Hence the BJT is a current amplifier.

Although the BJT is still used, many other types of transistors have been developed. For instance, the junction field effect transistor (JFET) and the metal-oxide-semiconductor field effect transistor (MOSFET) use a small variation in input voltage to control the size of an electric field, which in turn controls the current through the device. Consequently, FETs are referred to as voltage amplifiers.

Other developments in semiconductor have led to isolated gate FETs (IGFETs) and numerous other types of transistors. One of the greatest developments in semiconductor design occurred in the early 1960s with the invention of the integrated circuit (IC). Since then, the size of the transistor has shrunk to the point that several modern transistors can fit on the surface of a blood cell. Reducing the size of the transistor has resulted not only in more devices on a given IC wafer, but also improves the performance of the IC. This miniaturization has resulted in exponential improvements in the speed of computers and a corresponding reduction in the cost of all semiconductor devices. Indeed, this miniaturization led to Moore's Law, which states the speed of computers will double every eighteen months. Although many skeptics have predicted that this improvement cannot continue, Moore's law has been a surprisingly good predictor of computer speed and capacity for the past three decades. ∎

## 27.1 The Use of Capacitors in Amplifier Circuits

In the previous chapter, you likely noticed that most of the transistor circuits included capacitors, even though they were ignored in calculation of the dc operating points. In this section, you will learn the importance of capacitors in a transistor circuits and be able to calculate the values of these capacitors. At this point, a brief review of capacitors is worthwhile. You have already seen that capacitors are electrical components capable of storing electrical charge. Capacitors have a reactance (or impedance) to ac that is inversely proportional to the frequency of the signal applied to the component. The reactance of a capacitor is given as

$$X_C = \frac{1}{2\pi f C} \qquad [\Omega] \qquad (27\text{--}1)$$

From the above expression, we are able to observe two very important characteristics of capacitors. They are:

1. At dc ($f = 0$ Hz), a capacitor has infinite impedance, which means that a capacitor behaves as an open circuit.

2. As the frequency increases, the reactance of the capacitor decreases. If the frequency of a signal is sufficiently high, the capacitor will behave effectively as a short circuit.

The above characteristics are extremely useful in transistor amplifier circuits, since they allow capacitors to simultaneously prevent the dc operation of one stage from affecting other stages in the circuit, while at the same time allowing desired ac signals to pass readily between stages. Capacitors used in this manner are called **coupling capacitors,** since they couple the ac signal from one stage to the next.

### Coupling Capacitors

Consider the simplified circuit shown in Figure 27–1. A voltage source, represented by $v_S$ and a series resistance, $R_S$, is connected to a circuit having an input resistance, $R_{in}$.

The voltage, $v_{in}$ applied to the input of the circuit is found by applying the voltage divider rule as

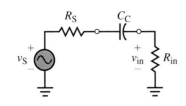

**FIGURE 27–1**

$$v_{in} = \left( \frac{R_{in}}{\sqrt{(R_{in} + R_S)^2 + (X_C)^2}} \right) v_S \qquad (27\text{--}2)$$

For frequencies above some **cutoff frequency,** the reactance of the capacitor will be very small relative to the size of the total resistance, $R = R_{in} + R_S$. Due to the negligible size of the capacitive reactance above the cutoff frequency, the expression for the input voltage can now be simply expressed as

$$v_{in} = \left( \frac{R_{in}}{R_{in} + R_S} \right) v_S \qquad (27\text{--}3)$$

The size of the coupling capacitor is selected to be such that $X_C \leq 0.1\ R$ at the lowest frequency of operation. This condition is referred to as **stiff coupling** and is used extensively throughout electronic design.

The simplified circuit shown in Figure 27–2, is intended to operate between a frequency range of 500 Hz and 10 kHz. Determine the size of the coupling capacitor that is required between the two stages if the output impedance of the first stage is 1200 $\Omega$ and the input impedance of the second stage is 800 $\Omega$.

**EXAMPLE 27–1**

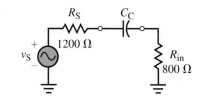

**FIGURE 27–2**

### Solution

For stiff coupling, the value of the capacitive reactance must be kept to $X_C \leq 0.1\,R$ for the lowest frequency of 500 Hz. Letting $X_C = 0.1\,R$, we get

$$X_C = (0.1)(1200\ \Omega + 800\Omega) = 200\ \Omega$$

By applying Equation 27–1, we get

$$C_C = \frac{1}{2\pi f X_C}$$

$$= \frac{1}{2\pi(500\ \text{Hz})(200\ \Omega)}$$

$$= 1.59\ \mu\text{F}$$

## Bypass Capacitors

Although resistors are useful for establishing the bias point of a transistor, they may adversely affect the ac operation of the circuit. Once again, we use capacitors to improve operation of the circuit. Placing a capacitor across a resistor has no affect on the dc operation of the circuit, since it is effectively an open circuit at dc. However, we have seen that as the frequency of a signal increases, the reactance of the capacitor will effectively approach a short circuit. If this capacitor is placed across any resistance, the resistance is effectively shorted for frequencies above the cutoff frequency, $f_c$. As one might expect, a capacitor that is used to bypass ac signals around a component (or circuit) is called a **bypass capacitor.** In most cases, the unwanted ac signal is simply bypassed to the circuit ground.

The value of a bypass capacitor is found in much the same way as the value of a coupling capacitor. For stiff bypass, the value of capacitive reactance, $X_C \leq 0.1R$ where the value of $R$ is the Thévenin resistance "seen" by the capacitor. The following example illustrates the principle.

The simplified circuit shown in Figure 27–3, is intended to operate between a frequency range of 500 Hz and 10 kHz. Determine the size of the bypass capacitor that is required across the resistor $R_E = 780\ \Omega$. The equivalent resistance of the rest of the circuit is 20 $\Omega$.

**EXAMPLE 27–2**

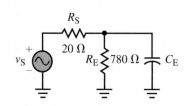

**FIGURE 27–3**

### Solution

The Thévenin resistance "seen" by the capacitor is

$$R = 20\ \Omega \| 780\ \Omega$$

$$= 19.5\ \Omega$$

For stiff bypass, we let $X_C = 0.1R = 1.95\ \Omega$ and so the value of the bypass capacitor is now determined to be

$$C_C = \frac{1}{2\pi f X_C}$$

$$= \frac{1}{2\pi(500\text{Hz})(19.5\ \Omega)}$$

$$= 163\ \mu\text{F}$$

The previous examples clearly illustrate how capacitors are used to couple desired ac signals between various stages and to bypass unwanted ac signals to ground. Whenever coupling or bypass capacitors are used in transistor circuits, the circuit is analyzed using the following simplifications:

1. Capacitors are replaced by open circuits in order to determine dc voltages and currents and

2. Capacitors are replaced by short circuits when we determine ac voltages and currents. In any design, the value of a bypass or coupling capacitor is determined by using a stiff design, namely that $X_C \leq 0.1R$ for the lowest frequency of operation. The value of $R$ is the Thévenin resistance external to the capacitor.

**PRACTICE PROBLEMS 1**

Given the circuit of Figure 27–4:

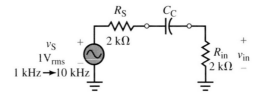

**FIGURE 27–4**

a. Determine the value of the coupling capacitor if the circuit is to operate in a frequency range from 1 kHz → 10 kHz.

b. Solve for the magnitude of the voltage, $v_{in}$ at a frequency of 1 kHz. How does the result compare to the voltage if the coupling capacitor had been replaced by a short circuit?

c. Repeat part b. for a frequency of 10 kHz.

*Answers*
a. 0.398 μF;  b. 0.498 V (as compared to 0.5 V);  c. 0.500 V

**PRACTICE PROBLEMS 2**

Given the circuit of Figure 27–5:

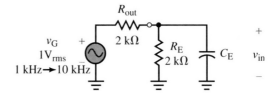

**FIGURE 27–5**

a. Determine the value of the bypass capacitor if the circuit is to operate in a frequency range from 1 kHz → 10 kHz.

b. Solve for the magnitude of the voltage, $v_{in}$, at a frequency of 1 kHz. How does the result compare to the voltage if the bypass capacitor had been replaced by a short circuit?

c. Repeat part b. for a frequency of 10 kHz.

*Answers*
a. 1.59 μF;  b. 0.0498 V (as compared to 0V);  c. 0.005 V

The operation of transistor amplifiers has been the source of much research and study. Numerous electrical models having been developed to explain the operation of the transistor; each of these models having advantages and disadvantages. For simplicity, our analysis examines only two models; the *T*-equivalent and the *h*-parameter small-signal models.

## T-Equivalent Model

The *T*-equivalent model of a transistor shown in Figure 27–6 is the simplest representation of a transistor, having only one resistor and a single current source, each of which can be determined from dc characteristics of the circuit under test. There are several important points that need to be made with respect to this model. First, the *T*-equivalent model is exactly the same regardless of whether the transistor is npn or pnp. This is because both transistor types behave exactly the same when an ac signal is applied. All current directions are instantaneous values and could just as easily be shown in the opposite direction since, as the name implies, an ac signal must alternate. Lastly, because we are working with ac currents and voltages, we show the currents in lower case letters to keep the distinction between ac and dc. You will also notice that relationship between ac currents in transistors is exactly the same as for dc currents, namely:

$$i_e = i_b + i_c \tag{27–4}$$

and

$$i_e = i_b + \beta_{ac}i_b = (\beta_{ac} + 1)i_b \tag{27–5}$$

Unless we are given other information, we assume that $\beta_{ac} = \beta_{dc}$. Although not always correct, this is generally a fairly good approximation. Finally, the value of the ac resistance in the emitter of the model is determined from the dc operating point as

$$r_e = \frac{26\text{ mV}}{I_{EQ}} \quad \text{at } 25°\text{ C} \tag{27–6}$$

The value, 26 mV, in the numerator of the above expression is due to the fact that a base-emitter junction behaves like a forward-biased diode. The resulting emitter resistance is typically very small (approximately 1 Ω to 50 Ω), as one might expect in a forward-biased diode. For example, if a transistor has an operating point of $I_{EQ} \approx I_{CQ} = 2.0$ mA, the emitter resistance would be

$$r_e = \frac{26\text{ mV}}{20\text{ mV}} = 1.3\ \Omega$$

## h-parameter Model

While the *T*-equivalent model circuit is very simple and generally provides a good model to explain most transistor operation, it is not accurate enough for other applications. For better representation of transistor ac operation, we use the more complex *h*-parameter model shown in Figure 27–7. This model consists of four variables, $h_{fe}$ (the forward current transfer ratio—unitless), $h_{ie}$ (the input impedance characteristic—in ohms, Ω), $h_{re}$ (the reverse voltage transfer ratio—unitless), and $h_{oe}$ (the output admittance characteristic—in siemens, S). Each of these parameters has a subscript *e*, indicating that the values are determined for the common emitter connection. Although less common, similar parameters may be found for common collector ($h_{fc}$, $h_{ic}$, $h_{rc}$, and $h_{oc}$) and for

## 27.2 BJT Small-Signal Models

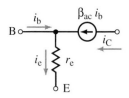

**FIGURE 27–6**   *T*-equivalent model of a BJT.

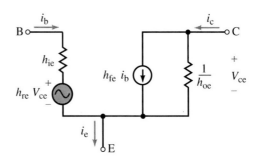

**FIGURE 27–7** *h*-parameter model of a BJT.

common base ($h_{fb}$, $h_{ib}$, $h_{rb}$, and $h_{ob}$) connections. This textbook uses only the common emitter model.

Notice that the *h*-parameter model has a current source that uses $h_{fe}$, while the *T*-equivalent model uses $\beta_{ac}$. These values are, in fact, the same, and the terms are used interchangeably. As mentioned previously, the value of $\beta_{ac}$ will often be close to the value of $\beta_{dc}$.

In order to find the values of the *h*-parameters, two methods are possible. The values can be measured by using an *h*-parameter tester or, more commonly, the values may be approximated from the manufacturer's specifications. Since the values of the *h*-parameters are dependent on the operating point, it is necessary to first determine the Q-point of the transistor. Figure 27–8 shows the *h*-parameter characteristics of a 2N3904 npn transistor.

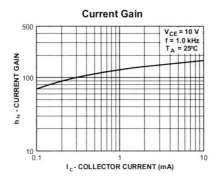

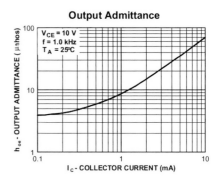

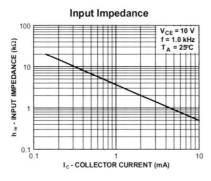

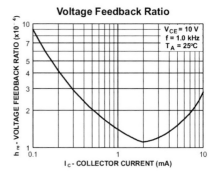

**FIGURE 27–8** *h*-parameter curves of a 2N3904 transistor. (*Courtesy of Fairchild Semiconductor Corporation*)

If we had a transistor with $I_C = 2$ mA (and $V_{CE} = 10$ V), we see that the values of the *h*-parameters are approximated as:

$$h_{fe} \approx 130, \; h_{oe} \approx 14 \; \mu S, \; h_{ie} \approx 2.0 \; k\Omega, \text{ and } h_{re} \approx 1.1 \times 10^{-4}$$

The current source in the collector circuit of each of the models shows why the BJT is referred to as a current amplifier. A small current applied at the base of a transistor is amplified into a collector current that can be 100 to 200 times larger than the base current.

## 27.3 Calculating $A_v$, $z_{in}$, $z_{out}$, and $A_i$ of a Transistor Amplifier

We are now ready to define some very important parameters of amplifier circuits; namely voltage gain ($A_v$), input impedance ($z_{in}$), current gain ($A_i$), output impedance ($z_{out}$), and power gain ($A_p$). Although we will analyze transistor circuits in this chapter, the above parameters apply equally well to any amplifier circuit. In the next chapter we will use the same parameters for circuits involving operational amplifiers. Imagine that any amplifier can be represented as a block diagram consisting of two ports as shown in Figure 27–9.

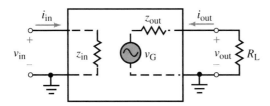

**FIGURE 27–9**    Two-port model of any amplifier circuit.

This model is called a two-port model since there are two distinct parts of the block diagram representing the amplifier; the input port and the output port. Although the model appears to show that these ports are isolated, the voltage source (which could just as easily have been the Norton equivalent with a current source and a parallel resistance) is dependent upon either voltage or current that occurs at the input. If we were to apply an input voltage, $v_{in}$, a current, $i_{in}$ would result in the input loop. We see that this current is dependent on the input impedance, $z_{in}$ of the amplifier and is easily calculated by using Ohm's law. The output circuit of the amplifier can be represented as a voltage source with a voltage, $v_{out}$, and an internal series impedance, $z_{out}$. Now, if some external load is applied to the output circuit, current would result in an output voltage across this load, $R_L$. The polarity of the output voltage, $v_{out}$, and the direction of the output current, $i_{out}$, are shown for reference purposes only. The actual voltage polarity and/or current direction may not necessarily be the same as those shown.

Whenever we analyze any amplifier circuit, we generally solve for five characteristics of the amplifier circuit: the voltage gain, the input impedance, the output impedance, the current gain, and the power gain. The use of the ac equivalent circuit is of fundamental importance in the analysis of all circuits.

### Voltage Gain, $A_v$

**Voltage gain** is defined as the ratio of the output voltage to input voltage.

$$A_v = \frac{v_{out}}{v_{in}} \qquad (27\text{–}7)$$

### Input impedance, $z_{in}$

The **input impedance** of any circuit is defined as the ratio of input voltage to input current.

$$z_{in} = \frac{v_{in}}{i_{in}} \qquad (27\text{--}8)$$

### Output Impedance, $z_{out}$

The **output impedance** of an amplifier is determined by looking back into the transistor's output terminals with the load resistance, $R_L$, removed. The definition of output impedance of a circuit is very similar to the approach that was used to find the Thévenin impedance of a circuit; namely that the output impedance of any circuit is expressed as the ratio of open-circuit output voltage to short-circuit output current.

$$z_{out} = \frac{v_{out(OC)}}{i_{out(SC)}} \qquad (27\text{--}9)$$

### Current Gain, $A_i$

As expected, **current gain** is defined as the ratio of output current to input current.

$$A_i = \frac{i_{out}}{i_{in}} \qquad (27\text{--}10)$$

Although the above expression is useful, there is an easier way to find the current gain of an amplifier once the voltage gain has been determined. The resulting expression can be used in any two-port circuit (i.e., any circuit consisting of two input terminals and two output terminals), regardless of the connection between the ports.

Remember that we defined voltage gain as

$$A_v = \frac{v_{out}}{v_{in}}$$

Applying Ohm's law on the circuit of Figure 27–9, results in

$$A_v = \frac{-i_{out}R_L}{i_{in}z_{in}}$$

Notice that the term in the numerator is negative. This is necessary to account for the reference direction of the output current, $i_{out}$. Finally, by using the definition of current gain we rewrite the equation as

$$A_i = -\frac{A_v z_{in}}{R_L} \qquad (27\text{--}11)$$

### Power Gain, $A_p$

As expected, it is a simple matter to find the power gain of the amplifier. **Power gain** is defined as the ratio of signal output power to signal input power, namely

$$A_p = \frac{P_{out}}{P_{in}} \qquad (27\text{--}12)$$

However, since power is determined as $P = V \cdot I$, we rewrite the expression as

$$A_p = \frac{v_{out}i_{out}}{v_{in}i_{in}} = |A_v A_i| \qquad (27\text{--}13)$$

The absolute value operation in the expression is necessary since power gain cannot have a negative value. Equation 27–13 is valid for all two-port systems regardless of the configuration. Although this expression seems to indicate that it is possible to have more output power than input power (a contradiction of the Law of Energy Conservation), what we have is an increase in signal (or ac) power. As we will observe later, the increase in signal power is the result of power conversion by the dc voltage source of the circuit.

In this section, we will examine several circuits and derive general equations that can be used to analyze circuits that have the same configuration. Although the circuit parameters can be easily found by simply plugging values into the appropriate equations, it is strongly recommended that you use applicable circuit theory in your analysis. The skills that you develop will help you to methodically analyze any circuit.

In order to determine how a transistor behaves with the application of an ac signal, we must first sketch the ac equivalent of a transistor circuit. To do this for any transistor circuit, we follow several important steps:

1. Find the operating point of the transistor to ensure that the transistor is in its active region.

2. Determine the ac parameters of the transistor model that you will use. If you use the $T$-equivalent model, you will need to calculate $r_e = 26$ mV/$I_E$. If you use the $h$-parameter model you will need $h_{fe}$ and $h_{ie}$. There are two other $h$-parameters that are seldom used. $h_{re}$ is very small and has negligible effect on any circuit operation. The value of $h_{oe}$ is only considered when $1/h_{oe}$ is within an order of magnitude of $R_C \| R_L$.

3. Remove all dc voltage sources from the given circuit and replace them with short circuits. (This step is similar to how we find the Thévenin equivalent circuit.)

4. Replace all coupling and bypass capacitors with short circuits. If the circuit was designed correctly, the values of these capacitors were designed to be stiff for the frequency range at which the transistor is to operate.

5. Replace the transistor with the appropriate model, whether the $T$-equivalent or the $h$-parameter.

6. Solve the resulting circuit for each of the required characteristics.

Let's examine how these steps can be applied to the common-emitter transistor amplifier circuit of Figure 27–10. If we assume that the operating point of the transistor has been found, we can apply Steps 3 and 4 to arrive at the equivalent circuit shown in Figure 27–11.

## 27.4 The Common-Emitter Amplifier

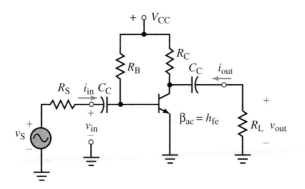

**FIGURE 27–10**   Fixed-bias CE amplifier.

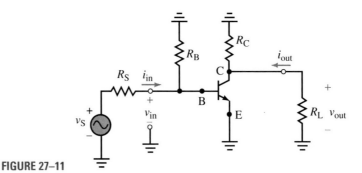

**FIGURE 27–11**

The circuit of Figure 27–11 is further redrawn in Figure 27–12 by substituting the transistor with the appropriate model (let's begin by using the *T*-equivalent) and by reconfiguring the resistors so that the grounds are at the bottom of the circuit. In order to help clarify the analysis, Figure 27–12 shows the circuit ground as a continuous connection. Notice also that the input and output terminals have been clearly identified. From the illustration we see that the output current is determined to be in the same direction as the ac collector current, $i_c$. However, since the output current is in the same direction as $i_c$, we conclude that the voltage across $R_L$ must be opposite to the polarity that is shown in the diagram.

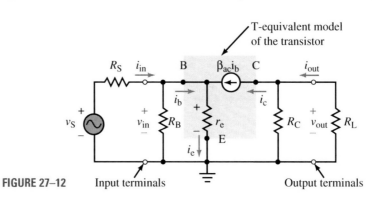

**FIGURE 27–12**    Input terminals            Output terminals

The polarities of all voltages are taken with respect to ground. Since the direction of the output current is into the collector (due to the current source in the transistor model), we see that the polarity of the output voltage must be negative. $R_C$ and $R_L$ are in a parallel connection and so we express the output voltage as $v_{out} = -i_c(R_C \| R_L)$.

Although the input voltage is across $R_B$, it is not useful to write the input voltage in terms of this component, since we know nothing of the current through $R_B$. Remember that Kirchhoff's voltage law states that the voltage at any point with respect to ground is the same, no matter which path is chosen. Consequently, we see that the input voltage may be written in terms of the current through $r_e$. This gives the input voltage as $v_{in} = i_e r_e$. The voltage gain is now easily written as

$$A_v = \frac{v_{out}}{v_{in}} = \frac{-i_c\left(R_C \| R_L\right)}{i_e r_e}$$

Now, since $i_c = \beta_{ac} i_b$ and $i_e = (\beta_{ac} + 1)i_b$ we express the voltage gain of the fixed-bias CE amplifier as

$$A_v = \frac{-\beta_{ac} i_b\left(R_C \| R_L\right)}{(\beta_{ac} + 1)i_b r_e} = -\frac{\beta_{ac}\left(R_C \| R_L\right)}{(\beta_{ac} + 1)r_e} \approx -\frac{\left(R_C \| R_L\right)}{r_e} \qquad \textbf{(27–14)}$$

Notice that the previous expression shows the voltage gain to be a negative value. This simply means that the output voltage is $180°$ out-of-phase (inverted) with respect to the input signal. This characteristic is true for all common-emitter circuits. In the final approximation, voltage gain is dependent on only the resistor values in the circuit and is not dependent on the ac beta (also specified as $h_{fe}$) of the transistor. This is because in most instances $h_{fe}$ is quite large and so $\beta_{ac}/(\beta_{ac} + 1) \approx 1$. Typical magnitudes of voltage gain for the fixed-bias CE amplifier are in the order of 50 to 150.

In order to determine the input impedance of the circuit, we begin by first solving for the input impedance (looking into the base) of the transistor. By applying Equation 27–8 to the base terminal of the transistor, we determine the input impedance of the transistor, $z_{in(Q)}$ as

$$z_{in(Q)} = \frac{v_b}{i_b} = \frac{i_e r_e}{i_b} = \frac{(\beta_{ac} + 1)i_b r_e}{i_b} = (\beta_{ac} + 1)r_e \qquad \textbf{(27–15)}$$

The input impedance at the input terminals of the circuit can now be found by placing the base resistance, $R_B$ in parallel with the input impedance of the transistor. The resultant input impedance of the fixed-bias CE transistor circuit is now found as

$$z_{in} = R_B \| (\beta_{ac} + 1)r_e \approx R_B \| (\beta_{ac} r_e) \qquad \textbf{(27–16)}$$

In general, the input impedance of the fixed-bias CE amplifier is moderately high and tends to be in a range of about 1 k$\Omega$ to 2 k$\Omega$.

Although Equation 27–9 can be used to solve for the output impedance of this circuit, there is a much easier approach for determining the output impedance of most (though not all) transistor circuits. In a manner similar to that used in determining the input impedance of the circuit, we begin by looking into the collector terminal of the transistor. Recall that when we were finding the Thévenin impedance of a circuit, we first begin by removing all voltage and current sources. Removing the current source, $\beta_{ac} i_b$ means that the output impedance of this transistor circuit is an open circuit, namely $z_{out(Q)} = \infty$. Consequently, the impedance at the output terminals is simply found as

$$z_{out} = R_C \qquad \textbf{(27–17)}$$

The current gain of any amplifier can be found by using Equation 27–11. If we substitute Equations 27–14 and 27–16 into Equation 27–11, we arrive at an expression for the current gain of the fixed-bias CE amplifier as follows:

$$A_i = -\frac{A_v z_{in}}{R_L}$$

$$= -\left( \frac{\beta_{ac}(R_C \| R_L)}{(\beta_{ac} + 1)r_e} \right)\left( \frac{R_B \| [(\beta_{ac} + 1)r_e]}{R_L} \right)$$

which, when simplified using the approximation that $\beta_{ac} \approx \beta_{ac} + 1$, results in

$$A_i \approx \frac{\beta_{ac} R_B R_C}{(R_C + R_L)(R_B + \beta_{ac} r_e)} \qquad \textbf{(27–18)}$$

Typical current gain for the fixed-bias CE amplifier tends to be between 50 and 100.

The previous equations were derived using the $T$-equivalent model of the transistor. Similar derivations are possible if we were to use the $h$-parameter model. Figure 27–13 shows the ac equivalent of the fixed-bias CE amplifier

**NOTES . . .**

The input impedance of the transistor is not equal to $r_e$ since $r_e$ is in the emitter circuit. Since we are trying to find the impedance looking into the base, we use the voltage and current at this terminal.

using the *h*-parameter model of the transistor. As mentioned previously, we will not consider the effects of $h_{re}$ for any ac model because the effects are minimal. In deriving the equations for the CE amplifier, we neglect the effects of the output impedance, $(1/h_{oe})$ of the transistor, since in most cases this impedance will be many times larger than the value of $R_C\|R_L$. However, as we will discover in Section 27.6 there are instances where the effects of $h_{oe}$ cannot be ignored.

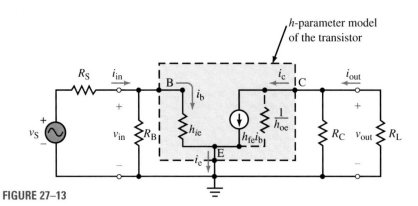

**FIGURE 27–13**

It is left as an exercise for the student to derive the following expressions using the *h*-parameter model of the transistor for the fixed-bias CE amplifier.

$$A_v = -\frac{h_{fe}\left(R_C\|R_L\right)}{h_{ie}} \tag{27-19}$$

$$z_{in} = R_B\|h_{ie} \tag{27-20}$$

$$z_{out} = R_C \tag{27-21}$$

$$A_i = \frac{h_{fe}R_B R_C}{\left(R_C + R_L\right)\left(R_B + h_{ie}\right)} \tag{27-22}$$

**EXAMPLE 27–3**

Given the fixed-bias CE amplifier circuit of Figure 27–14:

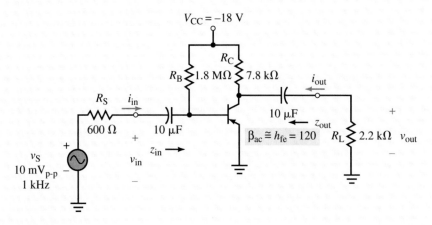

**FIGURE 27–14**

a. Find the dc operating point.

b. Sketch the ac equivalent circuit, using the *T*-equivalent model of the transistor.

c. Determine $A_v = v_{out}/v_{in}$, $z_{in}$, $z_{out}$, $A_i$, and $A_p$.

## Solution

a.
$$(1.8M\Omega)I_B + 0.7\text{ V} = 18\text{V}$$

$$I_B = \frac{18\text{ V} - 0.7\text{ V}}{1.8\text{ M}\Omega} = 9.61\ \mu\text{A}$$

$$I_C = (120)(9.61\ \mu\text{A}) = 1.15\text{ mA}$$

$$V_{CE} = -18\text{ V} + (7.8\text{ k}\Omega)(1.15\text{ mA}) = -9.00\text{ V}$$

$$r_e = \frac{26\text{ mV}}{1.15\text{ mA}} = 22.5\ \Omega$$

b. The ac equivalent of the circuit is shown in Figure 27–15. It is important to note that the ac equivalent of the transistor is not dependent on whether the transistor is npn or pnp since either transistor type will respond to an ac signal in exactly the same way.

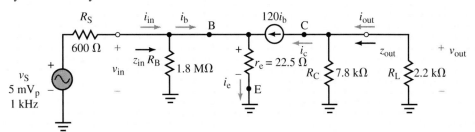

**FIGURE 27–15**

c. Voltage gain, $A_v = v_{out}/v_{in}$:

$$A_v = \frac{v_{out}}{v_{in}} = -\frac{i_c(R_C\|R_L)}{i_e r_e}$$

$$= -\frac{120i_b(7.8\text{ k}\Omega\|2.2\text{ k}\Omega)}{121i_b(22.5\text{ k}\Omega)}$$

$$= -75.6$$

Input impedance, $z_{in}$:

First, we find the input impedance of the transistor.

$$z_{in(Q)} = \frac{v_b}{i_b} = \frac{i_e r_e}{i_b} = \frac{(h_{fe}+1)i_b r_e}{i_b} = 121(22.5\ \Omega) = 2.72\text{ k}\Omega$$

The resultant input impedance is the parallel combination of $R_B$ and $z_{in(Q)}$. Due to its much greater size, $R_B$ has negligible effect on the input impedance of the amplifier circuit.

$$z_{in} = 2.72\text{ k}\Omega\|1.8\text{ M}\Omega \approx 2.72\text{ k}\Omega$$

Output impedance, $z_{out}$:

Due to the infinite output impedance of the $T$-equivalent transistor model, the output impedance of the amplifier is simply $z_{out} = 7.8\text{ k}\Omega$.

Current gain, $A_i$:

Using Equation 27–11, the current gain of the amplifier circuit is

$$A_i = -\frac{A_v z_{in}}{R_L} = -\frac{(-75.6)(2.72\text{ k}\Omega)}{2.2\text{ k}\Omega} = 93.5$$

Power gain, $A_p$:

Using Equation 27–14, we determine the power gain to be

$$A_p = |(-75.6)(93.5)| = 7070$$

**EXAMPLE 27–4**

For the fixed-bias CE amplifier circuit of Figure 27–14, let $h_{ie} = 2600 \ \Omega$ and $h_{oe} = 8.0 \ \mu S$.

a. Sketch the ac equivalent circuit, using the $h$-parameter model of the transistor.

b. Determine $A_v$, $z_{in}$, $z_{out}$, $A_i$, and $A_p$ using the $h$-parameter model.

c. If the signal generator has an unloaded output voltage of 10 mV$_{p-p}$, determine the expected output voltage. Sketch the waveforms of $v_S$, $v_{in}$, and $v_{out}$, showing amplitudes and relative phase angles.

**Solution**

a. The ac equivalent circuit is shown in Figure 27–16. Notice that the output impedance of the transistor is $1/h_{oe} = 125 \ k\Omega$. Since this value is much larger than $R_C$ and $R_L$ its effect may be neglected.

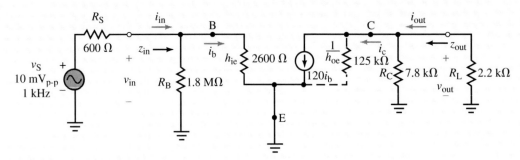

**FIGURE 27–16**

b.

$$A_v = \frac{v_{out}}{v_{in}} = \frac{-i_C(R_C\|R_L)}{i_B h_{ie}} = \frac{-(h_{fe}i_B)(R_C\|R_L)}{i_B h_{ie}} = \frac{-(120)(7.8 \ k\Omega\|R2.2 \ k\Omega)}{2.6 \ k\Omega} = -79.2$$

$$Z_{in(Q)} = \frac{v_b}{i_b} = \frac{h_{ie}i_B}{i_B} = h_{ie} = 2.6 \ k\Omega$$

$$Z_{in} = R_B\|Z_{in(Q)} = 1.8 \ M\Omega\|2.6 \ k\Omega \approx 2.6 \ k\Omega$$

$$Z_{out} = R_C\left\|\frac{1}{h_{oe}}\right. \approx R_C = 7.8 \ k\Omega$$

In general if $R_C\|R_L < 0.1(1/h_{oe})$ we may ignore the effect of $h_{oe}$

$$A_i = -\frac{A_v z_{in}}{R_L} = -\frac{(-79.2)(2.6 \ k\Omega)}{2.2 \ k\Omega} = 93.6$$

$$A_p = |A_v A_i| = (79.2)(93.6) = 7410$$

Notice that the values obtained by using the $h$-parameter model are somewhat different than those found using the $T$-equivalent model. For most circuits, the discrepancy is quite small. Because the $h$-parameter model is a closer representation of the actual behavior of a transistor, we find that this model provides a slightly better approximation than the $T$-equivalent model.

c. In order to solve for the output voltage, we must first determine the input voltage, $v_{in}$. A common error is to assume the input voltage is the same as the source voltage, $v_S$. This is not correct! As illustrated in Figure 27–17, we determine the input voltage by using the voltage divider rule between the input impedance, $z_{in}$ of the amplifier and the source resistance, $R_S$.

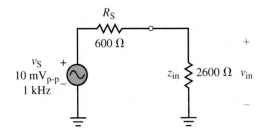

**FIGURE 27–17**

The input voltage is found as

$$v_{in} = \left(\frac{z_{in}}{z_{in} + R_S}\right)v_S = \left(\frac{2600\ \Omega}{2600\ \Omega + 600\ \Omega}\right)10\ \text{mV}_{p\text{-}p} = 8.12\ \text{mV}_{p\text{-}p}$$

Now since voltage gain is $A_v = v_{out}/v_{in} = -79.2$, we get

$$v_{out} = A_v v_{in} = (-79.2)(8.12\ \text{mV}_{p\text{-}p}) = 644\ \text{mV}_{p\text{-}p}$$

Notice that the output voltage is not written as $-644\ \text{mV}_{p\text{-}p}$ even though the voltage gain is preceded with a negative sign. By definition, peak-to-peak voltage is simply a magnitude. A negative sign would be meaningless in this context. Remember that the significance of the negative sign in the voltage gain simply means that the output voltage is $180°$ out-of- phase with respect to the input voltage. Figure 27–18 shows the waveforms as they would appear when observed with an oscilloscope.

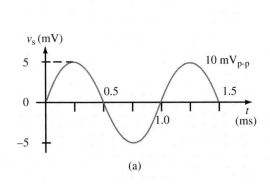

(a)

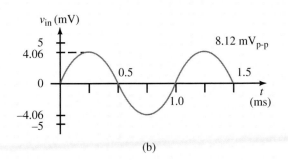

(b)

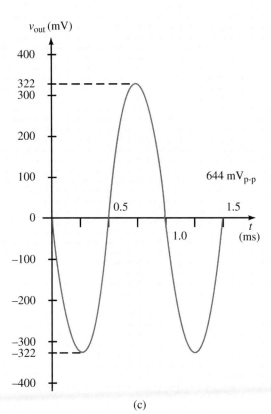

(c)

**FIGURE 27–18**

PRACTICE PROBLEMS 3

Given the amplifier circuit of Figure 27–19:

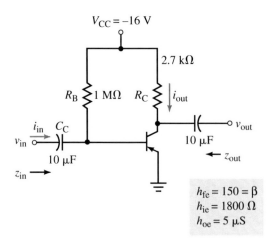

**FIGURE 27–19**

a. Determine the operating point.

b. Sketch the ac equivalent circuit, using the *h*-parameter model of the transistor.

c. Use the *h*-parameter model to calculate $A_v$, $z_{in}$, $z_{out}$, and $A_i$.

(Hint: When calculating the current gain, the load resistor is the component having the output current, $i_{out}$.)

*Answers*
a. $V_{CE} = -9.80$ V, $I_C = 2.30$ mA; c. $A_v = -225$, $z_{in} \approx 1.8$ kΩ, $z_{out} \approx 2.7$ kΩ, $A_i = 150$

PRACTICE PROBLEMS 4

Using the circuit of Figure 27–19, sketch the ac equivalent circuit using the *T*-equivalent model and calculate $A_v$, $z_{in}$, $z_{out}$, and $A_i$.

*Answers*
$r_e = 11.3$ Ω, $A_v = -237$, $z_{in} \approx 1.71$ κΩ, $z_{out} \approx 2.7$kΩ, $A_i = 150$

The methods that we used in analyzing the fixed-bias CE amplifier are easily applied to other CE amplifier circuits as well. The following example shows that with slight modifications in the analysis, we can use the same method to analyze other amplifier circuits such as the universal-bias CE amplifier, the most-commonly used transistor amplifier circuit.

**EXAMPLE 27–5**

Given the amplifier circuit of Figure 27–20:

a. Determine the dc operating point of the transistor.

b. Sketch the ac equivalent circuit using the *T*-equivalent model of the transistor.

c. Solve for $A_v$, $z_{in}$, $z_{out}$, and $A_i$.

d. Calculate the peak-to-peak value of the output voltage, $v_{out}$ for a supply voltage of $v_S = 10$ mV$_{p-p}$.

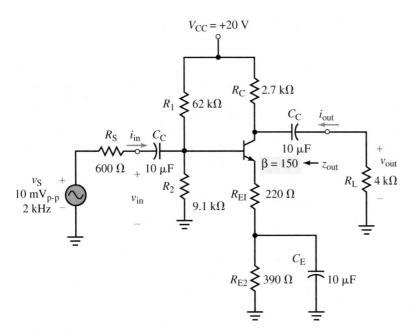

**FIGURE 27–20**

**Solution**

a. If we wish to use the voltage divider rule to determine the operating point, we must first examine the circuit to determine whether the following test is satisfied.

$$R_2 \leq 0.1 \, \beta_{dc} \, R_E$$

In this example, we see that the approximation is valid, since

$$9.1 \text{ k}\Omega \leq 0.1 \, (150) \, (0.61 \text{ k}\Omega) = 9.15 \text{ k}\Omega$$

(If the condition, $R_2 \leq 0.1 \, \beta_{dc} \, R_E$ had not been met then it would have been necessary find the Thévenin equivalent of the input of the circuit using $\beta_{dc}$). Now, using the approximation, we have the following:

$$V_B = \left( \frac{9.1 \, \Omega}{9.1 \, \Omega \, + \, 62 \text{ k}\Omega} \right) (20 \text{ V}) = 2.56 \text{ V}$$

$$V_E = 2.56 \text{ V} - 0.7 \text{ V} = 1.86 \text{ V}$$

$$I_E = \left( \frac{1.86 \text{ V}}{0.22 \, \Omega \, + \, 0.39 \text{ k}\Omega} \right) = 3.05 \text{ mA} \approx I_C$$

$$V_{CE} \approx 20 \text{ V} - 3.05 \text{ mA}(2.7 \text{ k}\Omega + 0.22 \text{ k}\Omega + 0.39 \text{ k}\Omega) = 9.91 \text{ V}$$

b. $r_E = \dfrac{26 \text{ mV}}{3.05 \text{ mA}} = 8.53 \, \Omega$

In the ac equivalent circuit, the bias resistors $R_1$ and $R_2$ are in a parallel connection from the transistor base to ground (Remember, the dc supply is replaced by a short circuit when doing ac analysis). The resulting ac equivalent circuit is shown in Figure 27–21.

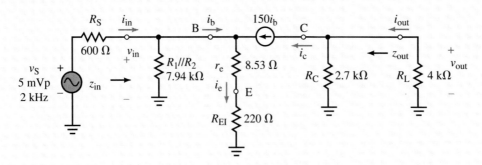

**FIGURE 27–21**

c.

$$A_v = \frac{v_{out}}{v_{in}} = -\frac{(150)i_b(2.7 \text{ k}\Omega \| 4 \text{ k}\Omega)}{(151)i_b(8.53 \text{ }\Omega + 220 \text{ }\Omega)} = -7.00$$

$$z_{in(Q)} = \frac{v_b}{i_b} = \frac{(151)i_b(8.53 \text{ }\Omega + 220 \text{ }\Omega)}{i_b} = 34.5 \text{ k}\Omega$$

$$z_{in} = R_1 \| R_2 \| z_{in(Q)} = 7.94 \text{ k}\Omega \| 34.5 \text{ k}\Omega = 6.45 \text{ k}\Omega$$

$$z_{out} \approx 2.7 \text{ k}\Omega$$

$$A_i = -\frac{A_v z_{in}}{R_L} = -\frac{(-7.00)(6.45 \text{ k}\Omega)}{4 \text{ k}\Omega} = 11.3$$

d. Using the voltage divider rule, we have

$$v_{in} = \left(\frac{6.45 \text{ k}\Omega}{6.45 \text{ k}\Omega + 0.6 \text{ k}\Omega}\right)(10 \text{ mV}_{p-p}) = 9.15 \text{ mV}_{p-p}$$

which results in

$$v_{out} = |(-7.00)(9.15 \text{ mV}_{p-p})| = 64.0 \text{ mV}_{p-p}$$

---

**PRACTICE PROBLEMS 5**

Given the circuit of Figure 27–22:

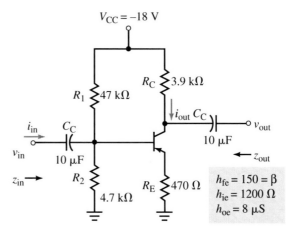

**FIGURE 27–22**

a. Determine the dc operating point of the transistor.

b. Sketch the ac equivalent circuit using the *h*-parameter model of the transistor.

c. Calculate $A_v$, $z_{in}$, $z_{out}$, and $A_i$.

*Answers*

a. $I_C \approx -1.99 \text{ mA}$, $V_{CE} \approx -9.29 \text{ V}$

b. $A_v = -8.11$, $z_{in} = 4.03 \text{ k}\Omega$, $z_{out} \approx 3.9 \text{ k}\Omega$, and $A_i = 8.38$.

Recall that the dc load line was used to determine the saturation current (maximum possible collector current) and the cutoff voltage (maximum possible collector-emitter voltage) that could occur in a transistor circuit. We found that the operating point or quiescent point (Q-point) of a transistor always occurred on the dc load line. In this section we will examine a similar line, called the **ac load line,** which is used to determine how the collector current and collector-emitter voltage behave when an ac signal is applied to the circuit.

## 27.5 The ac Load Line

The ac load line is used for determining the **maximum undistorted output signal** that can be expected for a given transistor amplifier. If we know the maximum undistorted output signal, we will be ready to calculate maximum power that we can expect to obtain from a particular transistor design.

Consider the CE amplifier circuit shown in Figure 27–23.

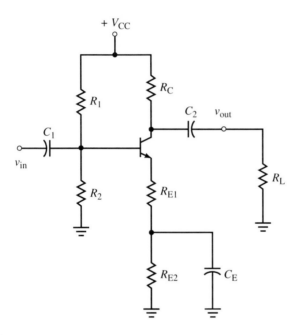

**FIGURE 27–23**

We know that the dc saturation current occurs when $V_{CE} = 0$ V, and is determined by considering the values of the resistors in the output loop of the transistor, namely

$$I_{C(DC-SAT)} = \frac{V_{CC}}{R_C + R_E}$$

Similarly, the dc cutoff voltage occurs when $I_C = 0$ mA, and in this circuit is simply given as

$$V_{CE(DC-OFF)} = V_{CC}$$

In determining the dc saturation and cutoff values, the capacitors are replaced by open circuits, since the value of capacitive reactance is infinite at dc ($f = 0$ Hz). As a result, we notice that the load resistor, $R_L$, has no effect on the dc operation of the circuit. This, however, is not the case when an ac signal is applied to the signal. When an ac signal is applied to the transistor, the bypass capacitor, $C_E$ effectively shorts a portion of the emitter resistance, $R_{E2}$ to ground and the coupling capacitor, $C_2$ introduces the load resistor, $R_L$ into the collector portion of the circuit. Figure 27–24 illustrates a simplified ac version of the output of the transistor amplifier. For simplicity, the bias resistors, $R_1$ and $R_2$, are not included in the illustration.

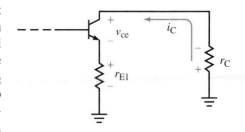

**FIGURE 27–24**

Now, using the direction and polarity of the ac current and voltage, we have the expressions

$$v_{CE} = -i_C(r_C + r_E) \qquad \textbf{(27–23)}$$

and

$$i_C = \frac{v_{CE}}{r_C + r_E} \qquad \textbf{(27–24)}$$

where $r_C$ is the "ac resistance" connected to the collector and is determined as $r_C = R_C \| R_L$ and $r_E$ is the "ac resistance" connected to the emitter and is given as $r_E = R_{E1}$. The resultant collector current and collector-emitter voltage in the circuit are determined (by superposition) as the summation of the dc and the ac components. Hence we have

$$i_C = I_{CQ} + i_c \qquad \textbf{(27–25)}$$

and

$$v_{CE} = V_{CEQ} + v_{ce} \qquad \textbf{(27–26)}$$

These results are more easily understood if we consider that the circuit has two load lines, the dc load line and the ac load line as shown in Figure 27–25.

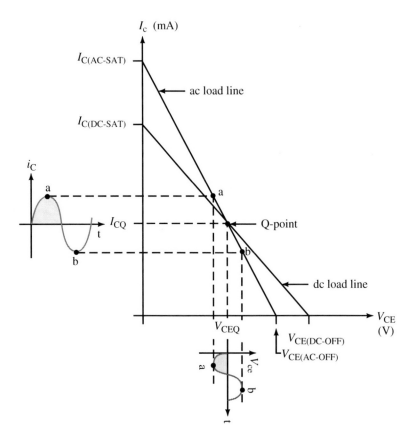

**FIGURE 27–25** dc load line and ac load line.

Notice that both the ac load line and dc load line intersect at the Q-point. Any ac signal must follow the ac load line. If there were no ac signal, then the collector current in the circuit must be equal to the dc value, $I_{CQ}$. The illustration also clearly shows that as the collector current, $i_c$ is increasing, the collector-emitter voltage, $v_{ce}$ is decreasing. Clearly the two values are 180° out-of-phase. This important characteristic was demonstrated when we calculated the voltage gain for each of the CE amplifiers previously in this chapter. This characteristic is also observed as the negative sign in Equations 27–23 and 27–24.

Now we will derive simplified expressions for the ac saturation current and the ac cutoff voltage. Remember that saturation is defined as that point on the dc load line where the current is maximum and where the collector-emitter voltage is zero. At ac saturation, Equation 27–31 becomes

$$0 = V_{CEQ} + v_{ce}$$

which gives

$$v_{ce} = -V_{CEQ}$$

Substituting this result into Equation 27–24 gives

$$i_C = \frac{V_{CEQ}}{r_C + r_E}$$

Finally, inserting this expression into Equation 27–25, we get

$$I_{C(AC\text{-}SAT)} = I_{CQ} + \frac{V_{CEQ}}{r_C + r_E} \qquad (27\text{-}27)$$

Using a similar approach to solve for ac cutoff ($i_C = 0$), we get

$$V_{CE(AC\text{-}OFF)} = V_{CEQ} + I_{CQ}(r_C + r_E) \qquad (27\text{-}28)$$

Equations 27–27 and 27–28 indicate that it is possible to find ac saturation and cutoff simply by determining the combined "ac resistance" in the collector-emitter circuit and then using the values of current and voltage at the operating point (Q-point). Once these values have been determined it is possible to determine the magnitude of the largest undistorted signal that is possible for the given transistor circuit.

If we examine the plot of $I_C$ vs. $V_{CE}$ shown in Figure 27–25, we see that the Q-point is not in the center of the ac load line. Since a sinusoidal ac signal is symmetrical about the time-axis, we see that if the collector current, $i_c$ were increased (due to an increase in base current caused by the input signal), point *b* will reach ac cutoff before point *a* reaches ac saturation. Therefore, we conclude that the maximum peak-to-peak undistorted collector current for this transistor is given as $i_{c(max)} = 2\,I_{CQ}$. If the Q-point were above the midpoint of the ac load line, the maximum peak-to-peak undistorted collector current for that condition would be given as $i_{c(max)} = 2\,(I_{C(AC\text{-}SAT)} - I_{CQ})$. From these results we concluded that in order to obtain the maximum undistorted signal at the output of a transistor amplifier, we would need to ensure that the amplifier is biased in the center of its ac load line.

EXAMPLE 27–6    Given the circuit of Figure 27–26:

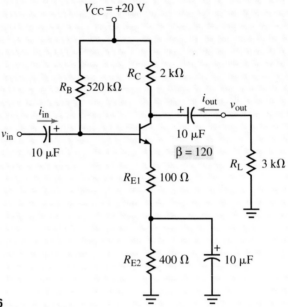

**FIGURE 27–26**

a. Determine the operating point of the transistor.

b. Sketch the simplified ac equivalent circuit of the output of the amplifier. (Do not model the transistor.)

c. Calculate the values of dc and ac saturation and cutoff.

d. Sketch a graph showing the dc load line and the ac load line.

e. Determine the maximum undistorted collector current and the maximum undistorted collector-emitter voltage. Solve for the maximum undistorted output voltage, $v_{out}$.

**Solution:**

a. The operating point of the transistor is found as

$$I_{BQ} = \frac{20\ V - 0.7\ V}{520\ k\Omega + 121(0.5\ k\Omega)} = 33.2\ \mu A$$

$$I_{CQ} = 120(33.2\ \mu A) = 3.99\ mA$$

$$V_{CEQ} = 20\ V - 3.99\ mA(2\ k\Omega + 0.5\ k\Omega) = 10.0\ V$$

b. Figure 27–27 shows the simplified ac circuit of the output of the transistor amplifier.

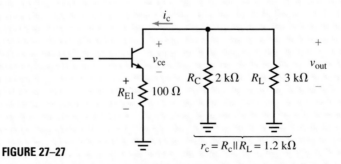

**FIGURE 27–27**

c. The values of dc saturation and cutoff are determined as

$$I_{C(DC\text{-}SAT)} = \frac{20 \text{ V}}{2 \text{ k}\Omega + 0.1 \text{ k}\Omega + 0.4 \text{k}\Omega} = 8.0 \text{ mA}$$

$$V_{CE(DC\text{-}OFF)} = 20 \text{ V}$$

The values of ac saturation and cutoff are determined as

$$I_{C(AC\text{-}SAT)} = 3.99 \text{ mA} + \frac{10 \text{ V}}{1.2 \text{ k}\Omega + 0.1 \text{ k}\Omega} = 11.70 \text{ mA}$$

$$V_{CE(AC\text{-}OFF)} = 10 \text{ V} + 3.99 \text{ mA}(1.2 \text{ k}\Omega + 0.1 \text{ k}\Omega) = 15.2 \text{ V}$$

d. The corresponding load lines are shown in Figure 27–28.

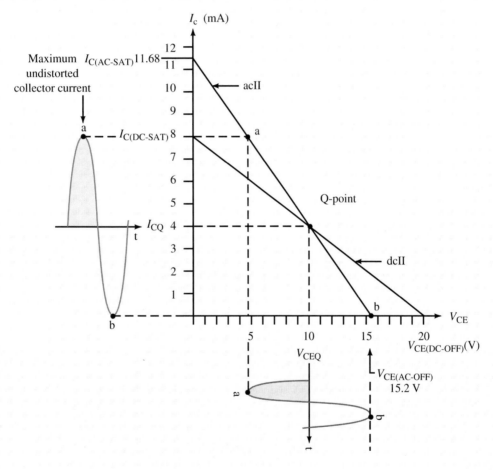

**FIGURE 27–28**

e. The maximum undistorted collector current is found to be

$$i_{c(max)} = 2(3.99 \text{ mA}) = 7.98 \text{ mA}_{p\text{-}p}$$

and the maximum undistorted collector-emitter voltage is found as

$$v_{ce(max)} = 2(15.2 \text{ V} - 10.0 \text{ V}) = 10.4 \text{ V}_{p\text{-}p}$$

The maximum undistorted output voltage can be found either by using Ohm's law

$$v_{out(max)} = i_c(R_C \| R_L) = 7.98 \text{ mA}(1.2 \text{ k}\Omega) = 9.58 \text{ V}_{p\text{-}p}$$

or by using the voltage divider rule

$$v_{out(max)} = v_{ce} + i_e r_E = 10.4 \text{ V} - 7.98 \text{ mA}(0.1 \text{ k}\Omega) = 9.58 \text{ V}_{p\text{-}p}$$

**Note:** The amplifier of Figure 27–26 has a voltage gain, of $A_v \approx -12$. Therefore, to ensure that the output is not distorted, the maximum signal that can be applied at the input is $v_{in(max)} = 0.80$ V$_{p-p}$ (or 0.40 V$_p$). If the level of the input signal goes slightly above this value, the positive-going portion of the output will be clipped, since the signal causes the transistor to go into ac cutoff. If the input signal is increased still further, ac saturation will occur, resulting in distortion of both the positive- and negative-going portions of the output signal.

---

**PRACTICE PROBLEMS 6**

Given the circuit of Figure 27–29:

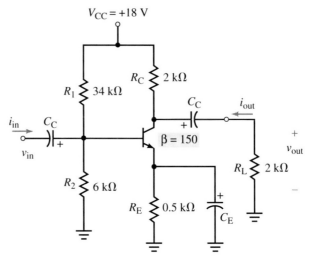

**FIGURE 27–29**

a.  Determine the operating point of the transistor.

b.  Sketch the simplified ac equivalent circuit of the output of the amplifier. (Do not model the transistor.)

c.  Calculate the values of dc and ac saturation and cutoff.

d.  Sketch a graph showing the dc load line and the ac load line.

e.  Determine the maximum undistorted collector current and the maximum undistorted collector-emitter voltage. Solve for the maximum undistorted output voltage, $v_{out}$.

*Answers*
a.  $I_{CQ} = 4.00$ mA, $V_{CEQ} = 8.00$ V; c. $I_{C(DC-SAT)} = 7.20$ mA, $V_{CE(DC-OFF)} = 18.00$ V, $I_{C(AC-SAT)} = 12.0$ mA, $V_{CE(DC-OFF)} = 12.00$ V; e. $i_{c(max)} = 8.00$ mA$_{p-p}$, $v_{ce(max)} = 8.00$ V$_{p-p}$

Although Equations 27–27 and 27–28 were specifically derived by finding the ac load line for npn transistors, it is possible to use these same expressions for finding the ac load line of pnp transistors as well. In such circuits, the collector current, $I_C$ and the collector-emitter voltage, $V_{CE}$ will each be negative.

---

## 27.6 The Common-Collector Amplifier

The common-collector amplifier has several important characteristics that make it particularly useful in certain instances. The distinguishing characteristics of the CC amplifier are:

1.  The input impedance tends to be very high, which means that this circuit will not adversely load the previous stage.

2. The output impedance of the CC amplifier is exceedingly low, which means that the following stage will not load the circuit.

3. The output voltage of the common-emitter is in-phase with the input voltage. For this reason this circuit is often referred to as a *voltage follower* circuit.

4. The common-collector circuit has an output voltage that is approximately equal to the input voltage. ($A_v \approx 1$). In actual fact, the output voltage is always slightly less than the input voltage.

5. The current gain of the CC amplifier is large, often just less than $h_{fe}$. Figure 27–30 shows a typical common-collector amplifier.

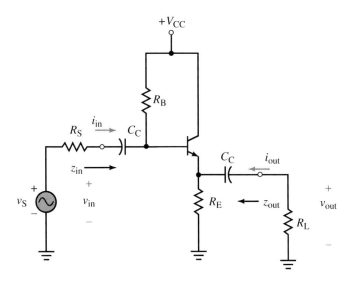

**FIGURE 27–30**

As in the common-emitter amplifier, the input signal is applied at the base of the circuit. However, the output is taken at the emitter. In the previous circuit, we see that any ac signal at the collector is connected to ground through the dc supply voltage, $V_{CC}$. As in previous circuits, we can use either the $T$-equivalent model or the $h$-parameter model of the transistor to assist in the ac analysis of the circuit. If the $T$-equivalent model of the transistor is used, the circuit will appear as shown in Figure 27–31.

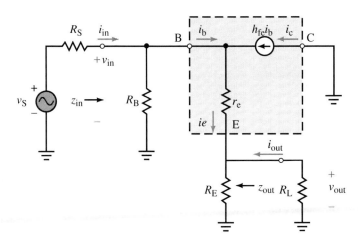

**FIGURE 27–31**    *T*-equivalent model of a CC amplifier.

For simplicity this circuit is redrawn in Figure 27–32. Notice that the only differences in the redrawn circuit are the locations of the collector and the emitter. All components are still in the same relative positions. Notice also that the output current, $i_{out}$ has a reference direction opposite to the direction of emitter current, $i_e$. Let's not worry about this apparent conflict right now!

The ac analysis of the resulting ac circuit is done in a manner similar to that used in previous transistor circuits.

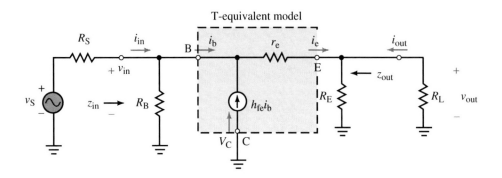

**FIGURE 27–32**

### Voltage Gain, $A_v$

Applying the same procedure as that used for CE amplifiers, we determine the voltage gain of the circuit is as follows:

$$A_v = \frac{v_{out}}{v_{in}} = \frac{i_e\left(R_E\|R_L\right)}{i_e r_e + i_e\left(R_E\|R_L\right)}$$

or

$$A_v = \frac{\left(R_E\|R_L\right)}{r_e + \left(R_E\|R_L\right)} \qquad (27\text{–}29)$$

Since $r_e$ tends to be very small in comparison to typical values of $R_E$ and $R_L$, its effect in the determination of the voltage gain is minimal and so we see that the denominator and the numerator cancel, allowing us to approximate the voltage gain as

$$A_v \approx 1 \qquad (27\text{–}30)$$

### Input Impedance, $z_{in}$

As in previous circuits, solve for the input impedance of the transistor (between the base terminal and the circuit ground) as

$$z_{in(Q)} = \frac{v_b}{i_b} = \frac{i_e r_e + i_e\left(R_E\|R_L\right)}{i_b} = \frac{\left(h_{fe} + 1\right)i_b\left(r_e + R_E\|R_L\right)}{i_b}$$

Simplifying, we get

$$z_{in(Q)} = \left(h_{fe} + 1\right)\left(r_e + R_E\|R_L\right) \qquad (27\text{–}31)$$

The input impedance of the entire circuit is found as the parallel combination

$$z_{in} = R_B\|z_{in(Q)} = R_B\|\left[\left(h_{fe} + 1\right)\left(r_e + R_E\|R_L\right)\right] \qquad (27\text{–}32)$$

which may be further approximated as

$$z_{in} \approx R_B \left\| \left[ (h_{fe})(R_E \| R_L) \right] \right. \tag{27-33}$$

## Current Gain, $A_i$

Recall that the current gain for any circuit is found by using the expression

$$A_i = \frac{i_{out}}{i_{in}} = -\frac{A_v z_{in}}{R_L}$$

For the circuit of Figure 27–32, we have

$$A_i = \frac{i_{out}}{i_{in}} = -\frac{\left[ \dfrac{R_E R_L}{r_e + R_E \| R_L} \right] \left[ R_B \left\| \left\{ (h_{fe} + 1)(r_e + R_E \| R_L) \right\} \right] \right.}{R_L} \tag{27-34}$$

The above expression shows that that the current gain is negative. Remember that this simply means that the actual output current is opposite to the reference direction, a condition that we noticed earlier.

## Output Impedance, $z_{out}$

The output impedance of the common collector circuit is always quite low (typically between 5 Ω and 50 Ω). Solving for the output impedance for the common collector circuit uses a technique that is similar for finding the input impedance. **Unlike the common emitter circuit, the output impedance of the transistor cannot be assumed to be an open circuit.** In a manner similar to that used when finding the Thévenin impedance, we begin by sketching an equivalent circuit as seen from the open output terminals. Recall that when Thévenin's Theorem is used in finding the impedance, it is necessary to "zero" all sources.

Figure 27–33 shows that the voltage source, $v_s$ is replaced by a short circuit, while the current source, $h_{fe}i_b$ is replaced by an open circuit. In order to find the output impedance of the transistor, it is necessary to use Ohm's law in combination with Kirchhoff's voltage law. The output impedance, as seen at the emitter of the transistor is

$$z_{out(Q)} = \frac{v_e}{i_e} = \frac{(R_S \| R_B)i_b + r_e i_e}{i_e} = \frac{(R_S \| R_B)i_b + r_e(h_{fe} + 1)i_b}{(h_{fe} + 1)i_b}$$

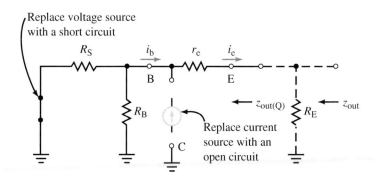

**FIGURE 27–33** Thévenin equivalent circuit of a common-collector output. (*T*-equivalent model)

which, when simplified becomes

$$z_{out(Q)} = \frac{v_e}{i_e} = \frac{R_S\|R_B}{h_{fe} + 1} + r_e \qquad (27\text{--}35)$$

The output impedance of the circuit is simply the parallel combination of the emitter resistance, $R_E$ and $z_{out(Q)}$

$$z_{out(Q)} = R_E \left\| \left( \frac{R_S\|R_B}{h_{fe} + 1} + r_e \right) \right. \qquad (27\text{--}36)$$

Since the value of $R_E$ is much larger than the output impedance of the transistor, we may make the approximation

$$z_{out(Q)} \approx \frac{R_S\|R_B}{h_{fe} + 1} + r_e \qquad (27\text{--}37)$$

The following example demonstrates how a typical common collector circuit is analyzed using the $T$-equivalent model.

**EXAMPLE 27–7**

Given the circuit of Figure 27–34:

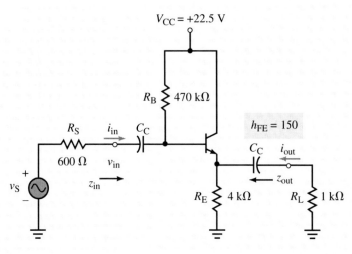

**FIGURE 27–34**

a. Find the dc operating point.

b. Sketch the ac equivalent circuit, using the $T$-equivalent model of the transistor.

c. Determine $A_v$, $z_{in}$, $z_{out}$, $A_i$, and $A_p$.

**Solution**

a.
$$I_B = \frac{22.5\text{ V} - 0.7\text{ V}}{470\text{ k}\Omega + (151)(4\text{ k}\Omega)} = 20.3\text{ }\mu\text{A}$$

$$I_C = 150(20.3\text{ }\mu\text{A}) = 3.04\text{ mA}$$

$$V_{CE} = 22.5\text{ V} - (4\text{ k}\Omega)(3.04\text{ mA}) = 10.3\text{ V}$$

$$r_e \approx \frac{26\text{ mV}}{3.04\text{ mV}} = 8.51\text{ }\Omega$$

b. The ac equivalent circuit is shown in Figure 27–35.

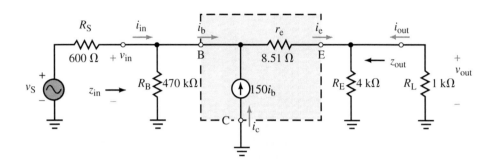

**FIGURE 27–35**

c. Although we have previously determined the voltage gain for the circuit as $A_v \approx 1$, the following calculation substantiates the result.

$$A_v = \frac{i_e(4 \text{ k}\Omega \| 1 \text{ k}\Omega)}{i_e(8.51 \ \Omega + 4 \text{ k}\Omega \| 1 \text{ k}\Omega)} = \frac{800 \ \Omega}{808.51 \ \Omega} = 0.989$$

The input impedance of the transistor is

$$z_{in(Q)} = \frac{v_b}{i_b} = \frac{i_e(8.51 \ \Omega + 4 \text{ k}\Omega \| 1 \text{ k}\Omega)}{i_b} = \frac{(151 i_b)(808.51 \ \Omega)}{i_b} = 122 \text{ k}\Omega$$

resulting in an input impedance for the circuit of

$$z_{in} = \frac{v_b}{i_b} = 470 \text{ k}\Omega \| 122 \text{ k}\Omega = 96.9 \text{ k}\Omega$$

The current gain is easily determined by using Equation 27–11.

$$A_i = -\frac{A_v z_{in}}{R_L} = -\frac{(0.989)(96.9 \text{ k}\Omega)}{1 \text{ k}\Omega} = -95.8$$

The power gain of the circuit is found to be

$$A_p = |A_v A_i| = (0.989)(95.8) = 94.7$$

In order to calculate the output impedance of the circuit, we first zero all sources and redraw the circuit as seen from the output terminals of the transistor. This circuit is shown in Figure 27–36.

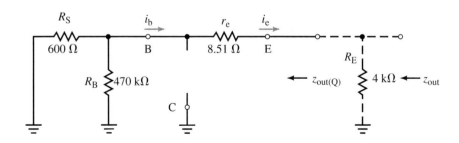

**FIGURE 27–36**

The output impedance of the transistor is found by using Kirchhoff's voltage law and Ohm's law.

$$z_{out(Q)} = \frac{v_e}{i_e} = \frac{i_b(0.6\ k\Omega \| 470\ k\Omega) + i_e(8.51\ \Omega)}{i_e}$$

Now, since $i_b = \dfrac{i_e}{h_{fe} + 1}$, we determine the output impedance of the transistor to be

$$z_{out(Q)} = \frac{\dfrac{i_e(0.6\ k\Omega \| 470\ k\Omega)}{151} + i_e(8.51\ k\Omega)}{i_e} = 3.97\ \Omega + 8.51\ \Omega = 12.5\ \Omega$$

Finally, the output impedance of the circuit becomes

$$z_{out} = 4\ k\Omega \| 12.5\ \Omega = 12.4\ \Omega$$

The previous calculations clearly demonstrate that the common-collector amplifier has very high input impedance and very low output impedance. As expected, the voltage gain is very close to 1.0, which shows that the output voltage is essentially equal to the input voltage and at the same time is in-phase with the input voltage. The power gain of the ac signal is obtained purely as a result of the current gain.

---

**PRACTICE PROBLEMS 7**

Given the circuit of Figure 27–37.

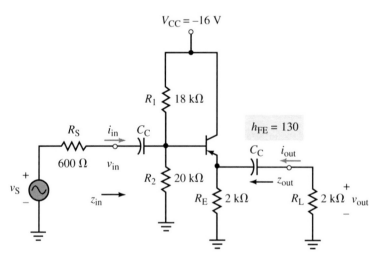

**FIGURE 27–37**

a. Find the dc operating point.

b. Sketch the ac equivalent circuit, using the $T$-equivalent model of the transistor.

c. Determine $A_v$, $z_{in}$, $z_{out}$, $A_i$, and $A_p$.

*Answers*
a. $I_E = 3.86\ mA \approx I_C$, $V_{CE} = -8.28\ V$; c. $A_v = 0.9933$, $z_{in} = 8.84\ k\Omega$, $z_{out} = 11.0\ \Omega$, $A_i = -4.39$, $A_p = 4.36$

Several techniques using the *h*-parameter model of a transistor are possible to analyze a common-collector amplifier. Although using the common collector model ($h_{ic}$, $h_{rc}$, $h_{fc}$, $h_{oc}$) of a transistor is possible, this technique is seldom used. Rather, the common emitter model ($h_{ie}$, $h_{re}$, $h_{fe}$, $h_{oe}$) is generally used, since the *h*-parameter values are readily available and the use of the CE model avoids a needless conversion between the model types. Substituting the CE *h*-parameter model for the transistor of Figure 27–30, we obtain the ac equivalent of Figure 27–38.

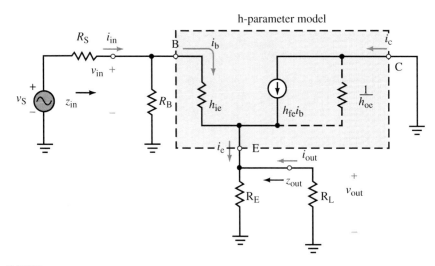

**FIGURE 27–38**

To further simplify the operation of the circuit, $h_{oe}$ is removed (since its effect is negligible on the operation of the input). The redrawn circuit, showing the output on the right hand side is illustrated in Figure 27–39.

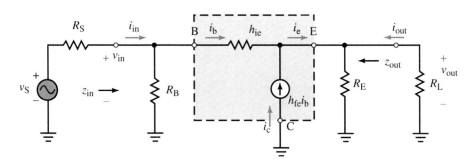

**FIGURE 27–39**

## Voltage Gain, $A_v$

The voltage gain of the circuit is determined from the following expression:

$$A_v = \frac{v_{out}}{v_{in}} = \frac{i_e\left(R_E\|R_L\right)}{i_b h_{ie} + i_e\left(R_E\|R_L\right)}$$

Now since $i_e = i_b + i_c = (h_{fe} + 1)i_b$, we have

$$A_v = \frac{\left(h_{fe} + 1\right)\left(R_E\|R_L\right)}{h_{ie} + \left(h_{fe} + 1\right)\left(R_E\|R_L\right)} \tag{27–38}$$

However, $h_{ie} << (h_{fe} + 1)(R_E \| R_L)$. The voltage gain may be simply stated as

$$A_v \approx 1 \qquad (27-39)$$

### Input Impedance, $z_{in}$

As always, we first determine the input impedance of the transistor (between the base terminal and the circuit ground).

$$z_{in(Q)} = \frac{v_b}{i_b} = \frac{i_b h_{ie} + i_e(R_E \| R_L)}{i_b} = \frac{i_b h_{ie} + (h_{ie} + 1)i_b(R_E \| R_L)}{i_b}$$

Simplifying, we get

$$z_{in(Q)} = h_{ie} + (h_{fe} + 1)\|(R_E R_L)$$

Now, the input impedance of the circuit is found as the parallel combination

$$z_{in} = R_B \| z_{in(Q)} = R_B \Big\| \Big[ h_{ie} + (h_{fe} + 1)(R_E \| R_L) \Big] \qquad (27-40)$$

which may be approximated as

$$z_{in} \approx R_B \Big\| \Big[ (h_{fe})(R_E \| R_L) \Big] \qquad (27-41)$$

### Current Gain, $A_i$

Using Equation 27–11, we obtain the current gain for the circuit of Figure 27–44 as

$$A_i = \frac{i_{out}}{i_{in}} = -\frac{A_v z_{in}}{R_L}$$

$$= \frac{\left[ \dfrac{(h_{fe} + 1)(R_E \| R_L)}{h_{ie} + (h_{fe} + 1)(R_E \| R_L)} \right] \left[ R_B \Big\| \Big\{ h_{ie} + (h_{fe} + 1)(R_E \| R_L) \Big\} \right]}{R_L} \qquad (27-42)$$

### Output Impedance, $z_{out}$

The output impedance of the common-collector circuit is always quite low (typically between 5 $\Omega$ and 50$\Omega$). The solution of the output impedance for the common-collector circuit uses a technique, which is similar to that used in finding the input impedance. First, we begin by sketching an equivalent circuit as seen from the output terminals. Recall that when Thévenin's theorem is used in finding the impedance, it is necessary to "zero" all sources. Figure 27–40

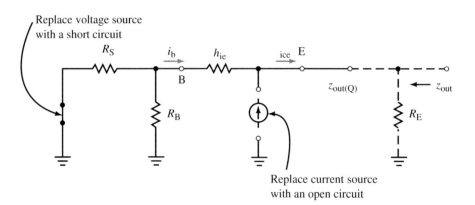

**FIGURE 27–40** Thévenin equivalent circuit of a common-collector output.

shows that the voltage source, $v_s$ is replaced by a short circuit, while the current source, $h_{fe}i_b$ is replaced by an open circuit.

In order to find the output impedance of the transistor, it is necessary to use Ohm's law and Kirchhoff's voltage law. The output impedance, as seen at the emitter of the transistor is found as

$$z_{out(Q)} = \frac{\left[\left(R_S \| R_B\right) + h_{ie}\right]i_b}{\left(h_{fe} + 1\right)i_b}$$

which is simplified as

$$z_{out(Q)} = \frac{\left(R_S \| R_B\right) + h_{ie}}{h_{fe} + 1} \qquad (27\text{--}43)$$

The output impedance of the circuit is found as the parallel combination of the emitter resistance, $R_E$ and $z_{out(Q)}$, namely

$$z_{out} = R_E \left\| \left[\frac{\left(R_S \| R_B\right) + h_{ie}}{h_{fe} + 1}\right]\right. \qquad (27\text{--}44)$$

Given the circuit of Figure 27–41.

**EXAMPLE 27–8**

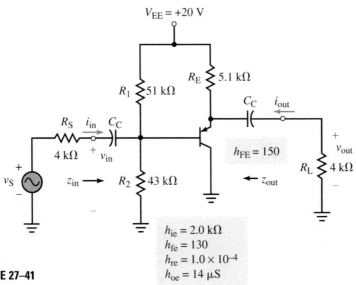

**FIGURE 27–41**

$h_{ie} = 2.0 \text{ k}\Omega$
$h_{fe} = 130$
$h_{re} = 1.0 \times 10^{-4}$
$h_{oe} = 14 \text{ μS}$

a. Find the dc operating point.

b. Sketch the ac equivalent circuit, using the $h$-parameter model of the transistor.

c. Determine $A_v$, $z_{in}$, $z_{out}$, $A_i$, and $A_p$.

**Solution**

a. The circuit of Figure 27–41 uses voltage divider bias, and so we have

$$V_B = \left(\frac{43 \text{ k}\Omega}{51 \text{ k}\Omega + 43 \text{ k}\Omega}\right)20 \text{ V} = 9.15 \text{ V}$$

$$V_E = 9.15 \text{ V} + 0.7 \text{ V} = 9.85 \text{ V}$$

$$I_E = \frac{20 \text{ V} - 9.85 \text{ V}}{5.1 \text{ k}\Omega} = 1.99 \text{ mA} \approx I_C$$

$$V_{CE} = -(20 \text{ V} - 9.85 \text{ V}) = -10.15 \text{ V}$$

b. The simplified ac equivalent circuit is shown in Figure 27–42.

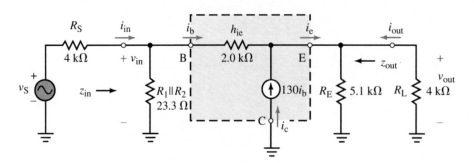

**FIGURE 27–42**

c. The voltage gain for the circuit is found as

$$A_v = \frac{(131)(5.1 \text{ k}\Omega\|4 \text{ k}\Omega)}{2.0 \text{ k}\Omega + (131)(5.1 \text{ k}\Omega\|4 \text{ k}\Omega)} = 0.993$$

The input impedance of the transistor (looking between the base and ground) is

$$z_{\text{in}(Q)} = 2.0 \text{ k}\Omega + (131)(5.1 \text{ k}\Omega\|4 \text{ k}\Omega) = 296 \text{ k}\Omega$$

The input impedance of the circuit is found as

$$z_{\text{in}} = 51 \text{ k}\Omega\|43 \text{ k}\Omega\|296 \text{ k}\Omega = 21.6 \text{ k}\Omega$$

This example illustrates that although the transistor has a very high input impedance, the bias resistors, $R_1$ and $R_2$, can dramatically reduce input impedance of the common collector circuit. In order to retain very high input impedance, it would be necessary to use an emitter bias configuration.

As in previous examples, we determine the output impedance of the transistor by first zeroing the sources and then examining the open output terminals. Figure 27–43 shows the equivalent impedance as seen between the emitter terminal and ground.

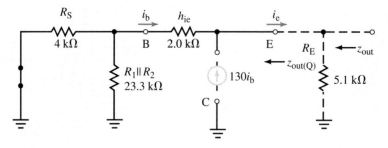

**FIGURE 27–43**

This results in output impedance for the circuit of

$$z_{\text{out}} = R_E \left\| \frac{\left(R_S\|R_1\|R_2\right) + h_{\text{ie}}}{h_{\text{fe}} + 1} = 5.1 \text{ k}\Omega \right\| \frac{\left(4 \text{ k}\Omega\|51 \text{ k}\Omega\|43 \text{ k}\Omega\right) + 2.0 \text{ k}\Omega}{131} = 34.1 \text{ }\Omega$$

Using Equation 27–11, we solve for the current gain as

$$A_i = -\frac{(0.993)(21.6 \text{ k}\Omega)}{4 \text{ k}\Omega} = -5.36$$

Finally, the power gain is found as

$$A_p = |A_v A_i| = (0.993)(5.36) = 5.32$$

Given the circuit of Figure 27–44.

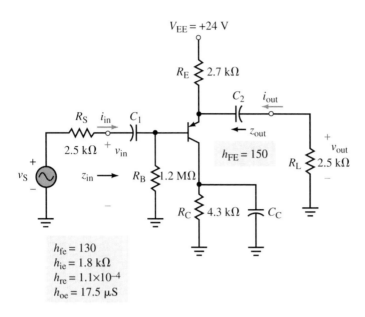

**FIGURE 27–44**

a. Find the dc operating point.

b. Sketch the ac equivalent circuit, using the *h*-parameter model of the transistor.

c. Determine $A_v$, $z_{in}$, $z_{out}$, $A_i$, and $A_p$.

*Answers*

a. $I_B = 14.5\ \mu A$, $I_C = 2.17\ mA$, $V_{CE} = -8.78\ V$

c. $A_v = 0.990$, $z_{in} = 150.\ k\Omega$, $z_{out} = 32.4\ \Omega$, $A_i = -59.5$, $A_p = 58.9$

When we examined the operation of field effect transistors you saw that when a voltage is applied to the gate of a FET, it affected the width of the channel between the drain and the source. It is for this reason that the FET is referred to as a voltage-controlled amplifier unlike the BJT, which is a current-controlled device. The small-signal ac model of JFETs and MOSFETs is precisely the same both types of transistors and is illustrated in Figure 27–45.

Notice that the impedance between the gate and the source is shown as an infinite resistance. Remember that in a JFET, the gate-source is always reverse-biased and so there can be no gate current. In both D-MOSFETs and E-MOSFETs, the gate is isolated from the channel by an insulating layer and, once again, there can be no gate current. Consequently, this model clearly shows that the ac drain current must be equal to the source current, namely

$$i_s = i_d \qquad (27\text{–}45)$$

The output impedance of the FET is $r_d$, which tends to be a fairly large value (around 20 kΩ to about 50 kΩ). As expected, the current source in the model shown in Figure 27–45 is dependent on the magnitude of the voltage applied between the gate and the source. Whereas in the *h*-parameter model of the BJT, the current source was determined on $h_{fe}$ (the forward current transfer ratio), here we see that the magnitude of the current source is determined by using a conductance characteristic, $g_m$. This conductance is obtained from the

## 27.7 The FET Small-Signal Model

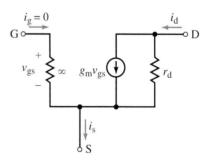

**FIGURE 27–45**   ac model of a field effect transistor.

transfer curve for the FET and for this reason, $g_m$ is called the *transconductance* of the FET. Just as in the BJT, this term provides the relationship between the input and the output of the FET. The transconductance of a FET is not constant, but rather is dependent on the operating point of the FET. Consider an n-channel FET having the transfer curve shown in Figure 27–46.

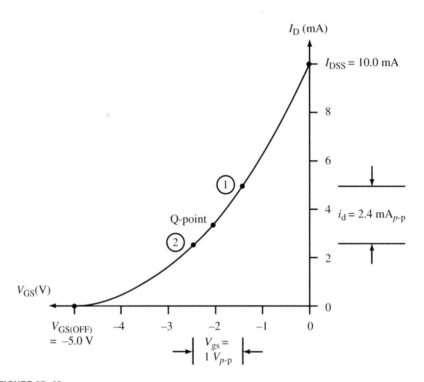

**FIGURE 27–46**

Let's assume that the operating point of the FET is at $V_{GSQ} = -2.0$ V and $I_{DQ} = 3.6$ mA and that an ac signal is applied between the gate and the source so that $v_{gs} = 1$ V$_{p-p}$. As the gate-source voltage alternates between $-2.5$ V and $-1.5$ V, the JFET will operate between points *1* and *2* on the transfer curve. The drain current will vary between 2.5 mA and 4.9 mA (2.4 mA$_{p-p}$). For small signals, the difference between points *1* and *2* will be relatively small and will be approximately linear. The slope of the line between the points *1* and *2* will be very close to the value of the transconductance, in this case

$$g_m \approx \frac{\Delta I_d}{\Delta V_{gs}} = \frac{4.9 \text{ mA} - 2.5 \text{ mA}}{-1.5 \text{ V} - (-2.5 \text{ V})} = \frac{2.4 \text{ mA}}{1.0 \text{ V}} = 2.5 \text{ mS}$$

The actual value of the transconductance at the Q-point is simply the slope of the tangent at the Q-point. This value can be determined graphically by sketching a line that is tangent at the Q-point and then calculating the slope of the tangent using

$$g_m \approx \frac{\Delta I_D}{\Delta V_{GS}} \tag{27–46}$$

Alternatively, we can use differential calculus to solve for the transconductance by solving for the derivative:

$$g_m = \frac{dI_D}{dV_{GS}} = \frac{d}{dV_{GS}}\left[ I_{DSS}\left(1 - \frac{V_{GSQ}}{V_{GS(OFF)}}\right)^2 \right]$$

which results in

$$g_m = \left( -\frac{2I_{DSS}}{V_{GS(OFF)}} \right)\left( 1 - \frac{V_{GSQ}}{V_{GS(OFF)}} \right) \qquad \textbf{(27–47)}$$

In the expression of Equation 27–47, the first term will always be positive and so this equation may be further simplified as

$$g_m = \left| \frac{2I_{DSS}}{V_{GS(OFF)}} \right|\left( 1 - \frac{V_{GSQ}}{V_{GS(OFF)}} \right) \qquad \textbf{(27–48)}$$

In the case of a JFET, the term contained within the absolute value symbol represents the maximum slope (hence maximum transconductance that is possible for the given transistor). This value is simply referred to as

$$g_{mo} = \left| \frac{2I_{DSS}}{V_{GS(OFF)}} \right| \qquad \textbf{(27–49)}$$

and is a constant for any given transistor. Therefore, we may simply express Equation 27–53 as

$$g_m = g_{mo}\left( 1 - \frac{V_{GSQ}}{V_{GS(OFF)}} \right) \qquad \textbf{(27–50)}$$

Given the transfer curve for an n-channel JFET illustrated in Figure 27–46.

a. Determine the transconductance of the JFET for an operating point having $V_{GSQ} = -2.0$ V,

b. Solve for $g_m$ if $V_{GSQ} = -3.0$ V,

c. Solve for $g_m$ if $V_{GSQ} = -1.0$ V.

**EXAMPLE 27–9**

**Solution**

a.

$$g_{mo} = \left| \frac{2I_{DSS}}{V_{GS(OFF)}} \right| = \left| \frac{2(10 \text{ mA})}{-5.0 \text{ V}} \right| = 4.0 \text{ mS}$$

$$g_m = (4.0 \text{ mS})\left( 1 - \frac{-2.0 \text{ V}}{-2.0 \text{ V}} \right) = 2.4 \text{ mS}$$

Note that this value is very close to the approximation that we determined previously.

b. $g_m = (4.0 \text{ mS})\left( 1 - \frac{-3.0 \text{ V}}{-5.0 \text{ V}} \right) = 1.6 \text{ mS}$

c. $g_m = (4.0 \text{ mS})\left( 1 - \frac{-1.0 \text{ V}}{-5.0 \text{ V}} \right) = 3.2 \text{ mS}$

The previous example clearly demonstrates that the transconductance, $g_m$ of a FET is dependent on the operating point. In order for a JFET to have a larger transconductance, it is necessary for the bias point of the transistor to be closer towards the value of $I_{DSS}$. For a D-MOSFET, the value of $g_{mo}$ and $g_m$ is found the same way as for a JFET (using $I_{DSS}$ and $V_{GS(OFF)}$). The transconductance of an E-MOSFET, however, is determined slightly differently. Recall from the previous chapter that the drain current of an E-MOSFET is found in terms of $V_{GS}$ as

$$I_D = k(V_{GS} - V_{GS(th)})^2$$

where

$$k = \frac{I_{D(ON)}}{\left(V_{GS(ON)} - V_{GS(th)}\right)}$$

Using differential calculus to solve for the transconductance of an E-MOSFET, we have:

$$g_m = \frac{dI_D}{dV_{GS}} = \frac{d}{dV_{GS}}\left[k\left(V_{GS} - V_{GS(th)}\right)^2\right] \qquad \text{(27–51)}$$

which becomes

$$g_m = 2k(V_{GS} - V_{GS(th)}) \qquad \text{(27–52)}$$

---

**EXAMPLE 27–10**

An E-MOSFET has the following characteristics:

$$V_{GS(th)} = 2.00 \text{ V}$$
$$I_{D(ON)} = 200 \text{ mA}$$
$$V_{GS(ON)} = 4 \text{ V}$$

If the operating point of the transistor occurs at $V_{GSQ} = 2.8$ V and $I_{DQ} = 32$ mA, find the value of the transconductance at the operating point. Sketch the small-signal ac equivalent circuit of the E-MOSFET.

$$k = \frac{I_{D(ON)}}{\left(V_{GS(ON)} - V_{GS(th)}\right)^2} = \frac{200 \text{ mA}}{(4 \text{ V} - 2 \text{ V})^2} = 50 \text{ mA} / \text{V}^2$$

$$g_m = 2k\left(V_{GS} - V_{GS(th)}\right) = 2(50 \text{ mA/V}^2)(2.8 \text{ V} - 2.0 \text{ V}) = 80 \text{ mS}$$

The resulting ac equivalent circuit of the E-MOSFET is shown in Figure 27–47.

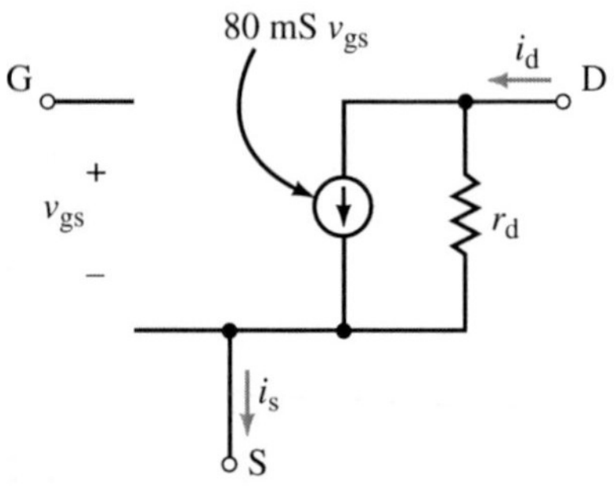

**FIGURE 27–47**

---

## 27.8 The Common-Source Amplifier

The analysis of FET amplifiers is remarkably similar to the methods used when analyzing BJT amplifiers using the *h*-parameter model. As always, it is necessary to first determine whether the amplifier is correctly biased. Unless this is the case, the circuit cannot operate as an amplifier. In the case of all FET amplifiers, we need the dc operating point to calculate the transconductance, $g_m$ of the transistor. The following examples show how the common source amplifier behaves very much like the common-emitter amplifier.

---

**EXAMPLE 27–11**

Given the JFET amplifier circuit of Figure 27–48:

a. Find $I_{DSQ}$, $V_{GSQ}$, and $V_{DSQ}$ at the operating point.

b. Solve for $g_{mo}$ and $g_m$ of the amplifier.

c. Sketch the small-signal ac equivalent circuit.

d. Determine $A_v$, $z_{in}$, and $z_{out}$ of the amplifier.

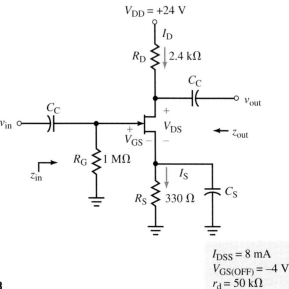

**FIGURE 27–48**

$I_{DSS} = 8$ mA
$V_{GS(OFF)} = -4$ V
$r_d = 50$ kΩ

## Solution

a. In order to find the operating point, we first must determine the dc load line
for the circuit. As before, we find two points on the dc load line by selecting suitable points.

Let $I_D = 0$: Since $I_G = 0$, $V_{GS} = 0$.

Let $I_D = 8.0$ mA: Now writing the loop equation for the input loop of the
circuit, we have

$$V_{GS} = 0(1 \text{ M}\Omega) - (8.0 \text{ mA})(0.33 \text{ k}\Omega) = -2.64 \text{ V}$$

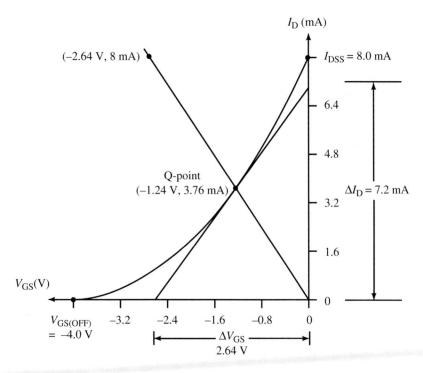

**FIGURE 27–49**

The load line is shown on the transfer curve of Figure 27–49. At the intersection of the transfer curve and the dc load line we obtain values as follows:

$I_{DQ} \approx 3.76$ mA and $V_{GSQ} \approx -1.24$ V

Now writing the output loop equation, we have the following:

$$(2.4 \text{ k}\Omega)I_D + V_{DS} + (0.33 \text{ k}\Omega)I_S = 24 \text{ V}$$

and since $I_S = I_D = 3.76$ mA, we have

$$V_{DSQ} = 24 \text{ V} - (2.4 \text{ k}\Omega)(3.76 \text{ mA}) - (0.33 \text{ k}\Omega)(3.76 \text{ mA}) = 13.74 \text{ V}$$

b. Using Equation 27–54, we have

$$g_{mo} = \left| \frac{2I_{DSS}}{V_{GS(OFF)}} \right| = \left| \frac{2(8.0 \text{ mA})}{-4.0 \text{ V}} \right| = 4.0 \text{ mS}$$

As indicated previously, there are two methods that can be used to solve for the transconductance of the FET: the graphical method and the algebraic method. In this example we will use both. **Graphical Method:** On the transfer curve of Figure 27–49, we simply sketch a line that is tangent at the Q-point. Recall that the value of the transconductance is simply expressed as the slope of the tangent line, namely

$$g_m = \left. \frac{\Delta I_d}{\Delta V_{gs}} \right|_{\text{at the point}}$$

and so we have

$$g_m = \frac{7.2 \text{ mA} - 0}{0 - (-2.64 \text{ V})} \approx 2.73 \text{ mS}$$

**Algebraic Method:** Using Equation 27–50, we have

$$g_m = g_{mo}\left(1 - \frac{V_{GSQ}}{V_{GS(OFF)}}\right)$$

$$= 4 \text{ mS}\left(1 - \frac{-1.24 \text{ V}}{-4.0 \text{ V}}\right) = 2.76 \text{ mS}$$

c. The small-signal ac equivalent circuit of Figure 27–48 is sketched by replacing all capacitors by short circuits and replacing the dc voltage source by a short circuit to ground. Notice that the source of the JFET is connected directly to ground through the bypass capacitor, $C_S$. The resulting circuit is shown in Figure 27–50.

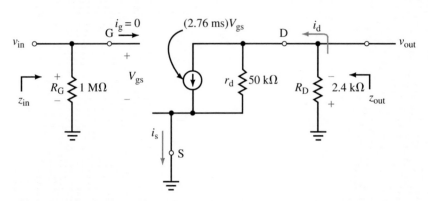

**FIGURE 27–50**

d. As in previous examples, we determine the voltage gain of the amplifier as follows:

$$A_v = \frac{v_{out}}{v_{in}} = \frac{-i_d R_D}{v_{gs}}$$

Now since $r_d$ (the output impedance characteristic of the FET) is much larger than $R_D$, we neglect its effect on the gain of the circuit. (This is because there is very little current through the larger resistance.) Consequently, we let $i_d \approx g_m v_{gs}$. The voltage gain is now rewritten as

$$A_v \approx \frac{-g_m v_{gs} R_D}{v_{gs}}$$

which when simplified, becomes

$$A_v \approx - g_m R_D \qquad\qquad \textbf{(27–53)}$$

The voltage gain of our circuit is now easily calculated as

$$A_v \approx - (2.76 \text{ mS})(2.4 \text{ k}\Omega) = -6.62$$

Here we see that a FET amplifier having a bypassed source resistor has a relatively low voltage gain. A similar BJT amplifier has a much larger voltage gain (typically over 100), if the circuit has a bypassed emitter resistor. This demonstrates one of the major characteristic differences between BJT amplifiers and FET amplifiers.

The input impedance of all FET amplifiers is taken to be infinity, since the value will always be extremely large (10 M$\Omega$ to several thousand M$\Omega$). Therefore, the input impedance of the circuit is determined simply by the value(s) of the bias resistors connected to the gate of the circuit. For the circuit of Figure 27–48, we have

$$z_{in} = R_G \qquad\qquad \textbf{(27–54)}$$

and so

$$z_{in} = 1 \text{ M}\Omega$$

Upon examining the ac equivalent circuit of Figure 27–50, we see that the output impedance characteristic, $r_d$ is very large in comparison to the drain resistor, $R_D$, and so we conclude that for this circuit, the output impedance may simply be taken as

$$z_{out} \approx R_D \qquad\qquad \textbf{(27–55)}$$

giving

$$z_{out} \approx 2.4 \text{ k}\Omega$$

---

If the bypass capacitor, $C_S$ is removed from the circuit of Figure 27–48:

a. Sketch the resulting small-signal ac equivalent circuit.

b. Determine $A_v$, $z_{in}$, and $z_{out}$ of the amplifier. (Hint: The input voltage will now include the voltage across $R_S = 330 \ \Omega$.)

PRACTICE PROBLEMS 9

*Answers*
b. $A_v = -3.47$, $z_{in} = 1 \text{ M}\Omega$, $z_{out} = 2.4 \text{ k}\Omega$

The analysis of D-MOSFETs is almost exactly the same as for JFETs, with the exception that D-MOSFETs can operate in the "enhancement" region. This means that it is possible to have the gate-to-source forward-biased. Remember that because the gate is isolated from the channel, there can be no current from the gate toward the source, once again resulting in an open circuit between the gate and the source in the ac small-signal model of the D-MOSFET.

E-MOSFET amplifiers follow an analysis process that is somewhat different than that used in JFET and D-MOSFET amplifiers. This is especially true if the circuit includes a source feedback resistor. The following example illustrates the point.

**EXAMPLE 27–12**

Given the E-MOSFET amplifier circuit of Figure 27–51:

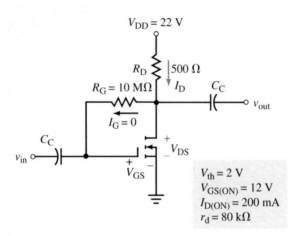

**FIGURE 27–51**

a. Find $I_{DSQ}$, $V_{GSQ}$, and $V_{DSQ}$ at the operating point.

b. Solve for $g_m$ of the amplifier.

c. Sketch the small-signal ac equivalent circuit.

d. Determine $A_v$, $z_{in}$, and $z_{out}$ of the amplifier.

**Solution**

a. Solving for the constant, $k$ of the E-MOSFET, gives

$$k = \frac{I_{D(ON)}}{\left(V_{GS(ON)} - V_{GS(th)}\right)^2} = \frac{200 \text{ mA}}{(12 \text{ V} - 2 \text{ V})^2} = 2.0 \text{ mA/V}^2$$

For this circuit we see that $V_{GS} = V_{DS}$ for all values, since there can be no gate current. We select suitable points and sketch the dc load line as shown in Figure 27–52.

Let $V_{GS} = 10V$:

$$I_D = \frac{22 \text{ V} - 10 \text{ V}}{500 \text{ }\Omega} = 24 \text{ mA}$$

Let $V_{GS} = 2V$:

$$I_D = \frac{22 \text{ V} - 2 \text{ V}}{500 \text{ }\Omega} = 40 \text{ mA}$$

From the graph, we see that at the Q-point, $I_D = 32$ mA and $V_{GSQ} = 6$ V $= V_{DSQ}$.

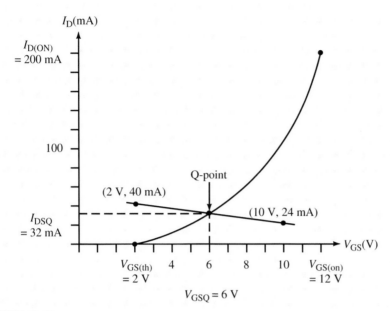

**FIGURE 27–52**

b. The transconductance at the operating point of the E-MOSFET is determined by applying Equation 27–57.

$$g_m = 2(2.0 \text{ mA} / \text{V}^2)(6.0 \text{ V} - 2.0 \text{ V}) = 16 \text{ mS}$$

c. Now the ac equivalent circuit of the E-MOSFET amplifier can be sketched as shown in Figure 27–53.

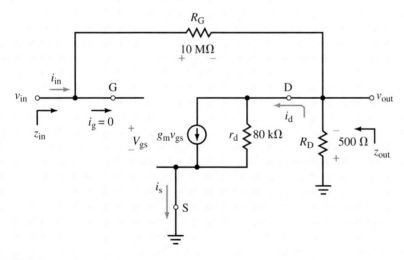

**FIGURE 27–53**

The ac equivalent circuit of Figure 27–53 shows that the resistance, $R_G$ provides a feedback path from the output to the input. While the resistor has very little effect on the voltage gain and the output impedance of the circuit, we will find that it does have a significant effect on the input impedance.

d. Due to the very large resistance and the relatively large output impedance of the E-MOSFET, there will be very little current through these values. Consequently, the voltage gain is determined to be

$$A_v \approx \frac{-g_m v_{gs} R_D}{v_{gs}}$$

which when simplified, becomes

$$A_v \approx -g_m R_D$$

Therefore, we have

$$A_v \approx -(16 \text{ mS})(0.5 \text{ k}\Omega) = -8.0$$

The output impedance of the transistor will be $z_{out(Q)} = 80 \text{ k}\Omega$. The 10-M$\Omega$ resistor has a negligible effect on the output impedance, due to the very small current through the component. Consequently, we conclude that the output impedance may be simply solved as

$$z_{out} = r_d \| R_D \approx R_D = 500 \ \Omega$$

The input impedance however, must be calculated by using Ohm's law as follows:

$$z_{in} = \frac{v_{in}}{i_{in}}$$

The input voltage is easily determined as $v_{in} = v_{gs}$. The difficulty occurs in calculating the input current. Although $i_g = 0$, the current $i_{in}$ is not zero. By examining the ac equivalent circuit, we see that the input current is the same as the current through the feedback resistor, $R_G$. Therefore, in order to solve for the current $i_{in}$, we simply need to find the voltage across $R_G$. If we go in a loop from the gate to source (ground) to drain, we obtain the voltage as

$$v_{RG} = v_{gs} + i_d R_D = v_{gs} + g_m v_{gs} R_D = v_{gs}(1 + g_m R_D)$$

Now we have

$$i_{in} = \frac{v_{gs}(1 + g_m R_D)}{R_G}$$

Finally, the input impedance is easily determined as

$$z_{in} = \frac{v_{in}}{i_{in}} = \frac{v_{gs}}{\dfrac{v_{gs}(1 + g_m R_D)}{R_G}} = \frac{R_G}{1 + g_m R_D} \qquad \textbf{(27–56)}$$

which for this example results in input impedance of

$$z_{in} = \frac{10 \ \Omega}{1 + (16 \text{ mS})(0.5 \text{ k}\Omega)} = 1.11 \text{ M}\Omega$$

Notice that the feedback resistor, $R_G$, which improves the dc operation of the amplifier, results in a decrease of input impedance when the circuit is operating with an ac signal. When working with any electronic circuit, there will always be tradeoffs that must be made.

In the circuit of Figure 27–51, the FET had a very large value of output impedance, $r_d$ in comparison to the drain resistance, $R_D$. If the value of $r_d$ in the transistor circuit is not much ($\geq 10$ times) larger than $R_D$, we would need to use the following expressions to solve for voltage gain and input impedance.

$$A_v \approx -g_m(r_d \| R_D) \qquad \textbf{(27–57)}$$

$$z_{in} = \frac{v_{in}}{i_{in}} = \frac{v_{gs}}{\dfrac{v_{gs}[1 + g_m(r_d \| R_D)]}{R_G}} = \frac{R_G}{1 + g_m(r_d \| R_D)} \qquad \textbf{(27–58)}$$

If $R_D = 100 \; \Omega$ in the circuit of Figure 27–51. (All other values remain unchanged.):

a. Find $I_{DSQ}$, $V_{GSQ}$, and $V_{DSQ}$ at the operating point.
b. Solve for $g_m$ of the amplifier.
c. Sketch the small-signal ac equivalent circuit.
d. Determine $A_v$, $z_{in}$, and $z_{out}$ of the amplifier.

*Answers*
a. $I_{DSQ} = 122$ mA, $V_{GSQ} = V_{DSQ} = 9.81$ V;  b. $g_m = 31.2$ mS;  d. $A_v = -3.12$,
   $z_{in} = 2.43$ MΩ, $z_{out} = 100 \; \Omega$

---

The common-drain amplifier is very similar to the common collector BJT amplifier that we examined previously. The characteristics of the common drain amplifier are:

   Voltage gain is always less than unity ($A_v < 1$).

   The output voltage is in-phase with the input voltage.

   The input impedance is typically very high.

   The output impedance is typically low.

   The main application of common-drain FET amplifiers is as a buffer between a circuit having high output impedance and one having low input impedance. The following example illustrates the similarity between the common drain FET amplifier and the common collector BJT amplifier.

## 27.9 The Common-Drain (Source Follower) Amplifier

Given the JFET amplifier circuit of Figure 27–54:

**EXAMPLE 27–13**

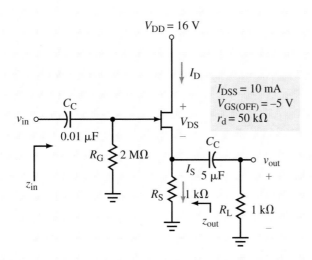

$V_{DD} = 16$ V

$I_{DSS} = 10$ mA
$V_{GS(OFF)} = -5$ V
$r_d = 50$ kΩ

**FIGURE 27–54**

a. Find $I_{DSQ}$, $V_{GSQ}$, and $V_{DSQ}$ at the operating point.
b. Solve for $g_{mo}$ and $g_m$ of the amplifier.
c. Sketch the small-signal ac equivalent circuit.
d. Determine $A_v$, $z_{in}$, and $z_{out}$ of the amplifier.

**Solution**

a. As in previous problems, we determine the operating point by finding the point at which the dc load line intersects the JFET transfer curve.

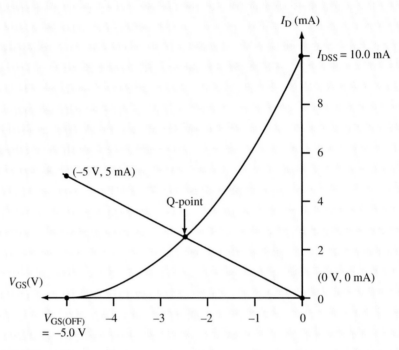

**FIGURE 27–55**

To find the dc load line, we arbitrarily select two points on the graph shown in Figure 27–55.

Let $I_S = I_D = 0$ mA:

Because $I_S = I_D = 0$ mA, we have $V_{GS} = 0$

Let $I_S = I_D = 5$ mA:

$$
\begin{aligned}
V_{GS} &= -I_D R_S \\
&= -(5 \text{ mA})(1 \text{ k}\Omega) \\
&= -5.0 \text{ V}
\end{aligned}
$$

At the intersection of the dc load line and the transfer curve, we have $I_{DQ} = 2.50$ mA and $V_{GSQ} = -2.50$ V. The value of $V_{GSQ}$ is found by applying Kirchhoff's voltage law at the output loop.

$$V_{DSQ} = 16 \text{ V} - (2.5 \text{ mA})(1 \text{ k}\Omega) = 13.5 \text{ V}$$

b. $g_{mo}$ is determined by applying Equation 27–54 as

$$V_{mo} = \left| \frac{2I_{DSS}}{V_{GS(OFF)}} \right| = \left| \frac{2(10 \text{ mA})}{-5 \text{ V}} \right| = 4.0 \text{ mS}$$

and the transconductance at the operating point is found from Equation 27–50 as

$$g_m = 4.0 \text{ mS}\left(1 - \frac{2.5 \text{ V}}{5.0 \text{ V}}\right) = 2.0 \text{ mS}$$

c. The small-signal ac equivalent circuit is shown in Figure 27–56.

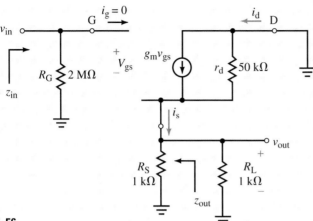

**FIGURE 27–56**

As was the case with the common collector circuit, we redraw the above equivalent circuit to make it easier to analyze. The redrawn circuit is shown in Figure 27–57.

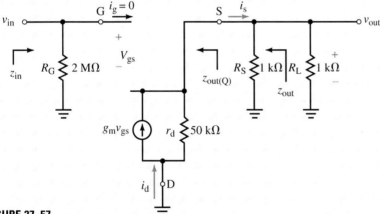

**FIGURE 27–57**

The direction of the current source in the drain circuit points away from the drain, just as it did in the original ac equivalent circuit. Notice also that $i_s = i_d = g_m v_{gs}$. Using this information, we write the expression for voltage gain as:

$$A_v = \frac{v_{out}}{v_{in}} = \frac{i_s\left(R_S \| R_L\right)}{v_{gs} + i_s\left(R_S \| R_L\right)}$$

$$= \frac{g_m v_{gs}\left(R_S \| R_L\right)}{v_{gs} + g_m v_{gs}\left(R_S \| R_L\right)}$$

which becomes

$$A_v = \frac{g_m\left(R_S \| R_L\right)}{1 + g_m\left(R_S \| R_L\right)} \tag{27–59}$$

From Equation 27–59, we see that the voltage gain for a source follower amplifier must always be less than unity and that the output voltage will always be in-phase with the input voltage.

For our circuit, we have

$$A_v = \frac{g_m\left(R_S\|R_L\right)}{1 + g_m\left(R_S\|R_L\right)} = \frac{2.0 \text{ mS}\left(1 \text{ k}\Omega\|1 \text{ k}\Omega\right)}{1 + 2.0 \text{ mS}\left(1 \text{ k}\Omega\|1 \text{ k}\Omega\right)} = 0.5$$

The input impedance (at the gate) of the FET is an open circuit, and so we conclude that

$$z_{in} = R_G = 2 \text{ M}\Omega$$

The output impedance (at the source) of the FET is determined by first finding the output impedance of the FET alone and then combining this with the source resistance, $R_S$. To simplify things a bit, we zero the input voltage (by replacing it with a short circuit to ground) as shown in Figure 27–58.

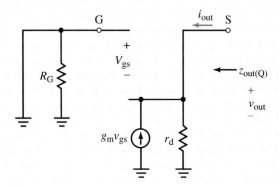

**FIGURE 27–58**

Since we are trying to find the output impedance at the source terminal of the FET, we begin with

$$z_{out(Q)} = \frac{v_{out}}{i_{out}}$$

But we see that

$$v_{out} = -v_{gs}$$

and

$$v_{out} = -v_{gs} = (g_m v_{gs} + i_{out})r_d$$

This last expression may be rewritten to solve for $i_{out}$ as

$$i_{out} = \frac{-v_{gs}}{r_d} - g_m v_{gs}$$

The expression for output impedance may now be rewritten as

$$z_{out(Q)} = \frac{-v_{gs}}{i_{out}} = \frac{-v_{gs}}{\dfrac{-v_{gs}}{r_d} - g_m v_{gs}} = \frac{1}{\dfrac{1}{r_d} + g_m}$$

which is the same as

$$z_{out(Q)} = r_d \left\| \frac{1}{g_m} \right.$$    **(27–60)**

If $r_d$ is large in comparison to $1/g_m$ then we approximate the output impedance of a common source FET amplifier as

$$z_{out(Q)} \approx \frac{1}{g_m}$$    **(27–61)**

And finally, the output impedance of the common source FET (without approximation) is taken as

$$z_{out} = z_{out(Q)} \| R_S = r_d \left\| \frac{1}{g_m} \right\| R_S$$    **(27–62)**

For the circuit of Figure 27–54, we have

$$z_{out} = 50 \text{ k}\Omega \left\| \frac{1}{2.0 \text{ mS}} \right\| 1 \text{ k}\Omega = 331 \ \Omega$$

Given the circuit of Figure 27–59:

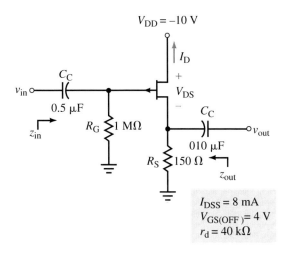

**FIGURE 27–59**

a. Find $I_{DSQ}$, $V_{GSQ}$, and $V_{DSQ}$ at the operating point.
b. Solve for $g_{mo}$ and $g_m$ of the amplifier.
c. Sketch the small-signal ac equivalent circuit.
d. Determine $A_v$, $z_{in}$, and $z_{out}$ of the amplifier.

*Answers*
a. $I_{DSQ} = 5.19$ mA, $V_{GSQ} = 0.79$ V, $V_{DSQ} = -9.22$ V; b. $g_{mo} = 4.0$ mS , $g_m = 3.22$ mS;
   d. $A_v = 0.76$, $z_{in}$ 1 M$\Omega$, and $z_{out} = 143 \ \Omega$

## 27.10 Troubleshooting a Transistor Amplifier Circuit

### NOTES . . .

It is extremely important to ensure that an electrolytic capacitor is correctly placed into a circuit. An incorrectly placed capacitor will tend to generate electrical noise, leading to poor circuit operation. It is also possible for an electrolytic capacitor to explode if the incorrect polarity is applied.

The most common problem encountered when a novice technologist builds a transistor amplifier circuit is the placement of electrolytic capacitors. If the capacitor is installed with incorrect polarity, it generally results in a "noisy" output signal. In such instances, the capacitor behaves as an antenna and picks up unwanted signals, usually 60 Hz. The signal may appear on an oscilloscope as shown in Figure 27–60.

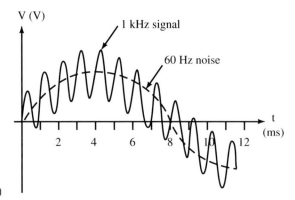

**FIGURE 27–60**

In the above illustration, we see that the desired 1-kHz component is superimposed on a fairly large 60 Hz component. Occasionally, the desired signal is entirely lost in the electrical "noise". The operation of the circuit is easily corrected. First, determine the proper polarity of the dc voltage across each capacitor and then place each electrolytic capacitor into the circuit accordingly. If an electrolytic capacitor has been inadvertently placed into a circuit with the wrong polarity, it is possible that the electrolyte in the capacitor may have been damaged. Therefore, if the problem persists, the capacitor will need to be replaced by a new one.

Another problem that may occur due to a faulty or incorrectly placed capacitor is that the measured voltage gain of a circuit is much different than the theoretical gain. A faulty capacitor will usually become an open circuit, although it is possible for it to develop an internal short. Consider the circuit shown in Figure 27–61.

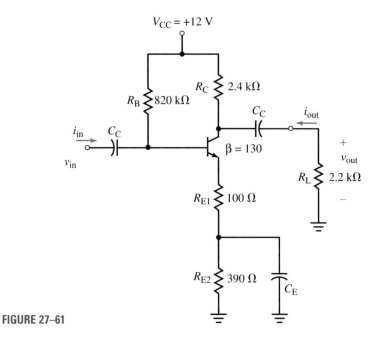

**FIGURE 27–61**

The theoretical gain of the above transistor (neglecting $r_e$) should be

$$A_v \approx -\frac{130i_b\left(2.4 \text{ k}\Omega \| 2.2 \text{ k}\Omega\right)}{131i_b\left(0.1 \text{ k}\Omega\right)} = -11$$

If the emitter bypass capacitor, $C_E$ becomes an open circuit due to an internal fault, the voltage gain will decrease due to the added emitter resistance, $R_{E2}$. In such a case, we would measure the voltage gain to be

$$A_v \approx -\frac{130i_b\left(2.4 \text{ k}\Omega \| 2.2 \text{ k}\Omega\right)}{131i_b\left(0.1 \text{ k}\Omega + 0.39 \text{ k}\Omega\right)} = -2.2$$

In the unlikely event that the emitter bypass capacitor becomes a short circuit, the dc operating point can be significantly affected. In this instance the base current would now be

$$I_B = \frac{12 \text{ V} - 0.7 \text{ V}}{820 \text{ k}\Omega + 131(0.1 \text{ k}\Omega)} = 13.6 \text{ }\mu\text{A}$$

rather than the actual value of

$$I_B = \frac{12 \text{ V} - 0.7 \text{ V}}{820 \text{ k}\Omega + 131(0.1 \text{ k}\Omega + 0.39 \text{ k}\Omega)} = 12.8 \text{ }\mu\text{A}$$

As we have observed in previous chapters, it is a good practice to develop a strategy in troubleshooting a faulty circuit. In the case where a transistor amplifier circuit is not operating as expected, the following steps may help to isolate the problem:

1. Remove all ac signal sources from the circuit. If the dc bias point of the transistor is not in the active region, then it will certainly not work correctly with the application of an ac signal.

2. Calculate the theoretical operating point of the transistor.

3. Determine the actual operating point by measuring $V_{CE}$ and solving for $I_C = V_{RC}/R_C$ if the circuit uses BJTs. If the amplifier circuit uses FETs, the operating point is found by measuring $V_{DS}$ and solving for $I_D = V_{RD}/R_D$. If the transistor is not operating at the expected bias point, determine the reason. You may need replace a faulty resistor or transistor. If the transistor is properly biased, then the problem is due to a problem in the ac operation of the circuit.

4. Verify that the coupling and bypass capacitors have been correctly placed into the circuit. If any of these capacitors are electrolytic, it is necessary to determine the correct polarity and install the capacitor accordingly. (There is a possibility that the capacitor was permanently damaged if an incorrect dc voltage was applied for any length of time.)

5. Ensure that all connections, especially ground wires, are kept as short as possible. This is particularly important if a transistor amplifier operates at high frequencies, since it is possible for ground-loop currents to be generated. These currents can result in the appearance of all manners of unwanted signals.

6. If the output signal is distorted, as shown in Figure 27–62, then the result is likely due to an input signal that is too large for the transistor. In order to return the transistor amplifier to linear operation (where the output signal resembles the input signal), it is necessary to lower the amplitude of the applied ac signal.

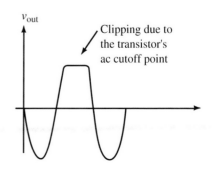

**FIGURE 27–62**

## 27.11 Computer Analysis of Transistor Amplifier Circuits

Computer analysis provides a powerful tool to analyze and predict the operation of complex circuits. Although the circuits that you are about to examine are not as complicated as circuits that appear in the "real world", you will find that the methods that are developed in entering and simulating the circuits will help when you work with much more complex circuits. Both PSpice and MultiSIM are excellent tools for simulating the operation of BJT and FET amplifiers.

### MultiSIM

The following example shows that we can simulate a complete transistor amplifier circuit, using actual component values that are commonly available in the lab. While the software is more forgiving than using actual components in the lab, you will find that if you connect components incorrectly, there will still be problems with the circuit operation.

**EXAMPLE 27–14**

Use MultiSIM to construct the circuit shown in Figure 27–26. In the circuit, use a 2N2712 as the npn transistor and set the signal source for a voltage of $v_{in} = 0.1\ V_p$ and a frequency of 1000 Hz. Use 10-$\mu$F electrolytic capacitors and place them with the correct polarities.

a. Use the oscilloscope to measure both the input and output voltages, and use these values to calculate the voltage gain of the amplifier.

b. Observe the effect of increasing the input voltage to 0.55 $V_p$, a value that is greater than the theoretical maximum allowable input signal ($v_{in(max)} = 0.4\ V_p$).

c. Compare the results to those of Example 27–6.

### Solution

a. Construct the circuit as you have done in previous chapters. Select an oscilloscope from the Instruments tool bar (to the right of the workspace). Place the oscilloscope into the circuit, so that Channel A displays the input voltage, $v_{in}$ and Channel B displays the output voltage, $v_{out}$. Your circuit should appear as shown in Figure 27–63.

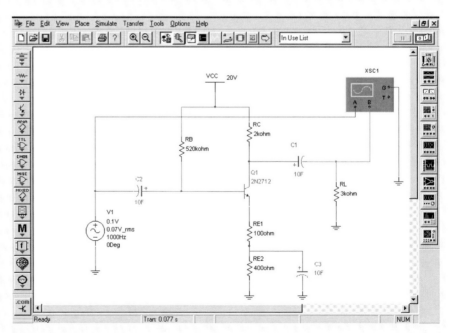

    **FIGURE 27–63**

You may find that it is useful to display each of the measurements in a different color. In order to change the color of a particular display simply right-click on the wire, click *color,* and select the desired color from the *basic colors* that are provided. For instance, Figure 27–63 shows that the input voltage (Channel A) will appear in red, while the output voltage (Channel B) will appear in blue. You will find it much easier to interpret the results shown on the oscilloscope if you select different colors for each of the channels.

In order to observe the display on the oscilloscope, double click on the instrument. Now, click on the *Run* button to simulate the design. You should observe that a display appears on the oscilloscope. However, the display will not likely provide you with useful results. Just like in the lab, you will need to adjust the controls on the oscilloscope to provide you with useful observations. In the *Timebase* setting of the oscilloscope, set the scale for 200 μS/Div. In the *Channel A* and *Channel B* settings, set the volts per division as 50 mV/Div and 500 mV/Div, respectively. Your display should now be much more useful.

You will find, though, that the display is constantly refreshing and shifting its horizontal position. This is easily corrected by clicking on either the *Sing.* button or the *Nor.* button in the *Trigger* setting. Your display should now appear as shown in Figure 27–64, providing you with a display that is easy to interpret.

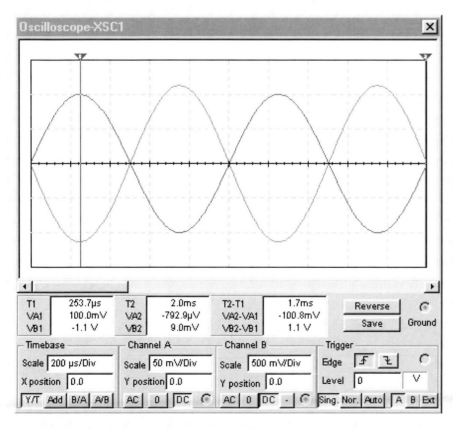

**FIGURE 27–64**

Let's use one more feature of the oscilloscope, the cursor. There are two cursors provided for this oscilloscope, one is red (labeled "1") and the other is blue (labeled "2"). Either cursor can be used to take measurements at any value of time by simply grabbing the cursor with the left mouse button and dragging it to the location. In this example, we see that when the input voltage is at its peak value, the output voltage will also be at a negative peak. From the results of the display, we observe the following:

$v_{in} = 100$ mV$_p$ and $v_{out} = 1.1$ V$_p$ and 180° out-of-phase with respect to the input.

Therefore, we conclude that this amplifier has a voltage gain of

$$A_v = \frac{v_{out}}{v_{out}} = -\frac{1.1 \text{ V}_p}{100 \text{ mV}_p} = -11$$

This result is consistent with the gain predicted in Example 27–6.

b. Increasing the input voltage to 0.55 V$_p$ results in the display of Figure 27–65.

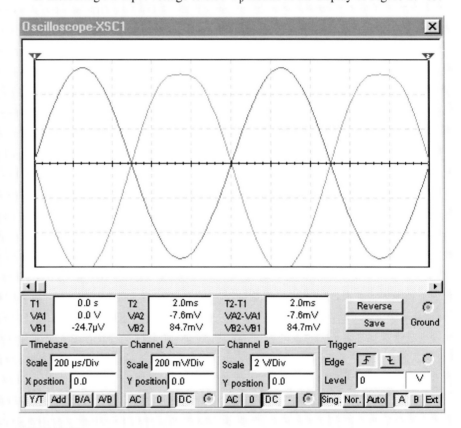

**FIGURE 27–65**

In the above display, we see that the positive-going portion of the output waveform is clipped due to the transistor going into ac cutoff. By adjusting the input voltage, it would be possible to determine the maximum input signal that would result in an undistorted output. It is left as an exercise for the student to show that this value occurs at around 0.52 V$_p$ (or 1.04 V$_{p-p}$).

c. In Example 27–6, the voltage gain of the circuit was approximately $A_v = -12$ and the maximum input signal that could be applied before distortion occurs, was 0.8 V$_{p-p}$. The observed results are relatively close to the predicted values. The variation is primarily due to the fact that the bias point is not equal to the predicted value. The original design would be more stable if we had used a universal-bias arrangement.

## PSpice

The student version of PSpice does not have the full complement of transistors that a complete version has. However, you will find that there is a wide enough selection to observe how this software is applied to analyzing complete transistor circuits. The following example illustrates some of the features of the software. You are encouraged to experiment with the software to see some of the many other circuit applications.

a. Use PSpice to input the circuit of Figure 27–20. Use a 2N3904 npn transistor.

b. Use the Probe postprocessor to observe both the input voltage (at the base of the transistor) and the output voltage appearing across the load resistor.

c. Determine the voltage gain of the circuit and compare the value to the predicted gain of Example 27–5.

**EXAMPLE 27–15**

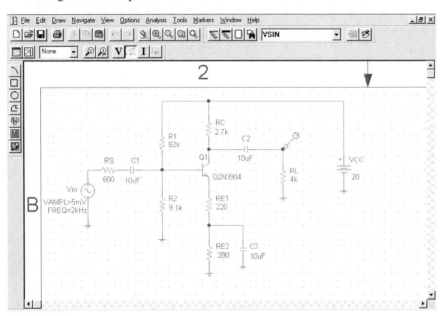

**FIGURE 27–66**

## Solution

a. The circuit components are entered as shown in Figure 27–66. These components are obtained from the ANALOG.slb, EVAL.slb, and SOURCE.slb libraries. Notice that the component and voltage source labels have been changed to reflect those of Figure 27–20. While not important, this step helps to recognize the function of the component in the original circuit. Remember that you will need to change all component values default values. In order for the program to function correctly, the attributes of the VSIN voltage source (ac input signal) must be changed to the following values:

$$\text{VOFF=0 \quad VAMPL=5mV \quad FREQ=2kHz}$$

Remember that each of the attributes must be saved before closing the comment box. Notice that a voltage/level marker is placed at $R_L$, so that the Probe postprocessor will immediately display the output voltage, $v_{out}$.

Before simulating the design, it is important to instruct PSpice to perform the correct analysis. Click on the *Setup Analysis* tool and enable transient analysis. Click on the *Transient* button and set the analysis to provide *Print Step:* 0.2ns and *Final Time:* 1ms. (Note: PSpice does not permit spaces between the magnitude and the units for these values.)

b. If all values are correctly entered, the simulation will result in a sinusoidal voltage display of $v_{out}$. In order to display the input voltage, $v_{in}$ as well as $v_{out}$, we need to have PSpice display an additional trace. This is done by first selecting *Add Plot* from the *Plot* menu. The previous step will provide us with a blank plot. Now, to display the input voltage, we now select *Add . . .* from the *Trace menu*. Since $v_{in}$ is the same as the voltage across $R_2$, we simply select *V(R2:1)* from the list of measurements that were determined by PSpice. The resulting display is shown in Figure 27–67.

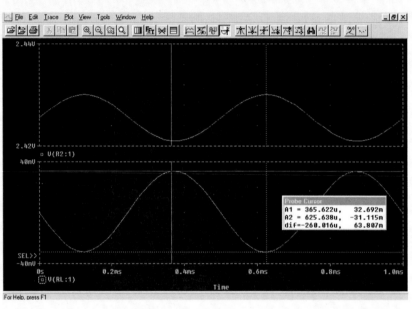

**FIGURE 27–67**

c. We use cursors to find the peak-to-peak voltages of both the input and output waveforms. The values are determined as $v_{in} = 9.138$ mV$_{p\text{-}p}$ and $v_{out} = 63.807$ mV$_{p\text{-}p}$. From the displays of Figure 27–67, we see that the output voltage is 180° out-of-phase with respect to the input. Consequently, the voltage gain for the circuit is determined to be

$$A_v = \frac{v_{out}}{v_{in}} = -\frac{63.807 \text{ mV}_{p\text{-}p}}{9.138 \text{ mV}_{p\text{-}p}} = -6.98$$

This value compares well to the value $A_v = -7.0$ that was found in Example 27–5.

---

PRACTICE PROBLEMS 12

a. Use PSpice to input the circuit of Figure 27–22. Make the following modifications to your circuit so that it will work correctly:
- Use a 2N3906 pnp transistor.
- Measure the output voltage at the collector of the transistor.
- Do not include a coupling capacitor at the collector (since this will result in an error in a PSpice simulation).
- Use a VSIN part having VOFF=0, VAMPL=5mV, FREQ=1kHz.

b. Use the Probe postprocessor to observe both the input voltage (at the base of the transistor) and the output voltage appearing at the collector of the transistor.

c. Determine the voltage gain of the circuit and compare the value to the predicted gain of Practice Problems 27–5.

*Answers*
b. $v_{in} = 9.967$ mV$_{p\text{-}p}$, $v_{out} = 79.256$ mV$_{p\text{-}p}$; c. $A_v = -7.95$ compares well with the theoretical gain of $A_v = -8.1$

## PROBLEMS

### 27.1 The Use of Capacitors in Amplifier Circuits

1. The coupling capacitor, illustrated in Figure 27–68 is used to pass ac signals from a signal source having an output impedance (resistance), $z_{out} = 1200 \, \Omega$ to a transistor circuit having an input impedance, $R_L = 800 \, \Omega$. The signal varies within a frequency range of 100 Hz → 20 kHz.

   a. Calculate the minimum value of coupling capacitor required.

   b. Determine the amplitude of the input voltage, $v_{in}$ if the coupling capacitor of part a. is used i) at 100 Hz and ii) at 20 kHz.

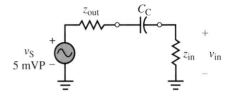

**FIGURE 27–68**

2. The coupling capacitor of Figure 27–68 is used to connect a circuit having $z_{out} = 600 \, \Omega$ and $z_{in} = 20 \, \Omega$ at a frequency range of 10 kHz → 200 kHz.

   a. Calculate the minimum value of coupling capacitor required.

   b. Determine the amplitude of the input voltage, $v_{in}$ if the coupling capacitor of part a. is used i) at 10 kHz and ii) at 200 kHz.

3. A bypass capacitor is placed across an emitter resistance, $R_E = 470 \, \Omega$, to increase the gain of a transistor amplifier. Determine the minimum value of bypass capacitor needed if the circuit is to operate between 500 Hz and 50 kHz.

4. A bypass capacitor is placed across an emitter resistance, $R_E = 1.2 \, k\Omega$ of a transistor amplifier. Determine the minimum value of bypass capacitor needed if the circuit is to operate between 500 Hz and 50 kHz.

### 27.4 The Common-Emitter Amplifier

5. Given that $V_{CC} = +22 \, V$, $R_C = 4.0 \, k\Omega$, $R_B = 1.1 \, M\Omega$, $R_L = 4.0 \, k\Omega$, and $\beta_{dc} = 150 = h_{fe} = \beta_{dc}$ in the circuit of Figure 27–69:

   a. Calculate the operating point of the transistor.

   b. Sketch the ac equivalent circuit using the $T$-equivalent model of the transistor.

   c. Use the ac equivalent circuit to find $A_v$, $z_{in}$, $z_{out}$, $A_i$, and $A_p$.

6. Given that $V_{CC} = +12 \, V$, $R_C = 2.2 \, k\Omega$, $R_B = 560 \, k\Omega$, $R_L = 3.3 \, k\Omega$, and $\beta_{dc} = 130 = h_{fe} = \beta_{dc}$ in the circuit of Figure 27–69:

   a. Calculate the operating point of the transistor.

   b. Sketch the ac equivalent circuit using the $T$-equivalent model of the transistor.

   c. Use the ac equivalent circuit to find $A_v$, $z_{in}$, $z_{out}$, $A_i$, and $A_p$.

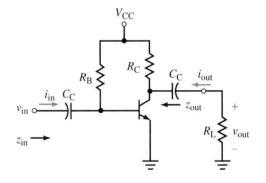

**FIGURE 27–69**

7. Consider the circuit of Figure 27–70.

   a. Given that $R_C = 3.3 \, k\Omega$, $R_B = 910 \, k\Omega$, and $\beta_{dc} = 150$, find the operating point of the transistor.

   b. Refer to the manufacturer's specifications of the 2N3906 transistor to obtain each of the $h$-parameters at the given operating point.

   c. Sketch the ac equivalent circuit using the appropriate values for the $h$-parameter model of the transistor.

   d. Use the ac equivalent circuit to find $A_v$, $z_{in}$, $z_{out}$, and $A_i$.

8. Refer to the circuit of Figure 27–70 and the values of part a. in Problem 7.

   a. Sketch the ac equivalent circuit using the $T$-equivalent model of the transistor.

   b. Use the ac equivalent circuit to find $A_v$, $z_{in}$, $z_{out}$, and $A_i$.

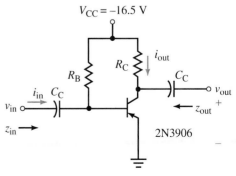

**FIGURE 27–70**

9. Refer to the circuit of Figure 27–71.

    a. Calculate the operating point of the transistor.

    b. Using the *h*-parameter values provided, sketch the ac equivalent circuit.

    c. Determine $A_v$, $z_{in}$, $z_{out}$, and $A_i$ for the circuit.

    d. Calculate the amplitudes of the input voltage, $v_{in}$ and the output voltage, $v_{out}$.

    e. Use graph paper to sketch two graphs, showing $v_{in}$ and $v_{out}$. Correctly label each graph with the amplitudes and the phase relationship.

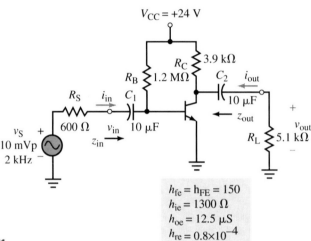

**FIGURE 27–71**

10. Refer to the circuit of Figure 27–72.

    a. Calculate the operating point of the transistor.

    b. Obtain the *h*-parameters of the transistor from the manufacturer's data sheets. Use the appropriate values to sketch the ac equivalent circuit.

    c. Determine $A_v$, $z_{in}$, $z_{out}$, and $A_i$ for the circuit.

    d. Calculate the amplitudes of the input voltage, $v_{in}$ and the output voltage, $v_{out}$.

    e. Use graph paper to sketch two graphs, showing $v_{in}$ and $v_{out}$. Correctly label each graph with the amplitudes and the phase relationship.

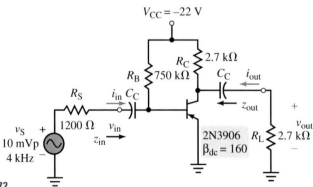

**FIGURE 27–72**

11. Given the circuit of Figure 27–73.

    a. Calculate the operating point of the transistor.

    b. Sketch the ac equivalent circuit using the *T*-equivalent model of the transistor.

    c. Use the ac equivalent circuit to find $A_v$, $z_{in}$, $z_{out}$, and $A_i$.

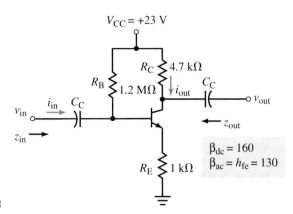

FIGURE 27–73

12. Assume that a bypass capacitor is placed across the emitter resistance, $R_E$ in the circuit of Figure 27–73.

  a. Will the dc operation of the circuit change?

  b. Sketch the ac equivalent circuit using the $T$-equivalent model of the transistor.

  c. Use the ac equivalent circuit to find $A_v$, $z_{in}$, $z_{out}$, and $A_i$.

  d. If a bypass capacitor is added across an emitter resistance of an emitter bias CE amplifier, what general statement can be made about the following?

    i. dc operating point

    ii. input impedance, $z_{in}$ of the circuit

    iii. voltage gain, $A_v$ of the circuit

13. Refer to the circuit of Figure 27–74. Given $V_{CC} = -18$ V, $R_S = 1200$ Ω, $R_B = 780$ kΩ, $R_C = 4.3$ kΩ, $R_{E1} = 180$ Ω, $R_{E2} = 820$ Ω, $R_L = 4.7$ kΩ

  a. Calculate the operating point of the transistor.

  b. Sketch the ac equivalent circuit using the $h$-parameter model of the transistor.

  c. Use the ac equivalent circuit to find $A_v$, $z_{in}$, $z_{out}$, and $A_i$.

  d. Given that $v_S = 5$ mV$_p$, determine the amplitudes of $v_{in}$ and $v_{out}$.

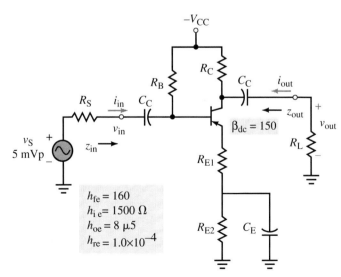

FIGURE 27–74                                                    ◀ MULTISIM

14. Refer to the circuit of Figure 27–74. Given $V_{CC} = -16$ V, $R_S = 2500$ Ω, $R_B = 680$ kΩ, $R_C = 2.7$ kΩ, $R_{E1} = 220$ Ω, $R_{E2} = 560$ Ω, $R_L = 3.3$ kΩ,

  a. Calculate the operating point of the transistor.

  b. Sketch the ac equivalent circuit using the $h$-parameter model of the transistor.

    c. Use the ac equivalent circuit to find $A_v$, $z_{in}$, $z_{out}$, and $A_i$.

    d. Given that $v_S = 5$ mV$_p$, determine the amplitudes of $v_{in}$ and $v_{out}$.

15. Assume that the emitter bypass capacitor in the circuit of Problem 13 is removed.

    a. Sketch the ac equivalent circuit using the $h$-parameter model of the transistor.

    b. Use the ac equivalent circuit to find $A_v$, $z_{in}$, $z_{out}$, and $A_i$.

    c. Given that $v_S = 5$ mV$_p$, determine the amplitudes of $v_{in}$ and $v_{out}$.

16. Assume that the emitter bypass capacitor in the circuit of Problem 14 is removed.

    a. Sketch the ac equivalent circuit using the $h$-parameter model of the transistor.

    b. Use the ac equivalent circuit to find $A_v$, $z_{in}$, $z_{out}$, and $A_i$.

    c. Given that $v_S = 5$ mV$_p$, determine the amplitudes of $v_{in}$ and $v_{out}$.

17. Refer to the circuit of Figure 27–75.

    Given that $V_{CC} = 16$ V, $R_1 = 47$ k$\Omega$, $R_2 = 4.7$ k$\Omega$, $R_E = 390$ $\Omega$, $R_C = 3.9$ k$\Omega$, $R_L = 3.9$ k$\Omega$:

    a. Calculate the operating point of the transistor.

    b. Sketch the ac equivalent circuit using the $T$-equivalent model of the transistor.

    c. Use the ac equivalent circuit to find $A_v$, $z_{in}$, $z_{out}$, and $A_i$.

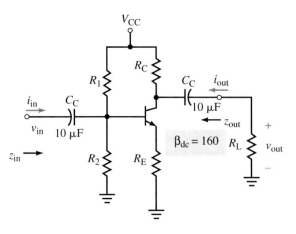

**FIGURE 27–75**

18. Refer to the circuit of Figure 27–75.

    Given that $V_{CC} = 22$ V, $R_1 = 91$ k$\Omega$, $R_2 = 10$ k$\Omega$, $R_E = 220$ $\Omega$, $R_C = 2.2$ k$\Omega$, $R_L = 2.2$ k$\Omega$:

    a. Use Thévenin's theorem to calculate the operating point of the transistor.

    b. Sketch the ac equivalent circuit using the $T$-equivalent model of the transistor.

    c. Use the ac equivalent circuit to find $A_v$, $z_{in}$, $z_{out}$, and $A_i$.

19. Refer to the circuit of Figure 27–76.

    Given that the circuit has $V_{CC} = -18.8$ V, $R_1 = 51$ k$\Omega$, $R_2 = 8.2$ k$\Omega$, $R_{E1} = 180$ $\Omega$,

    $R_{E2} = 670$ $\Omega$, $R_C = 3.3$ k$\Omega$, $R_L = 2.2$ k$\Omega$, $R_S = 1.5$ k$\Omega$:

    a. Calculate the operating point of the transistor.

    b. Obtain the $h$-parameters for the transistor. Sketch the ac equivalent circuit using the $h$-parameter model of the transistor.

    c. Use the ac equivalent circuit to find $A_v$, $z_{in}$, $z_{out}$, and $A_i$.

    d. Given that $v_S = 5$ mV$_p$, determine the amplitudes of $v_{in}$ and $v_{out}$.

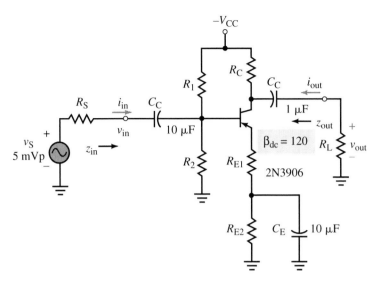

**FIGURE 27–76**

20. Refer to the circuit of Figure 27–76.

Given that the circuit has $V_{CC} = -20$ V, $R_1 = 67$ kΩ, $R_2 = 9.1$ kΩ, $R_{E1} = 470$ Ω, $R_{E2} = 470$ Ω, $R_C = 4.3$ kΩ, $R_L = 1.8$ kΩ, $R_S = 2$ kΩ.

a. Calculate the operating point of the transistor.

b. Obtain the *h*-parameters for the transistor. Sketch the ac equivalent circuit using the *h*-parameter model of the transistor.

c. Use the ac equivalent circuit to find $A_v$, $z_{in}$, $z_{out}$, and $A_i$.

d. Given that $v_S = 5$ mV$_p$, determine the amplitudes of $v_{in}$ and $v_{out}$.

21. Given the circuit of Figure 27–77:

a. Calculate the operating point of the transistor.

b. Sketch the ac equivalent circuit using the *T*-equivalent model of the transistor.

c. Use the ac equivalent circuit to find $A_v$, $z_{in}$, $z_{out}$, and $A_i$.

d. Given that $v_S = 5$ mV$_p$, determine the amplitudes of $v_{in}$ and $v_{out}$.

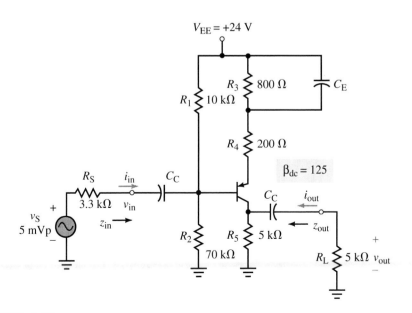

**FIGURE 27–77**

22. Given the circuit of Figure 27–78:

    a. Calculate the operating point of the transistor.

    b. Sketch the ac equivalent circuit using the $T$-equivalent model of the transistor.

    c. Use the ac equivalent circuit to find $A_v$, $z_{in}$, $z_{out}$, and $A_i$.

    d. Given that $v_S = 20$ mV$_p$, determine the amplitudes of $v_{in}$ and $v_{out}$.

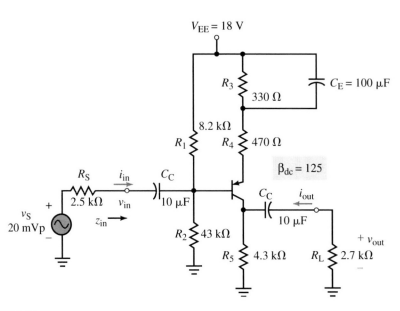

◀ MULTISIM

**FIGURE 27–78**

### 27.5   The ac Load Line

23. Given the circuit of Figure 27–79:

    a. Determine the operating point of the transistor.

    b. Sketch the simplified ac equivalent circuit of the output of the amplifier. (Do not model the transistor.)

    c. Calculate the values of dc and ac saturation and cutoff.

    d. Sketch a graph showing the dc load line and the ac load line.

    e. Determine the maximum undistorted collector current and the maximum undistorted collector-emitter voltage. Solve for the maximum undistorted output voltage, $v_{out}$.

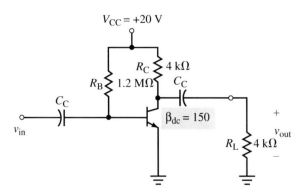

**FIGURE 27–79**

24. Repeat Problem 23 for the circuit of Figure 27–80.

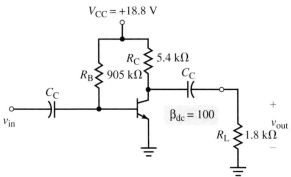

**FIGURE 27–80**

25. Repeat Problem 23 for the circuit of Figure 27–81.
26. Repeat Problem 23 for the circuit of Figure 27–82.

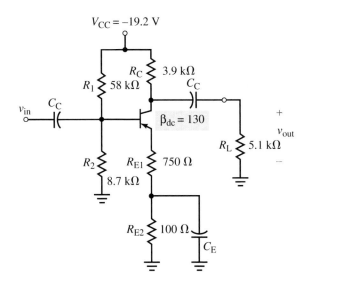

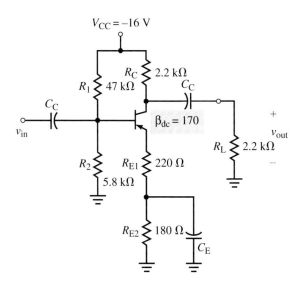

**FIGURE 27–81**                                                                        **FIGURE 27–82**

27. Refer to the circuit of Figure 27–74 and the component values of Problem 13.

   a. Determine the dc and ac cutoff and saturation values.

   b. Sketch a graph showing both the dc load line and the ac load line.

   c. Determine the maximum undistorted collector current and the maximum undistorted collector-emitter voltage. Solve for the maximum undistorted output voltage, $v_{out}$.

   d. Use the voltage gain calculated in Problem 13 to solve for the maximum input voltage, $v_{in}$, which can be applied to the circuit before the output signal is distorted.

28. Refer to the circuit of Figure 27–74 and the component values of Problem 14.

   a. Determine the dc and ac cutoff and saturation values.

   b. Sketch a graph showing both the dc load line and the ac load line.

   c. Determine the maximum undistorted collector current and the maximum undistorted collector-emitter voltage. Solve for the maximum undistorted output voltage, $v_{out}$.

   d. Use the voltage gain calculated in Problem 14 to solve for the maximum input voltage, $v_{in}$ that can be applied to the circuit before the output signal is distorted.

### 27.6 The Common-Collector Amplifier

29. Refer to the circuit of Figure 27–83. Let $V_{CC}$ = 16 V, $R_B$ = 67 k$\Omega$, $R_E$ = 470 $\Omega$

    a. Find the $V_{CEQ}$ and $I_{CQ}$ at the dc operating point.

    b. Sketch the ac equivalent circuit, using the T-equivalent model of the transistor.

    c. Determine $A_v$, $z_{in}$, $z_{out}$, $A_i$, and $A_p$ of the amplifier.

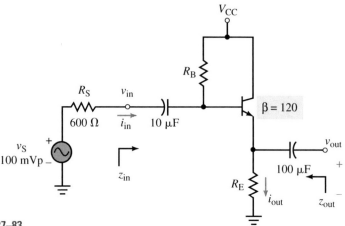

**FIGURE 27–83**

30. Refer to the circuit of Figure 27–83. Let $V_{CC}$ = 20 V, $R_B$ = 150 k$\Omega$, $R_E$ = 1.0 k$\Omega$

    a. Find the $V_{CEQ}$ and $I_{CQ}$ at the dc operating point.

    b. Sketch the ac equivalent circuit, using the T-equivalent model of the transistor.

    c. Determine $A_v$, $z_{in}$, $z_{out}$, $A_i$, and $A_p$ of the amplifier.

31. Refer to the circuit of Figure 27–84. Let $V_{CC}$ = 16 V, $R_1$ = 15 k$\Omega$, $R_2$ = 15 k$\Omega$, $R_E$ = 1.5 k$\Omega$, $R_L$ = 1.0 k$\Omega$

    a. Find the $V_{CEQ}$ and $I_{CQ}$ at the dc operating point.

    b. Sketch the ac equivalent circuit, using the T-equivalent model of the transistor.

    c. Determine $A_v$, $z_{in}$, $z_{out}$, $A_i$, and $A_p$ of the amplifier.

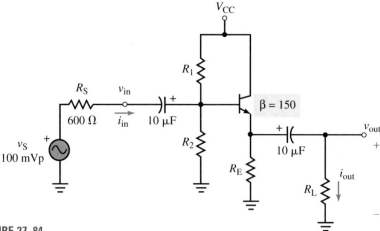

**FIGURE 27–84**

32. Refer to the circuit of Figure 27–84. Let $V_{CC} = 24$ V, $R_1 = 15$ kΩ, $R_2 = 20$ kΩ, $R_E = 2.0$ kΩ, $R_L = 2.4$ kΩ

    a. Find the $V_{CEQ}$ and $I_{CQ}$ at the dc operating point.

    b. Sketch the ac equivalent circuit, using the $T$-equivalent model of the transistor.

    c. Determine $A_v$, $z_{in}$, $z_{out}$, $A_i$, and $A_p$ of the amplifier.

33. Refer to the circuit described in Problem 29.

    a. Use the manufacture's specifications to find $h_{ie}$, $h_{fe}$, $h_{re}$, and $h_{oe}$.

    b. Sketch the ac equivalent circuit using the $h$-parameter model for the 2N3904 transistor. (Use the simplified $h$-parameter model.)

    c. Determine $A_v$, $z_{in}$, $z_{out}$, $A_i$, and $A_p$ of the amplifier.

34. Refer to the circuit described in Problem 30.

    a. Use the manufacture's specifications to find $h_{ie}$, $h_{fe}$, $h_{re}$, and $h_{oe}$.

    b. Sketch the ac equivalent circuit using the $h$-parameter model for the 2N3904 transistor. (Use the simplified $h$-parameter model.)

    c. Determine $A_v$, $z_{in}$, $z_{out}$, $A_i$, and $A_p$ of the amplifier.

35. Refer to the circuit described in Problem 31.

    a. Use the manufacture's specifications to find $h_{ie}$, $h_{fe}$, $h_{re}$, and $h_{oe}$.

    b. Sketch the ac equivalent circuit using the $h$-parameter model for the 2N3904 transistor. (Use the simplified $h$-parameter model.)

    c. Determine $A_v$, $z_{in}$, $z_{out}$, $A_i$, and $A_p$ of the amplifier.

36. Refer to the circuit described in Problem 32.

    a. Use the manufacture's specifications to find $h_{ie}$, $h_{fe}$, $h_{re}$, and $h_{oe}$.

    b. Sketch the ac equivalent circuit using the $h$-parameter model for the 2N3904 transistor. (Use the simplified $h$-parameter model.)

    c. Determine $A_v$, $z_{in}$, $z_{out}$, $A_i$, and $A_p$ of the amplifier.

## 27.7   The FET Small-Signal Model

37. An n-channel JFET has $I_{DSS} = 7.5$ mA and $V_{GS(OFF)} = -4.0$ V:

    a. Determine the transconductance of the JFET for an operating point of $V_{GSQ} = -2.0$ V.

    b. Solve for $g_m$ if $V_{GSQ} = -3.0$ V.

    c. Solve for $g_m$ if $I_{DSQ} = 6.0$ mA.

38. A p-channel JFET has $I_{DSS} = 9.0$ mA and $V_{GS(OFF)} = +5.0$ V:

    a. Determine the transconductance of the JFET for an operating point of $V_{GSQ} = +2.0$ V.

    b. Solve for $g_m$ if $V_{GSQ} = +1.5$ V.

    c. Solve for $g_m$ if $I_{DSQ} = 6.0$ mA.

39. A p-channel E-MOSFET has $V_{th} = 2.5$ V and $I_{D(ON)} = 10$ mA at $V_{GS(ON)} = +4.0$ V:

    a. Determine the transconductance of the E-MOSFET for an operating point of $V_{GSQ} = +3.0$ V.

    b. Solve for $g_m$ if $V_{GSQ} = +4.0$ V.

    c. Solve for $g_m$ if $I_{DSQ} = 6.0$ mA.

    d. Solve for $g_m$ if $I_{DSQ} = 12.0$ mA.

40. A p-channel E-MOSFET has $V_{th} = 3.0$ V and $I_{D(ON)} = 50$ mA at $V_{GS(ON)} = +5.0$ V:

    a. Determine the transconductance of the E-MOSFET for an operating point of $V_{GSQ} = +4.0$ V.

    b. Solve for $g_m$ if $V_{GSQ} = +5.0$ V.

    c. Solve for $g_m$ if $I_{DSQ} = 30$ mA.

    d. Solve for $g_m$ if $I_{DSQ} = 60$ mA.

## 27.8 The Common-Source Amplifier

41. Refer to the circuit of Figure 27–85. Let $V_{DD} = 22$ V, $R_G = 1.0$ MΩ, $R_D = 2.2$ kΩ, $R_S = 750$ Ω, and $R_L = 1.0$ kΩ.

    a. Find $I_{DSQ}$, $V_{GSQ}$, and $V_{DSQ}$ at the operating point.

    b. Solve for $g_{mo}$ and $g_m$ of the amplifier.

    c. Sketch the small-signal ac equivalent circuit.

    d. Determine $A_v$, $z_{in}$, and $z_{out}$ of the amplifier.

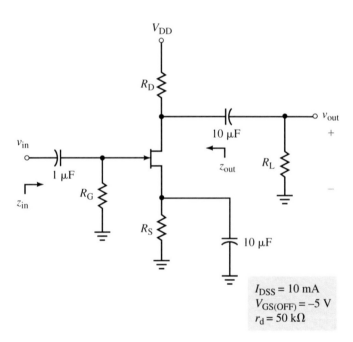

**FIGURE 27–85**

42. Refer to the circuit of Figure 27–85. Let $V_{DD} = 16$ V, $R_G = 2.0$ MΩ, $R_D = 3.9$ kΩ, $R_S = 1.0$ kΩ, and $R_L = 2.2$ kΩ.

    a. Find $I_{DSQ}$, $V_{GSQ}$, and $V_{DSQ}$ at the operating point.

    b. Solve for $g_{mo}$ and $g_m$ of the amplifier.

    c. Sketch the small-signal ac equivalent circuit.

    d. Determine $A_v$, $z_{in}$, and $z_{out}$ of the amplifier.

43. Refer to the circuit of Figure 27–86. Let $V_{DD} = 25$ V, $R_1 = 390$ kΩ, $R_2 = 100$ kΩ, $R_D = 3.3$ kΩ, $R_S = 2.2$ kΩ, and $R_L = 3.3$ kΩ.

    a. Find $I_{DSQ}$, $V_{GSQ}$, and $V_{DSQ}$ at the operating point.

    b. Solve for $g_{mo}$ and $g_m$ of the amplifier.

    c. Sketch the small-signal ac equivalent circuit.

    d. Determine $A_v$, $z_{in}$, and $z_{out}$ of the amplifier.

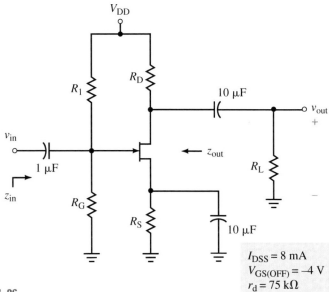

**FIGURE 27–86**

44. Refer to the circuit of Figure 27–86. Let $V_{DD} = 16$ V, $R_1 = 470$ k$\Omega$, $R_2 = 220$ k$\Omega$, $R_D = 1.1$ k$\Omega$, $R_S = 1.1$ k$\Omega$, and $R_L = 2.2$ k$\Omega$.

   a. Find $I_{DSQ}$, $V_{GSQ}$, and $V_{DSQ}$ at the operating point.

   b. Solve for $g_{mo}$ and $g_m$ of the amplifier.

   c. Sketch the small-signal ac equivalent circuit.

   d. Determine $A_v$, $z_{in}$, and $z_{out}$ of the amplifier.

45. Refer to the circuit of Figure 27–87.

   a. Find $I_{DSQ}$, $V_{GSQ}$, and $V_{DSQ}$ at the operating point.

   b. Solve for $g_{mo}$ and $g_m$ of the amplifier.

   c. Sketch the small-signal ac equivalent circuit.

   d. Determine $A_v$, $z_{in}$, and $z_{out}$ of the amplifier.

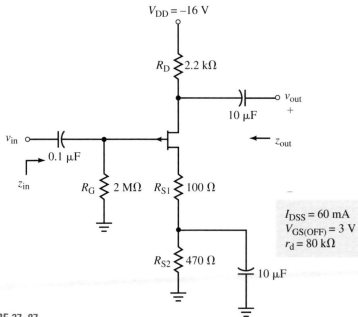

**FIGURE 27–87**

46. Repeat Problem 45 for the circuit of Figure 27–88.

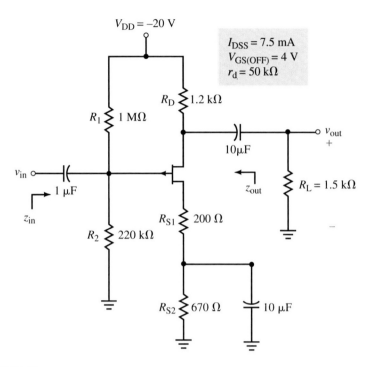

**FIGURE 27–88**

### 27.9   The Common-Drain (Source Follower) Amplifier

47. Refer to the circuit of Figure 27–89. Let $V_{DD} = 20$ V, $R_G = 1.0$ MΩ, $R_S = 1.0$ kΩ, and $R_L = 1.0$ kΩ.

  a. Find $I_{DSQ}$, $V_{GSQ}$, and $V_{DSQ}$ at the operating point.

  b. Solve for $g_{mo}$ and $g_m$ of the amplifier.

  c. Sketch the small-signal ac equivalent circuit.

  d. Determine $A_v$, $z_{in}$, and $z_{out}$ of the amplifier.

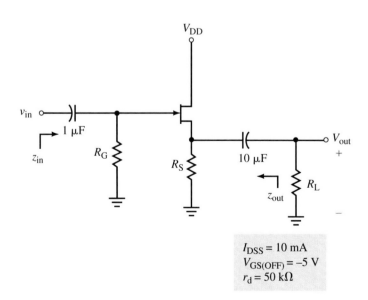

**FIGURE 27–89**

48. Repeat Problem 47 if $V_{DD} = 16$ V, $R_G = 2.0$ MΩ, $R_S = 470$ Ω, and $R_L = 910$ Ω.

49. Refer to the circuit of Figure 27–90. Let $V_{DD} = -20$ V, $R_1 = 820$ kΩ, $R_2 = 220$ kΩ, and $R_S = 820$ Ω.

    a. Find $I_{DSQ}$, $V_{GSQ}$, and $V_{DSQ}$ at the operating point.

    b. Solve for $g_{mo}$ and $g_m$ of the amplifier.

    c. Sketch the small-signal ac equivalent circuit.

    d. Determine $A_v$, $z_{in}$, and $z_{out}$ of the amplifier.

50. Repeat Problem 49 if $V_{DD} = -16$ V, $R_1 = 1.0$ MΩ, $R_2 = 220$ kΩ, and $R_S = 670$ Ω.

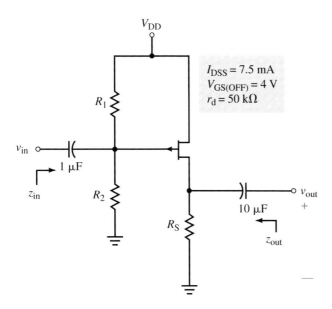

**FIGURE 27–90**

### 27.10   Troubleshooting a Transistor Amplifier Circuit

51. You have constructed the circuit of Figure 27–26. Upon measuring the voltage gain, you find that $A_v = -2.4$, rather than the expected value of $A_v = -12$. You have measured the operating point and found it to be close to the theoretical value. What is the most likely problem with the circuit?

52. The output of an amplifier circuit appears similar to that shown in Figure 27–60. List at least two problems that can cause such a problem.

53. a. If the coupling capacitor, $C_2$, in the circuit of Figure 27–71 were to develop a short circuit fault,

    i. what (if anything) would occur to the operating point of the transistor? Show calculations to support your conclusion.

    ii. what voltage gain would you expect the circuit to have? Show calculations.

    b. If the coupling capacitor, $C_2$, in the circuit of Figure 27–71 were to develop an open circuit fault,

    i. what (if anything) would occur to the operating point of the transistor? Show calculations to support your conclusion.

    ii. what voltage gain would you expect the circuit to have? Show calculations.

54. Refer to the circuit of Figure 27–74. Given $V_{CC} = -20$ V, $R_S = 600 \ \Omega$, $R_B = 910$ k$\Omega$, $R_C = 2.7$ k$\Omega$, $R_{E1} = 100 \ \Omega$, $R_{E2} = 560 \ \Omega$, $R_L = 2.7$ k$\Omega$.

    a. Calculate the operating point of the transistor.

    b. Determine the expected voltage gain of the amplifier circuit.

    c. If the emitter bypass capacitor, $C_E$, in the circuit were to develop a short circuit fault,

        i. what (if anything) would occur to the operating point of the transistor? Show calculations to support your conclusion.

        ii. what voltage gain would you expect the circuit to have? Show calculations.

    d. If the emitter bypass capacitor, $C_E$, in the circuit were to develop an open circuit fault,

        i. what (if anything) would occur to the operating point of the transistor? Show calculations to support your conclusion.

        ii. what voltage gain would you expect the circuit to have? Show calculations.

55. If the emitter bypass capacitor in the circuit of Problem 54 is an electrolytic capacitor, give two possible problems that could occur if it were inserted into the circuit with the wrong polarity.

56. Assume that the emitter bypass capacitor, $C_E$, in the circuit of Problem 19 develops an open-circuit fault.

    a. What effect would this have on the operating point? Give calculations to substantiate your answer.

    b. What effect would this have on the voltage gain and input impedance? Provide calculations to substantiate your answers.

### 27.11    Computer Analysis of Transistor Amplifier Circuits

◀ MULTISIM

57. Use MultiSIM to input the circuit of Figure 27–71. Use a 2N3904 transistor. Use the oscilloscope tool to simultaneously display the waveforms for $v_{in}$ and $v_{out}$. Determine the voltage gain, $A_v = v_{out}/v_{in}$ of the circuit.

◀ MULTISIM

58. Use MultiSIM to input the circuit of Figure 27–75. Use a 2N3904 transistor and the component values of Problem 17. Use the oscilloscope tool to simultaneously display the waveforms for $v_{in}$ and $v_{out}$. Determine the voltage gain, $A_v = v_{out}/v_{in}$ of the circuit.

◀ MULTISIM

59. Use MultiSIM to input the circuit of Figure 27–74. Use a 2N3906 transistor and the component values of Problem 13. Use the oscilloscope tool to simultaneously display the waveforms for $v_{in}$ and $v_{out}$. Determine the voltage gain, $A_v = v_{out}/v_{in}$ of the circuit.

◀ MULTISIM

60. Use MultiSIM to input the circuit of Figure 27–78. Use a 2N3906 transistor. Use the oscilloscope tool to simultaneously display the waveforms for $v_{in}$ and $v_{out}$. Determine the voltage gain, $A_v = v_{out}/v_{in}$ of the circuit.

◀ CADENCE

61. Use PSpice Capture to input the circuit of Figure 27–71. Use a 2N3904 transistor. Run the *Probe* postprocessor and obtain the waveforms for $v_{in}$ and $v_{out}$. Use the results to determine the voltage gain, $A_v = v_{out}/v_{in}$ of the circuit.

62. Use PSpice Capture to input the circuit of Figure 27–75. Use a 2N3904 transistor and the component values of Problem 17. Run the *Probe* postprocessor and obtain the waveforms for $v_{in}$ and $v_{out}$. Use the results to determine the voltage gain, $A_v = v_{out}/v_{in}$ of the circuit.

◀ CADENCE

63. Use PSpice Capture to input the circuit of Figure 27–74. Use a 2N3906 transistor and the component values of Problem 13. Run the *Probe* postprocessor and obtain the waveforms for $v_{in}$ and $v_{out}$. Use the results to determine the voltage gain, $A_v = v_{out}/v_{in}$ of the circuit.

◀ CADENCE

64. Use PSpice Capture to input the circuit of Figure 27–78. Use a 2N3906 transistor. Run the *Probe* postprocessor and obtain the waveforms for $v_{in}$ and $v_{out}$. Use the results to determine the voltage gain, $A_v = v_{out}/v_{in}$ of the circuit

◀ CADENCE

## ■ OBJECTIVES

On completion of this chapter, you will
be able to

- list the basic electrical characteristics of any operational amplifier (op-amp),

- sketch the equivalent circuit of an op-amp,

- correctly connect a dual power supply (V+ and V−) to an op-amp,

- explain the basic operation of a differential amplifier,

- calculate the common-mode voltage gain of an amplifier,

- calculate the common-mode rejection ratio (CMRR) of an amplifier,

- explain the importance of using negative feedback in an op-amp circuit,

- analyze and design inverting amplifier circuits using op-amps,

- analyze and design non-inverting amplifier circuits using op-amps,

- determine the effect of input offset voltage, input offset current, and input bias current on the output of an op-amp circuit,

- use manufacturer's specifications to determine the bandwidth of an op-amp for a given voltage gain,

- use the specified slew rate of an op-amp to calculate the maximum amplitude for a sinusoidal output waveform at a given frequency,

- modify an op-amp circuit to correctly compensate for variation due to input offset,

- use PSpice and MultiSIM software to observe the operation of an op-amp circuit.

# Operational Amplifiers

# 28

**CHAPTER PREVIEW**

This chapter examines the basic characteristics and operation of perhaps the most useful and versatile linear integrated circuit used in the electronics industry. In this chapter you will use your knowledge of impedance to analyze and design circuits using the operational amplifier. Although the actual circuit of the op-amp is complicated, we will treat this device as a simple block that uses quite simple concepts with which you are now familiar. This chapter examines the op-amp circuit using Ohm's law, Kirchhoff's current law, and Kirchhoff's voltage law. You will discover that we are no longer interested in exactly what goes on inside a given device, but rather we examine its operation as part of a complete system. ∎

**PUTTING IT IN PERSPECTIVE**

ANALOG COMPUTERS, WHICH USED VACUUM tubes to perform arithmetic and feedback operations, were developed prior to World War II. These operational amplifiers were very slow and extremely inefficient, often requiring more than one voltage source. Due to the very slow reaction times, there were few practical uses for these amplifiers.

As so often is the case, war resulted in acceleration of research in feedback systems. The allies had made remarkable advances in radar, but needed some mechanism to aim antiaircraft guns using the information provided by radar. George A. Philbrick, a graduate of Massachusetts Institute of Technology and a researcher working with analog computers and operational amplifiers, was certain that the operational amplifier could be improved to provide improved response time necessary for real-time analysis of radar information. The operational amplifier design was greatly improved, thanks to the research of Loebe Julie, who worked for Professor Ragazzini at Columbia University, New York. Ultimately, the operational amplifier was successfully used in aiming antiaircraft guns.

After World War II, George Philbrick redesigned the operational amplifier into a modular package that was marketed in 1952 as the "K2-W" operational amplifier. The module consisted of two vacuum tubes that provided a gain of about 20,000 and a gain-bandwidth product of about 1 MHz, similar to many modern operational amplifiers.

With improvements in semiconductor technology, the modern operational amplifier is miniscule compared to the size of the original "K2-W". Modern op-amps need much less power to operate, requiring only 1/2 W of power compared to the almost 5 W for a K2-W. Perhaps the greatest improvement is that modern op-amps are a fraction of the cost of the older versions. ∎

## 28.1 Introduction to the Operational Amplifier

The operational amplifier (op-amp) is one of the most versatile devices used in the electronics industry. George Philbrick of Huntington Engineering Labs originally designed the op-amp circuit in the late 1940s using vacuum tubes. Since digital computers were not yet available, the op-amp was used as an analog computer to perform mathematical operations (hence the name) such as addition, subtraction, multiplication, and solving differential equations. Modern op-amps are linear integrated circuits and are often included as part of even more complex ICs. A typical op-amp has several important characteristics:

- very high input impedance (generally several megohms)
- very low output impedance (generally less than $100 \, \Omega$)
- very high open-loop voltage gain (20,000 to 200,000)

Op-amps are used throughout electronics as comparators, voltage amplifiers, oscillators, active filters, and instrumentation amplifiers, to name just a few applications.

Figure 28–1 shows the symbol of a basic op-amp. The op-amp has two input terminals, the **inverting input** ($-$) and the **non-inverting input** ($+$) and a single output terminal. The impedance between the two input terminals and

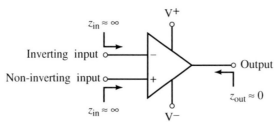

(a) Basic operational amplifier (op-amp)

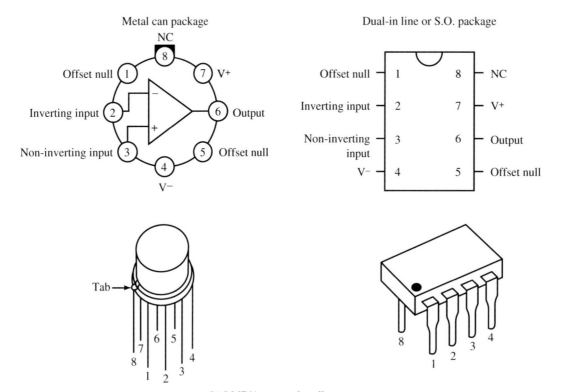

(b) LM741 connection diagrams

(*Courtesy of National Semiconductor Corporation*)

**FIGURE 28–1**

between each of the terminals and ground is very high and so we normally approximate $z_{in} \approx \infty$. The output impedance of the op-amp (looking from the output terminal to circuit ground) is very low and so $z_{out} \approx 0$. Figure 28–2 shows that the ideal op-amp may be represented as two separate parts, the input, which is effectively an open circuit, and the output that consists of an ideal voltage source in series with $z_{out} = 0 \ \Omega$.

In addition to the characteristics shown in Figure 28–2, the ideal op-amp has infinite bandwidth and has unlimited output voltage. Clearly, it is not possible to have a real op-amp with these characteristics. In Section 28.6 we will examine the specifications of op-amps and see the limitations of the device.

Input signals can be applied at either of the two input terminals. Figure 28–3 shows the effect of applying a sinusoidal signal to each of the input terminals, with the other input grounded. When an op-amp is connected in this manner, it is said to be operating as a **single-ended amplifier,** since the input signal is applied at only one terminal, with the other grounded.

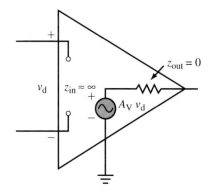

**FIGURE 28–2**

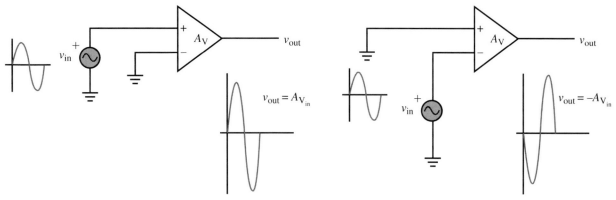

(a) Op-amp used as a non-inverting amplifier

(b) Op-amp used as an inverting amplifier

**FIGURE 28–3**

Figure 28–4(a) shows that it is also possible to connect an op-amp so that the signal is applied directly between the two inputs, without using a ground connection. The voltage applied between the two input terminals is referred to as $v_d$, the difference voltage. In such instances, the op-amp is said to be operating as a **double-ended amplifier** or **differential amplifier** since it is amplifying the difference between the two inputs. When used as a differential amplifier, the op-amp may also have two different signals (relative to ground) applied to the two input terminals as illustrated in Figure 28–4(b).

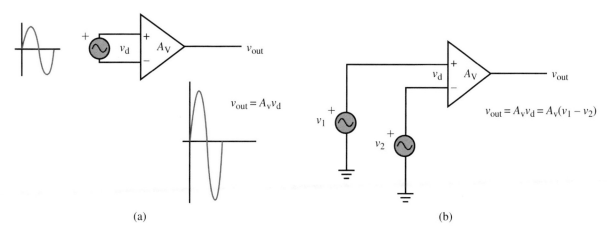

(a)

(b)

**FIGURE 28–4**

In order for an op-amp to operate, it is normally connected to two dc power supplies, one positive with respect to ground, the other negative. (Although less common, some op-amps require only a single power supply). Figure 28–5 shows the correct connection when using a dual power supply. In the lab, you will normally find that a single control changes voltage on both power supplies simultaneously. Notice that the ground terminal is connected between both supplies.

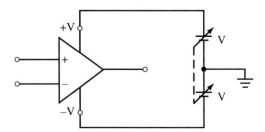

**FIGURE 28–5**

## 28.2 The Differential Amplifier and Common-Mode Signals

### The Differential Amplifier

Figure 28–6 shows the schematic of the 741 operational amplifier. While the circuit is complex (21 transistors), the basic operation of the device can be understood by examining only two transistors, which together form the differential amplifier. In the circuit of Figure 28–6, the transistors $Q_1$ and $Q_2$ form

Schematic Diagram

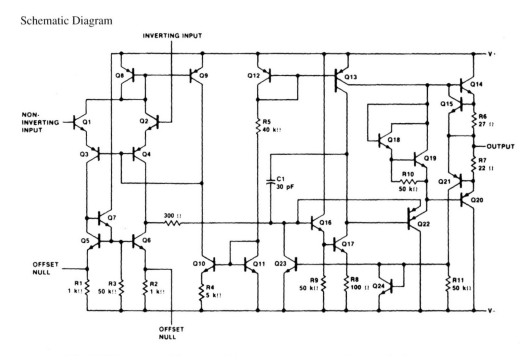

**FIGURE 28–6**   Schematic of the LM741 op-amp. *(Courtesy of National Semiconductor Corporation)*

part of the differential amplifier. Although we will not analyze the circuit in detail, it is worthwhile to briefly examine the operation of the differential amplifier stage. As the name implies, the differential amplifier amplifies only the difference between the signals appearing between the two inputs. The amplifier will reject any signal that is common to both inputs. Consider the transistor amplifier circuit shown in Figure 28–7.

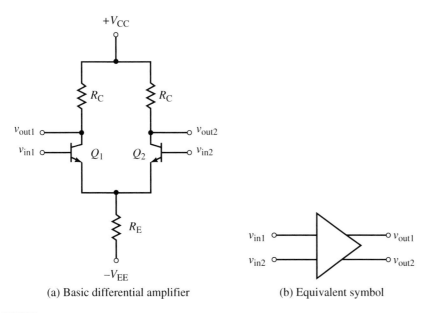

(a) Basic differential amplifier      (b) Equivalent symbol

**FIGURE 28–7** The differential amplifier.

The components in the differential amplifier circuit are selected so that $Q_1$ and $Q_2$ have identical properties and both collector resistors are equal in value. When these components are constructed on a single IC, it is fairly easy to ensure that the required conditions are met. Consider that both inputs are grounded as illustrated in Figure 28–8.

We are able to easily determine the operating point of the transistors. Since both transistors are identical, the current through each emitter (and each collector) will be the same and so we may conclude that

$$I_{C1} = I_{C2} \approx I_{E1} = I_{E2} = \frac{I_E}{2} \qquad \textbf{(28–1)}$$

Also, we see that both emitters will be at the same potential, namely

$$V_E = -0.7 \text{ V}$$

Applying Ohm's law, gives

$$I_E = \frac{V_E - \left(-V_{EE}\right)}{R_E} = \frac{-0.7 \text{ V} - \left(-V_{EE}\right)}{R_E} = \frac{V_{EE} - 0.7 \text{ V}}{R_E} \qquad \textbf{(28–2)}$$

The voltage at the collector of each transistor is determined as

$$V_C = V_{CC} - I_C R_C \approx V_{CC} - \frac{I_E}{2} R_C \qquad \textbf{(28–3)}$$

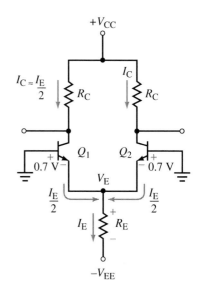

**FIGURE 28–8**

**EXAMPLE 28–1**

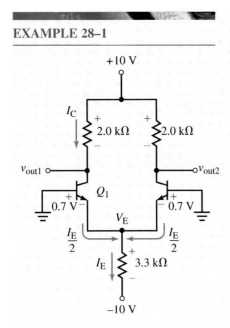

**FIGURE 28–9**

Given the circuit of Figure 28–9, find $I_C$ and $V_C$.

**Solution**
The voltage at each emitter (relative to ground) is $V_E = -0.7$ V and so we determine that

$$I_E = \frac{-0.7 \text{ V} - (-10 \text{ V})}{3.3 \text{ k}\Omega} = 2.82 \text{ mA}$$

and so

$$I_C \approx \frac{I_E}{2} = \frac{2.82 \text{ mA}}{2} = 1.41 \text{ mA}$$

Finally,

$$V_C = V_{CC} - I_C R_C = 10 \text{ V} - (1.41 \text{ mA})(2.0 \text{ k}\Omega) = 7.18 \text{ V}$$

In the above example, it is important to note that with the base of each transistor connected to ground, each collector will be at the same potential, namely 7.18 V. If the output is taken between the two output terminals we have the difference in potential between the terminals as $v_{out} = v_{out1} - v_{out2} = 0$ V.

Now, let's examine the effect of applying alternating voltages to each of the base terminals. Figure 28–10 illustrates what will happen to the voltages at various locations if a sinusoidal voltage is applied to the base of $Q_1$.

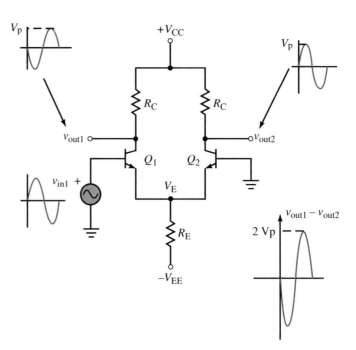

**FIGURE 28–10**

As $v_{in1}$ increases, it results in a corresponding increase in collector current, $I_{C1}$. This increase in collector current results in a decrease in $v_{out1} = V_{C1} = V_{CC} - I_{C1}R_C$. Since the base of $Q_2$ is at ground, the voltage $V_E$ will remain unchanged at $V_E = -0.7$ V. Consequently, there would be no change in $I_E$. In order for Kirchhoff's current law to be satisfied, the increase in collector current $I_{C1}$, would need to cause a decrease the collector current $I_{C2}$ of the other transistor, $Q_2$. This decrease in $I_{C2}$ results in an increased voltage at the collector of $Q_2$. Now, if we were to determine the output voltage as $v_{out} = v_{out1} - v_{out2}$, we would observe an output voltage that is 180° out-of-phase with respect to the input and which is significantly larger.

Using a similar approach, if a sinusoidal voltage were applied at the base of $Q_2$ (with the base of $Q_1$ grounded), the signal appearing at $v_{out1}$ would be in phase with the input and $v_{out2}$ would be 180° out-of-phase. In this case, the output voltage $v_{out} = v_{out1} - v_{out2}$, would be in phase with the input, $v_{in2}$.

What would happen if the input to each transistor's base were the same? In this case, both collector currents would increase simultaneously. The voltage $V_E$ would also increase. More important though, is that the voltage at both collectors would always remain equal, since now there is no imbalance. This means that both outputs would change at exactly the same rate, and the difference, $v_{out} = v_{out1} - v_{out2} = 0$V. This means that if the same signal is applied to each input (referred to as a **common-mode signal**), the output will be zero.

Lastly, if the input signals were applied 180° out-of-phase, the output voltage, $v_{out} = v_{out1} - v_{out2}$ would have twice the magnitude as when only one signal was applied to the base of a transistor (with the other base grounded).

Figure 28–11, shows the effect of applying sinusoidal signals to one or both inputs of a differential amplifier. In the representation shown, the input, $v_{in1}$, is the inverting input and the input, $v_{in2}$, is the non-inverting input.

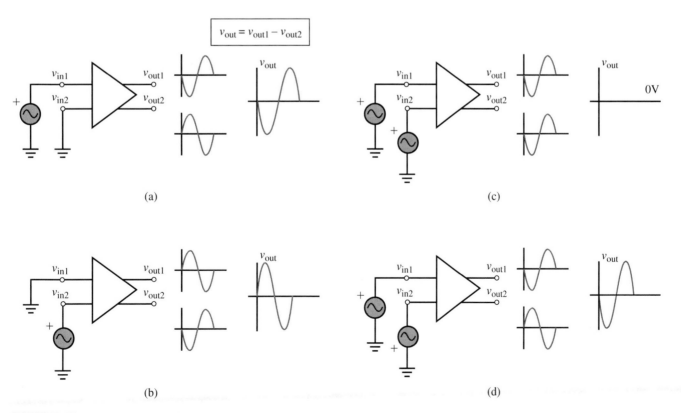

**FIGURE 28–11**

## Common-Mode Signals

One of the characteristics of the ideal operational amplifier is that if the same (common-mode) signal is applied to both inputs, the output will be zero. When an op-amp is manufactured, it is impossible to make all transistors in the differential amplifiers exactly the same. This means that even when the same signal is applied to both inputs, there will be slight imbalances in the op-amp that result in a non-zero output.

Consider the op-amp shown in Figure 28–12. We define the **differential voltage gain** of the amplifier as

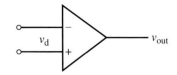

**FIGURE 28–12**

$$A_{vd} = \frac{v_{out}}{v_d} \qquad \textbf{(28–4)}$$

Another name for differential voltage gain is *open-loop voltage gain, $A_{vol}$*. The term *open-loop* refers to the fact that there is no feedback connection between the output and the input. As mentioned previously, the typical open-loop voltage gain for an op-amp is very large, normally between 20,000 and 200,000.

Now, if we were to connect a common-mode signal, $v_c$ as shown in Figure 28–13, one expects that the output would be zero. However, due to slight unbalances within the differential amplifiers of the op-amp, there will normally be some detectable output signal. We define the *common-mode voltage gain* of the amplifier as

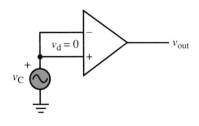

**FIGURE 28–13**

$$A_{vc} = \frac{v_{out}}{v_c} \qquad \textbf{(28–5)}$$

The **common-mode rejection ratio (CMRR)** is the ability of an op-amp (or any other differential amplifier) to reject common-mode signals and is defined as

$$CMRR = \frac{A_{vd}}{A_{vc}} \qquad \textbf{(28–6)}$$

Since the common-mode voltage gain is much smaller that the differential voltage gain, the CMRR of an op-amp will be very large. Therefore, the common-mode rejection ratio is normally expressed in decibels as

$$[CMRR]_{dB} = 20 \log CMRR \qquad \textbf{(28–7)}$$

Typical values of common-mode rejection ratio for an op-amp are in the order of 70 to 90 dB.

**EXAMPLE 28–2**

An op-amp has a differential voltage gain of 200,000. Calculate its CMRR (in dB) if the output voltage is measured to be 2.0 $V_{p\text{-}p}$ when the input terminals are connected together and a 0.1 $V_{p\text{-}p}$ voltage is applied between the inputs and ground.

**Solution**
The common-mode voltage gain is

$$A_{vc} = \frac{v_{out}}{v_c} = \frac{2\ V_{p\text{-}p}}{0.1\ V_{p\text{-}p}} = 20$$

The common-mode rejection ratio is determined as

$$[CMMR]_{dB} = 20 \log \frac{A_{vd}}{A_{vc}} = 20 \log \frac{200,000}{20} = 80\ dB$$

One of the most important considerations in any electronic circuit is the amount of noise relative to the desired signal strength. We have all heard the effects of noise (or *static*) on an audio signal when we listen to far away radio stations. The static can be annoying at best and if large enough, can completely obliterate the desired signal. Imagine that the circuit shown in Figure 28–14 represents a signal being sent over a long distance.

As one might expect, the signal will decrease in amplitude as it moves from the source to the amplifier, since there will be losses in the line itself. Meanwhile, because the line behaves as an antenna, noise will be induced onto the line in series with the desired signal, with the result that the longer the line, the more noise. If we were to apply both the signal and noise to a single-ended amplifier as shown in Figure 28–14, both the signal and noise would be amplified equally. The desired signal would be lost in the noise.

Now, consider that we use an op-amp as a differential amplifier as shown in Figure 28–15. In this case, we see that neither input terminal is connected to ground. The desired signal is connected directly between the inverting and non-inverting terminals of the amplifier and so the signal provides a differential voltage. As in the first case, noise will once again be generated on the line. Since both lines are in the same electrical environment, and since neither line is connected to ground, each line will receive the same amount of induced noise induced (relative to ground). Because the noise is a common-mode signal, the differential amplifier will eliminate it and only the desired signal will appear at the output of the op-amp.

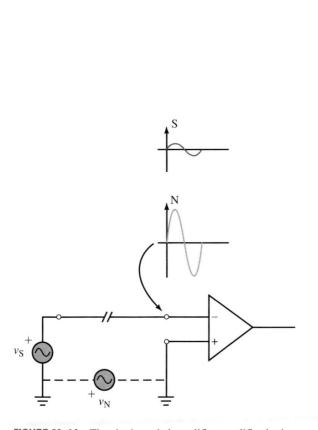

**FIGURE 28–14**  The single-ended amplifier amplifies both signal and noise equally.

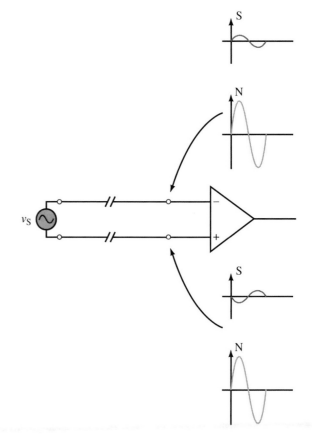

**FIGURE 28–15**  The differential amplifier amplifies only the signal, canceling the noise.

**EXAMPLE 28–3**

The input of an amplifier has a signal with amplitude of 1.0 mV and noise having amplitude of 100 mV.

a. If the above signal and noise are applied to the input of a single-ended amplifier having a differential voltage gain of 100:
   i) Calculate the signal voltage and the noise voltage at the output of the amplifier.
   ii) Determine the ratio of the signal voltage to the noise voltage at the output of the amplifier.
   iii) Will the signal be lost?

b. If the given signal and noise are applied to the input of a differential amplifier having a differential voltage gain of 100 and a CMMR of 10,000 (or 80 dB), repeat the calculations of part a.

**Solution**

a.  i) The signal and the noise will both be amplified by the same factor. The output signal voltage will be $v_s = 100(1.0 \text{ mV}) = 100 \text{ mV}$ and the output noise voltage will be $v_n = 100(100 \text{ mV}) = 10.0 \text{ V}$
   ii) The **signal-to-noise voltage ratio** will be

$$\frac{S}{N} = \frac{v_s}{v_n} = \frac{100 \text{ mV}}{10 \text{ V}} = 0.01$$

   iii) Since the signal voltage is $\frac{1}{100}$ of the noise, we can safely conclude that the signal will be lost in the noise.

b. i) Recall that the CMRR was defined as $\text{CMRR} = \frac{A_{vd}}{A_{vc}}$. Therefore, the common-mode voltage gain is determined as

$$A_{vc} = \frac{A_{vd}}{\text{CMRR}} = \frac{100}{10,000} = 0.01$$

Now, since the desired signal is a differential voltage, we determine the output signal to have a value of

$$v_s = 100(1.0 \text{ mV}) = 100 \text{ mV}$$

The noise is a common-mode voltage, and so its level at the output of the op-amp will be

$$v_n = 0.01(100 \text{ mV}) = 1 \text{ mV}$$

   ii) The signal-to-noise voltage ratio for the differential amplifier will be

$$\frac{S}{N} = \frac{v_s}{v_n} = \frac{100 \text{ mV}}{1 \text{ mV}} = 100$$

   iii) Since the signal voltage is now 100 times larger than the noise, the signal will no longer be lost in the noise. In fact, the noise will be barely perceptible.

The previous example shows that if used correctly a differential amplifier can significantly reduce the amount of noise on a long line. This is especially important when working with audio or digital signals that must go through an electrically noisy environment, such as one having a large amount of 60 Hz wiring or in a location having many electric motors. The example also illustrates the importance of preventing ground loops (Figure 28–14), that can dramatically increase the noise in an amplifier.

One of the characteristics of an op-amp is that it has a very large differential voltage gain (in the order of 100,000). With a application of a very small input voltage, the output voltage will easily become saturated. Consider the op-amp circuit shown in Figure 28–16.

If the dc supply voltages for the op-amp are $\pm 15$ V as shown, the output voltage, $v_{out}$, could never exceed the values of the supply. (In fact the saturation voltage, $V_{SAT}$ will normally be one or two volt less than the supply voltage.) Consequently, if we assume that the op-amp has a differential voltage gain of 100,000, the maximum signal that could be applied between the inputs would be 150 $\mu V_p$. If we were to apply 1 mV directly to the input of an op-amp, we expect an output of $v_{out} = (100{,}000)(1 \text{ mV}) = 100$ V. Clearly this can't occur, and so the output voltage would have a magnitude of $\pm V_{SAT}$. Figure 28–17 shows what would happen if we were to connect a 1 mV dc source to each of the input terminals. Even if no input voltage were applied to the input terminals, the amount of electrical noise at the input will almost always be large enough to cause the op-amp to be saturated. This causes the output of the op–amp to have a value of either $+V_{SAT}$ or $-V_{SAT}$ even when no signal is applied to an input terminal.

## 28.3 Negative Feedback

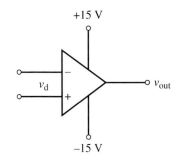

**FIGURE 28–16**

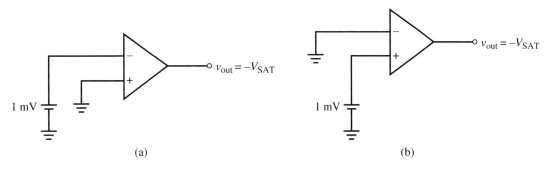

(a)                                                     (b)

**FIGURE 28–17**   The differential voltage gain of an op-amp results in saturation with the application of a small input signal.

In order to make the op-amp more useful, *negative feedback* as shown in Figure 28–18, is used to reduce the voltage gain of the amplifier. Negative feedback takes a portion of the output signal and returns in to the inverting input of the op-amp. Because of the negative feedback, the voltage, $v_d$ will be decreased, resulting in a corresponding decrease in the output voltage. The net result is that the voltage gain of the entire circuit is reduced.

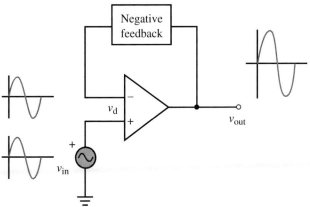

**FIGURE 28–18**

## 28.4 The Inverting Amplifier

Figure 28–19 shows an op-amp that uses negative feedback between the output and the inverting input terminal and has the input signal applied to the inverting input. This circuit is called the *inverting amplifier* since, as we will find, the output is 180° out-of-phase with respect to the input. By using basic circuit theory, several important characteristics of this amplifier become apparent. Using a feedback resistor results in a significant decrease in the voltage gain of the circuit. The voltage gain will no longer be equal to the open-loop voltage gain, but rather will be a much smaller value called the **closed-loop voltage gain,** $A_{vcl}$. You will find that even though the open-loop gain of the op-amp may vary from 20,000 to 200,000, the gain of the overall amplifier will not change at all. Additionally, you will find that by using feedback, the output impedance of the circuit will be reduced to almost zero.

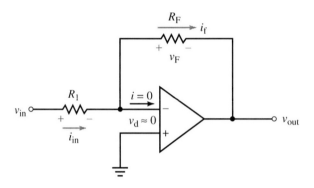

**FIGURE 28–19**   The inverting amplifier.

The op-amp of Figure 28–19 shows some very important characteristics of a typical op-amp circuit. The differential voltage, $v_d$ will be about 100,000 times smaller than the output and so we say that $v_d \approx 0$. We therefore determine that the inverting input $(-)$ is at a **virtual ground,** since the potential at this point essentially zero. Additionally, there will be negligible current entering the op-amp due to the very high input impedance of the op-amp. By Kirchhoff's voltage law, we can solve for the input current of the circuit as

$$i_{in} = \frac{v_{in}}{R_1}$$

None of the input current enters the op-amp, and so the current must follow the path through $R_F$. We see therefore that $i_f = i_{in}$. Now applying Kirchhoff's voltage law at the output, the output voltage must be equal in magnitude to the voltage across the feedback resistor, namely

$$v_{out} = -v_f + v_d = -i_f R_F$$

Since $i_f = i_{in}$, the closed-loop voltage gain for the circuit is determined to be

$$A_{vcl} = \frac{v_{out}}{v_{in}} = -\frac{i_{in} R_F}{i_{in} R_1}$$

which, when simplified gives the voltage gain for the inverting amplifier as

$$A_{vcl} = -\frac{R_F}{R_1} \qquad\qquad (28\text{–}8)$$

The above result shows that the voltage gain of an amplifier is dependent only on the values of resistance that are used. The voltage gain of the circuit is not at all dependent on the open-loop voltage gain, thereby making the circuit operation much more stable.

Using the definition of input impedance allows us to solve for the input impedance of the inverting amplifier as

$$z_{in} = \frac{v_{in}}{i_{in}} = \frac{i_{in}R_1 + v_d}{i_{in}} \approx \frac{i_{in}R_1}{i_{in}}$$

which gives the input impedance for the inverting amplifier as

$$z_{in} \approx R_1 \qquad \text{(28–9)}$$

As you have already seen, the op-amp can be modeled as a circuit having a dependent source. Due to the dependent voltage source and the feedback resistor, we can no longer simply zero all sources to find the output impedance. Rather, it is necessary to apply the circuit theory that you learned in Chapter 19 to determine the output impedance of the circuit by solving for the ratio of the open-circuit voltage to short-circuit current.

$$z_{out} = \frac{v_{out(OC)}}{i_{out(SC)}} \qquad \text{(28–10)}$$

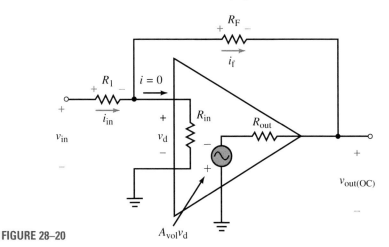

**FIGURE 28–20**

Figure 28–20 shows the inverting amplifier using the complete model of the op-amp. As determined previously, the open-circuit voltage of the circuit is simply found as

$$v_{out(OC)} = -\frac{R_F}{R_1} v_{in} \qquad \text{(28–11)}$$

In order to find the short circuit current, we examine the circuit shown in Figure 28–21, which shows the output terminal shorted to ground. Now, applying Kirchhoff's current law at the output terminal, we have

$$i_{out(SC)} = i_f - i_1 \qquad \text{(28–12)}$$

Applying Ohm's law in the output loop easily solves the current $i_1$ as

$$i_1 = \frac{A_{vol}v_d}{R_{out}} \qquad \text{(28–13)}$$

Further, we see that the voltage across $R_F$ is equal to the differential voltage, $v_d$. Therefore we have

$$i_f = \frac{v_d}{R_F} \qquad \text{(28–14)}$$

Substituting Equations 28–13 and 28–14 into Equation 28–12 gives

$$i_{out(SC)} = \frac{v_d}{R_L} - \frac{A_{vol}v_d}{R_{out}}$$

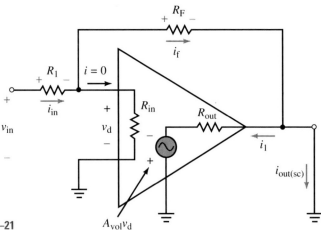

**FIGURE 28–21**

which can be rewritten as

$$i_{out(SC)} = v_d \left( \frac{1}{R_L} - \frac{A_{vol}}{R_{out}} \right) \qquad (28\text{–}15)$$

In the circuit of Figure 28–21, we see that the differential voltage is found by applying the Ohm's law to the loop containing $R_1$ and $R_F$. (The input resistance of the op-amp is much larger than $R_F$, and so can be neglected.)

$$v_d = \frac{R_F}{R_1 + R_F} v_{in} \qquad (28\text{–}16)$$

Substituting this result into Equation 28–15 gives

$$i_{out(SC)} = \left( \frac{R_F v_{in}}{R_1 + R_F} \right) \left( \frac{1}{R_L} - \frac{A_{vol}}{R_{out}} \right)$$

$$= -\left( \frac{R_F v_{in}}{R_1 + R_F} \right) \left( \frac{A_{vol}}{R_{out}} - \frac{1}{R_L} \right)$$

Now, substituting the above result and Equation 28–11 into Equation 28–10 we determine the output impedance as

$$z_{out} = \frac{v_{out(OC)}}{i_{out(SC)}}$$

$$= \frac{-\dfrac{R_F v_{in}}{R_1}}{-\left( \dfrac{R_F v_{in}}{R_1 + R_F} \right) \left( \dfrac{A_{vol}}{R_{out}} - \dfrac{1}{R_L} \right)}$$

$$= \frac{\dfrac{1}{R_1}}{\left( \dfrac{1}{R_1 + R_F} \right) \left( \dfrac{A_{vol}}{R_{out}} - \dfrac{1}{R_L} \right)}$$

$$= \frac{R_1 + R_F}{R_1} \left( \frac{1}{\left( \dfrac{A_{vol}}{R_{out}} - \dfrac{1}{R_L} \right)} \right)$$

Finally, since $\dfrac{A_{vol}}{R_{out}}$ is much larger than $\dfrac{1}{R_L}$ and since the closed-loop voltage

gain is $A_{vcl} = -\dfrac{R_F}{R_1}$, we simplify the above expression as

$$z_{out} = \left(1 - A_{vcl}\right)\left(\dfrac{R_{out}}{A_{vol}}\right) \qquad (28\text{–}17)$$

EXAMPLE 28–4

Given the circuit of Figure 28–22, find the voltage gain, input impedance, and output impedance. Sketch both the input and output voltage waveforms. The 741 op-amp has $R_{in} = 2.0\ \text{M}\Omega$, $R_{out} = 75\ \Omega$ and open-loop gain of $A_{vol} = 200{,}000$.

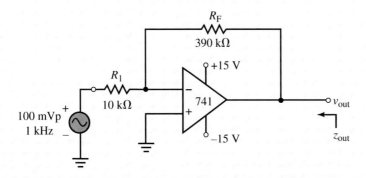

**FIGURE 28–22**

**Solution**

The voltage gain is

$$A_{vcl} = -\dfrac{R_F}{R_1} = -\dfrac{390\ \text{k}\Omega}{10\ \text{k}\Omega} = -39$$

The input impedance is

$$z_{in} = R_1 = 10\ \text{k}\Omega$$

The output impedance is

$$z_{out} = \left[1 - (-39)\right]\left(\dfrac{75\ \Omega}{200{,}000}\right) = 0.015\ \Omega$$

The output voltage will have amplitude of

$$v_{out} = \left|A_{vcl}v_{in}\right| = \left|(-39)(0.10\ \text{V}_p)\right| = 3.9\ \text{V}_p$$

Figure 28–23 shows the sketch of both the input and output voltages. This example clearly illustrates the simplicity of working with op-amps and also demonstrates that the output impedance is negligible.

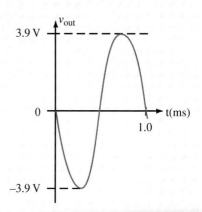

**FIGURE 28–23**

PRACTICE PROBLEMS 1

Using a 741 op-amp, design an inverting amplifier for a closed-loop gain of $-5$ and an input impedance of 15 k$\Omega$. Use the characteristics of Example 28–4 to solve for the output impedance. What conclusion can you make about output impedance as it relates to closed-loop gain?

*Answers*
$R_1 = 15$ k$\Omega$, $R_F = 75$ k$\Omega$, $z_{out} = 2.25$ m$\Omega$. As the voltage gain decreases, so too does the output impedance.

## 28.5 The Non-Inverting Amplifier

As the name implies, the non-inverting amplifier shown in Figure 28–24 has an output that is in phase with the input. In a manner similar to the previous section, we will determine expressions for the voltage gain, input impedance, and output impedance of this amplifier. Although the inverting amplifier had input impedance that was relatively low (determined by the value of the series resistance at the input terminal), you will discover that the input impedance of the non-inverting amplifier is many times larger than the already-large input resistance of the op-amp.

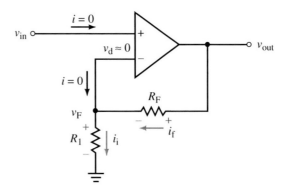

**FIGURE 28–24**    The non-inverting amplifier.

The voltage gain of the non-inverting amplifier is determined by starting with the definition of voltage gain, namely

$$A_v = \frac{v_{out}}{v_{in}}$$

By examining the circuit and applying Kirchhoff's voltage law, we are able to rewrite the voltage gain as

$$A_v = \frac{R_F i_F + R_1 i_1}{v_d + R_1 i_1}$$

Now, since the differential voltage is essentially zero and since $i = 0$ results in $i_f = i_1$, the expression is further simplified as

$$A_v = \frac{R_F i_F + R_1 i_F}{R_1 i_F}$$

which gives the closed-loop voltage gain of the non-inverting amplifier as

$$A_{vcl} = \frac{R_F}{R_1} + 1 \qquad\qquad \textbf{(28–18)}$$

The input impedance is determined by including the equivalent circuit of the op-amp as illustrated in Figure 28–25. When calculating the input impedance, we

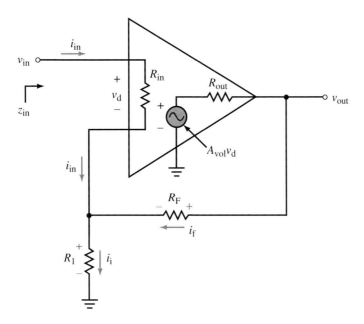

**FIGURE 28–25**

can no longer assume that $i_{in} = 0$ nor $v_d = 0$. Let's begin with the definition of input impedance and then simplify the resulting expression wherever possible.

$$z_{in} = \frac{v_{in}}{i_{in}} = \frac{v_d + R_1 i_1}{i_{in}} \approx \frac{R_1 i_1}{i_{in}} \qquad (28\text{–}19)$$

Now, since $i_{in}$ is much smaller than $i_1$, we can simplify the numerator by letting

$$i_1 = i_f = \frac{A_{vol} v_d}{R_{out} + R_F + R_1} \approx \frac{A_{vol} v_d}{R_F + R_1}$$

Applying Ohm's law allows us to rewrite the denominator as

$$i_{in} = \frac{v_d}{R_{in}}$$

Substituting these values into Equation 28–19 gives

$$z_{in} = \frac{v_d + R_1 \left( \dfrac{A_{vol} v_d}{R_F + R_1} \right)}{\dfrac{v_d}{R_{in}}} = \frac{1 + R_1 \left( \dfrac{A_{vol}}{R_F + R_1} \right)}{\dfrac{1}{R_{in}}}$$

which, when simplified gives the input impedance as

$$z_{in} = \left( 1 + \frac{A_{vol}}{A_{vcl}} \right) R_{in} \qquad (28\text{–}20)$$

Lastly, we solve for the output impedance of the non-inverting amplifier in much the same way as for the inverting amplifier. First, remember that we already have the open-circuit voltage for the non-inverting amplifier as

$$v_{out(OC)} = \left( \frac{R_F}{R_1} + 1 \right) v_{in} \qquad (28\text{–}21)$$

The short-circuit current is found by placing a short between the output terminal and ground as illustrated in Figure 28–26.

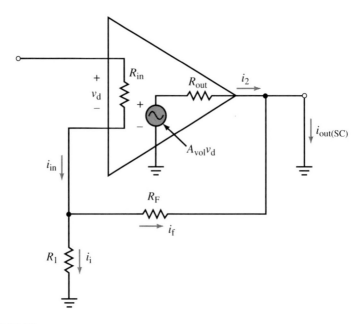

**FIGURE 28–26**

Applying Kirchhoff's current law gives the output short-circuit as

$$i_{out(SC)} = i_2 + i_f$$

However, $i_f$ will be very small since $i_{in} \approx 0$. Also, by voltage divider, $v_d \approx v_{in}$ and so we write

$$i_{out(SC)} = i_2 = \frac{A_{vol}v_{in}}{R_{out}} \qquad (28-22)$$

Now the output impedance is written as

$$z_{out} = \frac{v_{out(OC)}}{i_{out(SC)}} = \frac{A_{vcl}v_{in}}{\dfrac{A_{vol}v_{in}}{R_{out}}}$$

which becomes

$$z_{out} = \left(\frac{A_{vcl}}{A_{vol}}\right) R_{out} \qquad (28-23)$$

**EXAMPLE 28–5**

Given the circuit of Figure 28–27, find the voltage gain, input impedance, and output impedance. The 741 op-amp has $R_{in} = 2.0$ MΩ, $R_{out} = 75$ Ω and open-loop gain of $A_{vol} = 200,000$.

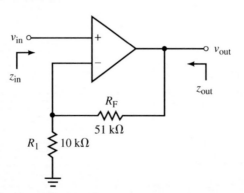

**FIGURE 28–27**

**Solution**

The voltage gain is

$$A_{\text{vcl}} = \frac{R_F}{R_1} + 1 = \frac{51 \text{ k}\Omega}{10 \text{ k}\Omega} + 1 = 6.1$$

The input impedance is

$$z_{\text{in}} = \left(1 + \frac{A_{\text{vol}}}{A_{\text{vcl}}}\right)R_{\text{in}} = \left(1 + \frac{200,000}{6.1}\right)2.0 \text{ M}\Omega = 65.6 \text{ G}\Omega$$

The output impedance is

$$z_{\text{out}} = \left(\frac{A_{\text{vcl}}}{A_{\text{vol}}}\right)R_{\text{out}} = \left(\frac{6.1}{200,000}\right)75 \Omega = 0.0023 \Omega = 2.3 \text{ m}\Omega$$

The previous example illustrates that the non-inverting amplifier has extremely high input impedance and very low output impedance. These characteristics make this design an ideal choice as a **buffer** circuit. The buffer circuit, also referred to as a **voltage follower,** has a unity voltage gain ($A_v = 1$) and provides an interface between two parts of a circuit that would normally be affected by loading. The following example illustrates how a buffer can be used between a high output impedance source and a low input impedance load.

Given the circuit of Figure 28–28:

EXAMPLE 28–6

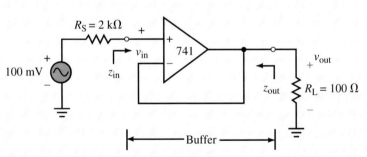

**FIGURE 28–28**

a. Solve for the voltage gain.
b. Determine the input impedance and output impedance of the buffer.
c. Calculate the output voltage.
d. Compare this to the output voltage that would have occurred if the buffer had not been used.

**Solution**

a. Notice that the feedback path results in $R_F = 0$, and $R_1 = \infty$. So the voltage gain of the amplifier will be

$$A_v = \frac{R_F}{R_1} + 1 = \frac{0}{\infty} + 1 = 1$$

b.

$$z_{in} = \left(1 + \frac{A_{vol}}{A_{vcl}}\right) R_{in} = \left(1 + \frac{200,000}{1}\right) 2\ M\Omega = 400\ G\Omega$$

$$z_{out} = \left(\frac{1}{200,000}\right) 75\ \Omega = 0.375\ m\Omega$$

c. The calculations of part b show that there will be no loading of the circuit. Now, since $v_{in} = 100$ mV, we have $v_{out} = A_v v_{in} = 1(100$ mV$) = 100$ mV.

d. If the circuit had not used a buffer, the output voltage would have been

$$v_{out} = \left(\frac{R_L}{R_S + R_L}\right) v_{in} = \left(\frac{100\ \Omega}{2000\ \Omega + 100\ \Omega}\right)(100\ mV) = 4.76\ mV$$

This example clearly shows the importance of using a buffer circuit to prevent loading effects.

---

**PRACTICE PROBLEMS 2**

Given the circuit of Figure 28–29, find the voltage gain, output voltage, input impedance, and output impedance. The 741 op-amp has $R_{in} = 2.0$ M$\Omega$, $R_{out} = 75$ $\Omega$ and open-loop gain of $A_{vol} = 200,000$.

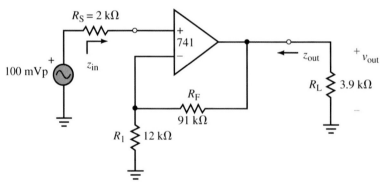

**FIGURE 28–29**

*Answers*
$A_v = 8.58$, $v_{out} = 858$ mV$_p$, $z_{in} = 46.6$ G$\Omega$, $z_{out} = 3.22$ m$\Omega$.

---

**PRACTICE PROBLEMS 3**

Use a 741 op-amp to design an inverting amplifier for a closed-loop gain of 10. Let $R_1 = 20$ k$\Omega$. Use the characteristics of Example 28–5 to solve for the input and the output impedance of your design.

*Answers*
$R_F = 180$ k$\Omega$, $z_{in} = 40.0$ G$\Omega$, $z_{out} = 3.75$ m$\Omega$.

---

**28.6  Op-Amp Specifications**

In this section, we examine typical electrical specifications of the op-amp. Although our examination uses the characteristics of the 741C op-amp summarized in Figure 28–30, you will find that all op-amps have similar characteristics.

| Parameter | Conditions | LM741A | | | LM741 | | | LM741C | | | Units |
|---|---|---|---|---|---|---|---|---|---|---|---|
| | | Min | Typ | Max | Min | Typ | Max | Min | Typ | Max | |
| Input Offset Voltage | $T_A = 25°C$ $R_S \leq 10\ k\Omega$ $R_S \leq 50\ k\Omega$ | | 0.8 | 3.0 | | 1.0 | 5.0 | | 2.0 | 6.0 | mV mV |
| | $T_{AMIN} \leq T_A \leq T_{AMAX}$ $R_S \leq 50\ k\Omega$ $R_S \leq 10\ k\Omega$ | | | 4.0 | | | 6.0 | | | 7.5 | mV mV |
| Average Input Offset Voltage Drift | | | | 15 | | | | | | | $\mu V/°C$ |
| Input Offset Voltage Adjustment Range | $T_A = 25°C, V_S = \pm 20V$ | $\pm 10$ | | | | $\pm 15$ | | | $\pm 15$ | | mV |
| Input Offset Current | $T_A = 25°C$ $T_{AMIN} \leq T_A \leq T_{AMAX}$ | | 3.0 | 30 70 | | 20 85 | 200 500 | | 20 | 200 300 | nA nA |
| Average Input Offset Current Drift | | | | 0.5 | | | | | | | $nA/°C$ |
| Input Bias Current | $T_A = 25°C$ $T_{AMIN} \leq T_A \leq T_{AMAX}$ | | 30 | 80 0.210 | | 80 | 500 1.5 | | 80 | 500 0.8 | nA $\mu A$ |
| Input Resistance | $T_A = 25°C, V_S = \pm 20V$ $T_{AMIN} \leq T_A \leq T_{AMAX},$ $V_S = \pm 20V$ | 1.0 0.5 | 6.0 | | 0.3 | 2.0 | | 0.3 | 2.0 | | $M\Omega$ $M\Omega$ |
| Input Voltage Range | $T_A = 25°C$ $T_{AMIN} \leq T_A \leq T_{AMAX}$ | | | | $\pm 12$ | $\pm 13$ | | $\pm 12$ | $\pm 13$ | | V V |
| Large Signal Voltage Gain | $T_A = 25°C, R_L \geq 2\ k\Omega$ $V_S = \pm 20V, V_O = \pm 15V$ $V_S = \pm 15V, V_O = \pm 10V$ | 50 | | | 50 | 200 | | 20 | 200 | | V/mV V/mV |
| | $T_{AMIN} \leq T_A \leq T_{AMAX},$ $R_L \geq 2\ k\Omega,$ $V_S = \pm 20V, V_O = \pm 15V$ $V_S = \pm 15V, V_O = \pm 10V$ $V_S = \pm 5V, V_O = \pm 2V$ | 32 25 10 | | | | | | 15 | | | V/mV V/mV V/mV |
| Output Voltage Swing | $V_S = \pm 20V$ $R_L \geq 10\ k\Omega$ $R_L \geq 2\ k\Omega$ | $\pm 16$ $\pm 15$ | | | | | | | | | V V |
| | $V_S = \pm 15V$ $R_L \geq 10\ k\Omega$ $R_L \geq 2\ k\Omega$ | | | | $\pm 12$ $\pm 10$ | $\pm 14$ $\pm 13$ | | $\pm 12$ $\pm 10$ | $\pm 14$ $\pm 13$ | | V V |
| Output Short Circuit Current | $T_A = 25°C$ $T_{AMIN} \leq T_A \leq T_{AMAX}$ | 10 10 | 25 | 35 40 | | 25 | | | 25 | | mA mA |
| Common-Mode Rejection Ratio | $T_{AMIN} \leq T_A \leq T_{AMAX}$ $R_S \leq 10\ k\Omega, V_{CM} = \pm 12V$ $R_S \leq 50\Omega, V_{CM} = \pm 12V$ | 80 | 95 | | 70 | 90 | | 70 | 90 | | dB dB |
| Supply Voltage Rejection Ratio | $T_{AMIN} \leq T_A \leq T_{AMAX},$ $V_S = \pm 20V$ to $V_S = \pm 5V$ $R_S \leq 50\Omega$ $R_S \leq 10\ k\Omega$ | 86 | 96 | | 77 | 96 | | 77 | 96 | | dB dB |
| Transient Response Rise Time Overshoot | $T_A = 25°C$, Unity Gain | | 0.25 6.0 | 0.8 2.0 | | 0.3 5 | | | 0.3 5 | | $\mu s$ % |
| Bandwidth (Note 6) | $T_A = 25°C$ | 0.437 | 1.5 | | | | | | | | MHz |
| Slew Rate | $T_A = 25°C$, Unity Gain | 0.3 | 0.7 | | | 0.5 | | | 0.5 | | $V/\mu s$ |
| Supply Current | $T_A = 25°C$ | | | | | 1.7 | 2.8 | | 1.7 | 2.8 | mA |

**FIGURE 28–30**  Electrical characteristics of the LM741 op-amp ($V_S = \pm 15$ V). *(Courtesy of National Semiconductor Corporation)*

## Input Offset Voltage, $V_{io}$

There will always be imbalances in any differential amplifier. In the op-amp circuits that we have analyzed up to now, we have assumed that the op-amps are ideal, namely that there is no current entering the inverting or the non-inverting inputs. We have also assumed that the differential voltage between the input terminals is exactly zero. Although these assumptions are very good, they are not exactly correct. It is important to understand that real op-amp circuits may not work exactly as expected. If we examine the circuit shown in Figure 28–31, we see that the output voltage should ideally be zero. However, due to imbalances in the differential amplifier, there will be a slight error in the output voltage resulting in a value between a few microvolts and several millivolts. The specification sheet for the 741C op-amp indicates that a typical **input offset voltage** of 2 mV should be expected.

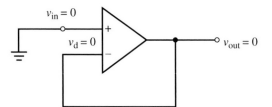

**FIGURE 28–31**

What possible effect could such small voltages have on the overall operation of the op-amp? Consider that the input offset voltage, $V_{io}$ is modeled as a battery in series with the non-inverting $(+)$ terminal of the op-amp as shown in Figure 28–32. We will discover that this insignificant value can have a dramatic effect on the operation of the amplifier. For example, if we were to connect an op-amp as illustrated in Figure 28–33(a), we see that the offset voltage will be multiplied by the open-loop gain of the op-amp, resulting in the output that will be equal to $\pm V_{SAT}$, depending on the polarity of the offset voltage.

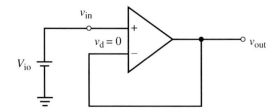

**FIGURE 28–32**

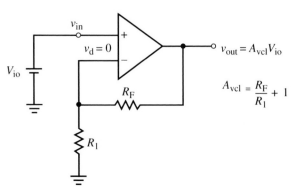

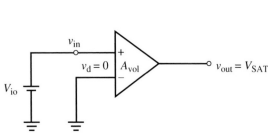

(a) Effect of input offset voltage on the output voltage of an op-amp having no feedback

(b) Effect of input offset voltage on the output voltage of an op-amp using negative feedback

**FIGURE 28–33**

If the amplifier uses a feedback resistor as illustrated in Figure 28–33(b), the output will normally be less than the saturation voltage, but the offset voltage will nonetheless be amplified, in this case by the closed loop gain of the amplifier. The following example shows how to measure the input offset voltage of an op-amp.

**EXAMPLE 28–7**

The 741C op-amp shown in Figure 28–34 is measured to have output voltage of 180 mV. Determine the input offset voltage for this amplifier. Compare the result to the value of $V_{io}$ specified by the manufacturer.

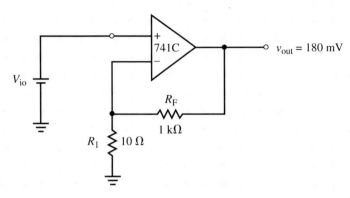

**FIGURE 28–34**

**Solution**
The voltage gain of the amplifier is

$$A_v = \frac{R_F}{R_1} + 1 = \frac{1000\ \Omega}{10\ \Omega} + 1 = 101$$

and so we have

$$V_{io} = \frac{V_{out}}{A_{vcl}} = \frac{180\ mV}{101} = 1.78\ mV$$

The manufacturer specifies that the input offset voltage has a typical value of 2 mV. The above result is consistent with the manufacturer's specification.

## Input Bias Current, $I_B$

By examining the schematic of the op-amp, we see that the circuit consists of numerous transistors. Remember that in order for a transistor to operate correctly, it must be properly biased. The bias current for the base of the transistor connected to the inverting input terminal is referred to as $I_{B(-)}$, while the bias current for the base of the transistor connected to the non-inverting input terminal is referred to as $I_{B(+)}$. The base bias currents needed to operate the transistors of the differential amplifier will generally require slightly different bias currents for the two input terminals. We define the input bias current as the average of the two bias currents, namely

$$I_B = \frac{\left| I_{B(+)} \right| + \left| I_{B(-)} \right|}{2} \tag{28–24}$$

The 741C op-amp has a typical bias current of 80 nA. If the op-amp were designed using FET differential amplifiers, the bias current would have been in the order of pA ($10^{-12}$ A).

### Input Offset Current, $I_{os}$

The difference between the magnitude of the two bias currents is called the **input offset current** and is given as

$$I_{OS} = \left| I_{B(+)} \right| - \left| I_{B(-)} \right| \tag{28–25}$$

The 741C op-amp has a typical input offset current of 20 nA. Let's examine the effect of the input offset current on an amplifier.

Consider the voltage follower shown in Figure 28–35(a). If we imagine that the input offset current is applied to the inverting terminal as shown, we see that the output voltage of the amplifier will not be zero, but rather will be equal to the voltage across the feedback resistor.

$$V_{out} = R_F I_{B(-)} \tag{28–26}$$

Figure 28–35(b) shows that the result will be similar for the inverting amplifier. Figure 28–35(c) shows that if a resistor is placed between the inverting terminal and the summing junction, the effect of the input bias current is magnified. Although normally this would have an undesirable effect on the operation of the circuit, inserting a multiplying resistor, $R_M$, allows us to measure the very small value of $I_{os}$. The voltage at the summing junction will be

$$V = R_M I_{B(-)}$$

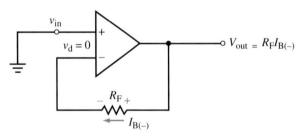

(a) Effect of input bias current on the voltage follower circuit

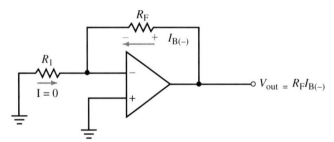

(b) Effect of input bias current on the inverting amplifier

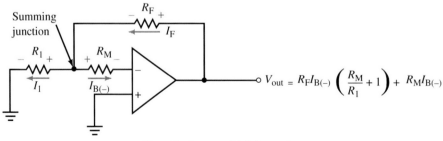

(c) Effect of using a multiplying resistor

**FIGURE 28–35**

and so the current through $R_1$ will be determined from Ohm's law as

$$I_1 = \frac{R_M I_{B(-)}}{R_1}$$

The current through the feedback resistor is determined by applying Kirchhoff's current law and is found to be

$$I_F = I_1 + I_{B(-)} = \frac{R_M I_{B(-)}}{R_1} + I_{B(-)} = I_{B(-)}\left(\frac{R_M}{R_1} + 1\right)$$

and so the output voltage is found by Kirchhoff's voltage law as

$$v_{out} = R_F I_F + R_M I_{B(-)}$$

which gives

$$V_{out} = R_F I_{B(-)}\left(\frac{R_M}{R_1} + 1\right) + R_M I_{B(-)} \qquad \textbf{(28–27)}$$

The following example shows that the multiplying resistor is easily used to find the value of the input offset current.

**EXAMPLE 28–8**

The circuit of Figure 28–36 is constructed to measure the value of the input offset current. The output voltage is measured to be $v_{out} = 0.6$ V. Determine the input offset current, $I_{io} = I_{B(-)}$.

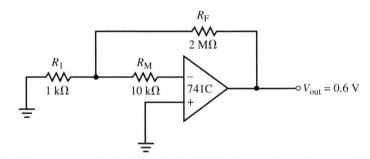

**FIGURE 28–36**

**Solution**

$$0.6\text{ V} = (2\text{ M}\Omega)I_{B(-)}\left(\frac{10\text{ k}\Omega}{1\text{ k}\Omega} + 1\right) + (10\text{ k}\Omega)I_{B(-)}$$

$$I_{io} = I_{B(-)} \approx \frac{0.6\text{ V}}{(2\text{ M}\Omega)(11)} = 0.0273\text{ }\mu\text{A} \equiv 27.3\text{ nA}$$

## Input Resistance

We have already done an in-depth examination of this characteristic. Although the input resistance of an op-amp has a value around 2 MΩ, we have observed that by using the inverting amplifier, the input impedance of a circuit can be significantly reduced. Conversely, using a non-inverting amplifier results in greatly increased input impedance for the circuit.

### Open Loop Voltage Gain, $A_{vol}$ and Bandwidth, *BW*

The open loop voltage gain and the bandwidth of the op-amp are closely related. Figure 28–37 shows that although the open loop voltage gain at low frequencies is very high (200,000) the gain very quickly decreases as the frequency of operation increases. For example, at a frequency of 10 Hz, the open loop gain of the 741C op-amp is 100,000, while at a frequency of 100 kHz, the gain has decreased to a value of 10. Notice that the product of gain and bandwidth is constant everywhere along the graph between 10 Hz and 1 Mz. We conclude, therefore, that the **gain-bandwidth product** for the 741 op-amp is a constant $10^6$ Hz. This means that if we were to use negative feedback to set the closed loop gain of the amplifier, the bandwidth would be easily determined as

$$[BW]_{Hz} = \frac{10^6 \text{ Hz}}{A_{vcl}} \qquad (28\text{–}28)$$

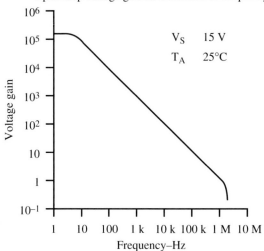

FIGURE 28–37

---

A non-inverting amplifier has a gain of 20. Determine its bandwidth.

*Answer*
50 kHz

### Slew Rate, $\Delta V/\Delta t$

The **slew rate** of an amplifier is a measure of how fast the output voltage can change. The lowest slew rate occurs for an amplifier having unity gain ($A_v = 1$). Imagine that a perfect square wave having amplitude of 10 V is applied to the input of a unity gain amplifier.

As illustrated in Figure 28–38, the output will not rise instantaneously, but rather have a slope determined by the slew rate of the op-amp. For the 741C op-amp, the value of slew rate is 0.5 V/μs. This means that it will take 20 μs for the output to go from 0 V to 10 V. The slew rate affects not only square wave inputs but results in distortion of any waveform that rises at a rate faster than 0.5 V/μs.

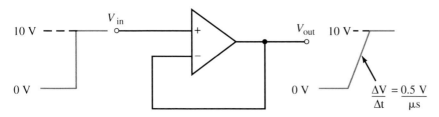

**FIGURE 28–38**

Consider that a sine wave is applied to the input of an amplifier. The input voltage is written as $v(t) = A \sin \omega t$. The instantaneous rate of change of the sinusoidal is determined by taking the derivative of this function, namely

$$\frac{dv}{dt} = \omega A \cos \omega t$$

Consequently, the maximum rate of change of the sinusoidal is simply

$$\left[\frac{dv}{dt}\right]_{max} = \omega A$$

which simplifies to

$$\text{slew rate} = 2\pi f A$$

This means that we can determine the maximum frequency or the maximum amplitude from the slew rate of an amplifier.

$$f_{max} = \frac{\text{slew rate}}{2\pi A} \qquad \textbf{(28–29)}$$

$$A_{max} = \frac{\text{slew rate}}{2\pi f} \qquad \textbf{(28–30)}$$

Determine the maximum peak undistorted output voltage that can be obtained from a non-inverting 741C op-amp having a gain of 5.

**EXAMPLE 28–9**

**Solution**
For a gain of 5, the bandwidth of the 741C op-amp is

$$[BW]_{Hz} = \frac{10^6}{A_{vcl}} = \frac{10^6}{5} = 200 \text{ kHz}$$

The maximum amplitude at the output of the amplifier is

$$A_{max} = \frac{\text{slew rate}}{2\pi f} = \frac{0.5 \text{ V/}\mu s}{2\pi \,(200 \text{ kHz})} = 0.398 \text{ V}_p$$

This means that the maximum sinusoidal signal that can be applied to the input of the amplifier is approximately 80 mV$_p$.

Determine the maximum sinusoidal frequency that can be applied to a unity gain non-inverting 741C op-amp if the amplitude of the input is 10 V$_p$.

PRACTICE PROBLEMS 5

*Answer*
8 kHz

### Bias Compensation

We have observed that input bias current and input bias voltage can have a dramatic effect on the operation of an op-amp circuit. The effects of bias current can be minimized if the impedance seen between the non-inverting terminal and ground is the same as the impedance seen from the inverting terminal to ground. For example, placing a resistor, $R_C = R_1 \| R_F$ in series with the non-inverting input compensates for the effects of bias current in the circuit of Figure 28–39. If the signal source has a large internal resistance, its effect must also be included in the calculation.

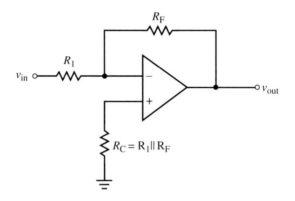

**FIGURE 28–39**

**EXAMPLE 28–10**

Given the circuit of Figure 28–40, determine the value of the compensating resistor, $R_C$.

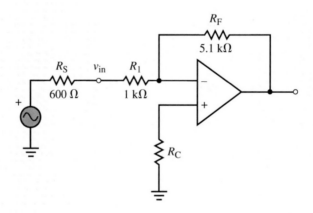

**FIGURE 28–40**

**Solution**

In this circuit, we must consider the effect of the source resistance, $R_S = 600\ \Omega$.

$$R_C = (R_S + R_1)\|R_F = (0.600\ \text{k}\Omega + 1\ \text{k}\Omega)\|5.1\ \text{k}\Omega = 1.22\ \text{k}\Omega$$

Manufacturers of op-amps have included null circuits that compensate for offset voltage. For example, the 741C op-amp has two external connections, −OFFSET NULL (pin 1) and +OFFSET NULL (pin 5), that permit very simple correction for offset voltage. Figure 28–41 shows the proper connections to minimize offset error for the 8-pin 741C DIP package.

The procedure used to null an op-amp is itemized below:

1. Remove all ac voltage sources and replace them with short circuits to ground.

2. Connect a 10-kΩ potentiometer between the offset null pins as illustrated in Figure 28–41.

3. Connect the wiper (center terminal) of the potentiometer to the negative supply.

4. With a dc coupled oscilloscope or a sensitive dc voltmeter connected between the output terminal and ground, adjust the wiper until the output voltage has dropped to zero as measured on the most sensitive scale.

5. Reinsert the ac voltage sources and do not readjust the potentiometer.

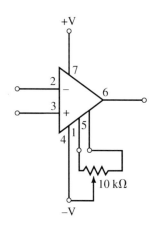

**FIGURE 28–41** Connection of an offset voltage adjustment resistor.

## 28.7 Troubleshooting an Op-Amp Circuit

Once an op-amp circuit is working, very little can go wrong unless there is a power surge resulting in a catastrophic failure. Most problems are encountered when the circuit is first built. The most important connection (and yet the most common source of errors) when building op-amp circuits occurs in connecting the dual power supply. Refer to the circuit of Figure 28–42, which shows all connections for an op-amp. The two supplies must be connected to the circuit reference point (ground) as illustrated.

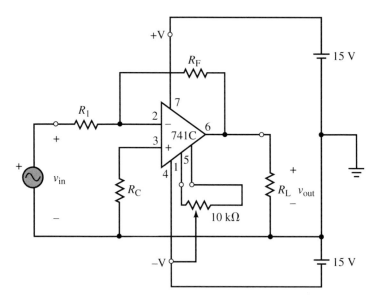

**FIGURE 28–42**

Notice that the input and the output of the amplifier use the same reference point as well. At this point it is worth noting that the reference point should only have one external connection to an earth ground, if required. Otherwise it is possible to generate a ground loop that acts as antenna, which picks up external noise, generally in the form of 60 Hz hum. For the same reason, it is good practice to keep all connecting wires short. If, after all other precautions, the amplifier is still picking up external noise, it may help to connect a small capacitor (e.g. 0.01 μF) across the feedback resistor, $R_F$.

In the unlikely event that a resistor in the op-amp circuit becomes faulty, it is possible to use voltage measurements to determine the origin of the fault. For example, if $R_F$ of an inverting amplifier were to be open-circuited, there would be no feedback path. Consequently, the op-amp would have a gain equal to $A_{vol}$, resulting in an output voltage $v_{out} = \pm V_{SAT}$. On the other hand, if $R_F$ were to be short-circuited, the entire output signal would be returned to the input, resulting in total cancellation, and so $v_{out} = 0$ V, regardless of the input value.

If $R_1$ of an inverting amplifier were to be short-circuited, the entire input voltage would be applied directly to the differential input of the op-amp, once again resulting in an output voltage $v_{out} = \pm V_{SAT}$. If $R_1$ were to be open-circuited, none of the input signal would appear at the op-amp, and so $v_{out} = 0$ V, regardless of the input value.

## 28.8 Computer Analysis of Op-Amp Circuits

In this section, we will use MultiSIM to show typical results that will be observed when measuring quantities in the lab. Although PSpice may be used to predict similar results, this software is used to create an op-amp model and allows us to measure both input impedance and output impedance of a non-inverting op-amp circuit. These values will be very difficult to observe in a lab, since the input impedance of the circuit will normally be in the order of many GΩ, while the output impedance will be in the order of a few mΩ. The PSpice simulation is used to demonstrate the validity of the equations used to solve for these values.

### MultiSIM

**EXAMPLE 28–11**

Use MultiSIM to model the circuit of Figure 28–22. Apply a 1-kHz sinusoidal signal having amplitude of 100 mV$_p$ and use an oscilloscope to display both the input and the output waveforms. Calculate the voltage gain from the measurements.

**Solution**
The completed MultiSIM circuit is shown in Figure 28–43.

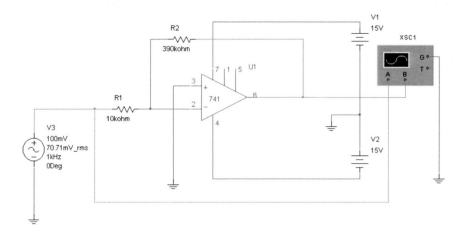

**FIGURE 28–43**

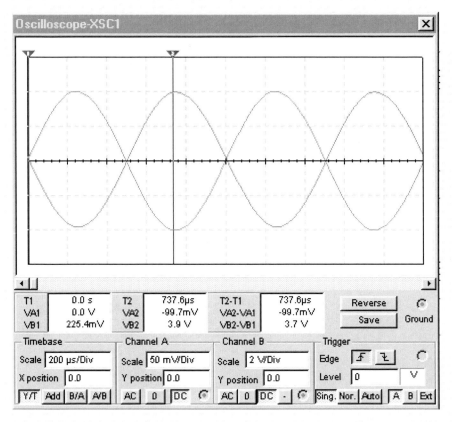

**FIGURE 28–44**

The waveforms appearing on the oscilloscope are shown in Figure 28–44. As expected, the output is 180° out-of-phase with respect to the input. The cursors allow us to calculate the gain of the amplifier as

$$A_v = \frac{v_{out}}{v_{in}} = -\frac{3.9 \text{ V}}{0.1 \text{ V}} = -39$$

The result is consistent with the gain determine in the calculations of Example 28–4.

PRACTICE PROBLEMS 6

Use MultiSIM to model the circuit of Figure 28–27. Apply a 1-kHz sinusoidal signal having amplitude of 100 mV$_p$ and use an oscilloscope to display both the input and the output waveforms. Calculate the voltage gain from the measurements.

*Answer*
$A_v = +6.1$ The output is in phase with the input.

## PSpice

**EXAMPLE 28–12**

Use PSpice to create the model of a 741 op-amp. The model shall use $R_{in} = 2\ M\Omega$, $A_{vol} = 200{,}000$, and $R_{out} = 75\ \Omega$. Use the op-amp model to simulate the circuit shown in Figure 28–27. Apply an input voltage of 10 mV to the circuit and determine voltage gain, input impedance, and output impedance of the amplifier. Compare the results to those found in Example 28–5.

**Solution**

The circuit is constructed using the VSRC voltage source and changing the properties of the component (by pointing to the component and double-clicking) so that DC = 0V and AC = 1V. Figure 28–45 shows the PSpice capture file. Notice that the voltage controlled voltage source is used to model the open loop voltage gain (200,000) of the 741 op-amp.

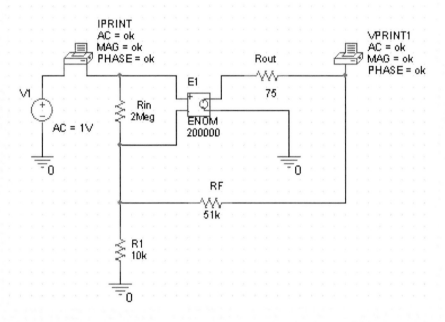

**FIGURE 28–45**

After entering the complete circuit and making the required changes to the circuit properties, the circuit can be simulated using an ac sweep. Once the Probe Postprocessor window appears, we obtain the desired voltage and current values by clicking on the <u>V</u>iew menu item and selecting Output F<u>i</u>le. The pertinent data from the output file is given as

| FREQ | VM(N00083) | VP(N00083) |
|---|---|---|
| 1.000E+03 | 6.100E+00 | 0.000E+00 |

and

| FREQ | IM(V_PRINT1) | IP(V_PRINT1) |
|---|---|---|
| 1.000E+03 | 1.527E-11 | 0.000E+00 |

The above data indicates that the output voltage is in phase with the input voltage and that $v_{out} = 6.1$ V. Therefore the gain of the amplifier is $A_v = 6.1$, as found in Example 28–5. The input impedance is determined by applying Ohm's law to the input of the circuit, namely

$$z_{in} = \frac{1\ V}{1.527 \times 10^{-11}\ A} = 65.5\ G\Omega$$

The above result is almost identical to the calculated value of $z_{in} = 65.6$ GΩ. In order to find the output impedance, we need to determine the short circuit output current by replacing the VPRINT1 device with an IPRINT device. With an input voltage of 1 V, we can expect the short circuit current to be exceptionally large. Remember that we have modeled the 741 op-amp with its equivalent circuit, without regard to the actual circuit limits. Placing the IPRINT device between the output terminals and ground provides the following value for the short circuit current.

```
FREQ         IM(V_PRINT2)    IP(V_PRINT2)
1.000E+03    2.656E+03       0.000E+00
```

Clearly the short circuit current of 2656 A is much larger than the 741 op-amp is able to provide (25 mA). Although the current value is unrealistically large, we are nonetheless able to apply Thévenin's theorem for dependent sources to calculate the output impedance as follows:

$$z_{out} = \frac{V_{OC}}{I_{SC}} = \frac{6.1\ V}{2656\ A} = 2.30\ m\Omega$$

This value is precisely the value that was found in Example 28–5. We are therefore able to see that by using negative feedback, the input impedance of a non-inverting amplifier is increased to effectively an open circuit, while the output impedance is reduced to virtually zero.

# PROBLEMS

## 28.1  Introduction to the Operational Amplifier

1. What are the three characteristics of a typical operational amplifier?

2. a. If a signal is applied to the inverting input, with the non-inverting input grounded, in what mode is the op-amp working?

   b. If a signal is applied between the inverting input and the non-inverting input, in what mode is the op-amp working?

## 28.2  The Differential Amplifier and Common-Mode Signals

3. Given that the circuit of Figure 28–46 has $V_{CC} = +15$ V, $V_{EE} = -15$ V, $R_E = 2.7$ kΩ, and $R_{C1} = R_{C2} = 2.2$ kΩ, find $I_{C1}$ and $V_{C1}$.

4. Repeat Problem 1 if the circuit of Figure 28–46 has $V_{CC} = +12$ V, $V_{EE} = -12$ V, $R_E = 1.8$ kΩ, and $R_{C1} = R_{C2} = 1.2$ kΩ

5. An amplifier has a differential voltage gain of 200 and a common-mode voltage gain of 0.01. Calculate the common-mode rejection ratio in decibels.

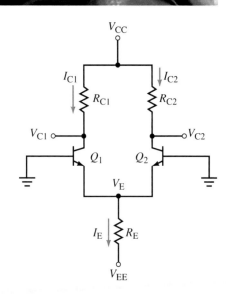

**FIGURE 28–46**

6. An op-amp is specified to have an open-loop voltage gain of 100,000 and a common-mode rejection ratio of at least 75 dB.

    a. If the amplifier is measured to have a common-mode gain of 0.02, calculate the actual $[CMRR]_{dB}$.

    b. Does the op-amp meet the manufacturer's specification?

7. An op-amp circuit has a differential voltage gain of 200 and CMRR of 80 dB. If the output signal voltage of the amplifier is 10 $V_{p-p}$, determine the maximum common-mode input voltage that can be applied to the amplifier to ensure that the output signal-to-noise ratio is no less than 1000 (60 dB).

8. Repeat Problem 5 if the op-amp were to have a differential voltage gain of 20. (All other values remain unchanged.)

### 28.4    The Inverting Amplifier

9. If $R_F = 100$ k$\Omega$ and $R_1 = 20$ k$\Omega$ in the circuit of Figure 28–47, determine the voltage gain, input impedance, and output impedance of the amplifier. Solve for $v_{out}$ if $v_{in} = -2.0$ V.

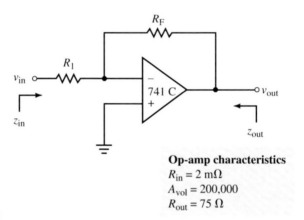

**Op-amp characteristics**
$R_{in} = 2$ m$\Omega$
$A_{vol} = 200,000$
$R_{out} = 75$ $\Omega$

**FIGURE 28–47**

10. If $R_F = 68$ k$\Omega$ and $R_1 = 15$ k$\Omega$ in the circuit of Figure 28–47, determine the voltage gain, input impedance, and output impedance of the amplifier. Solve for $v_{out}$ if $v_{in} = +0.5$ V.

11. Design the amplifier circuit of Figure 28–47 to have input impedance of 12 k$\Omega$ and a voltage gain of magnitude 5.

12. Design the amplifier circuit of Figure 28–47 to have input impedance of 7.5 k$\Omega$ and a voltage gain of magnitude 4.

### 28.5    Non-inverting Amplifier

13. If $R_F = 100$ k$\Omega$ and $R_1 = 20$ k$\Omega$ in the circuit of Figure 28–48, determine the voltage gain, input impedance, and output impedance of the amplifier. Solve for $v_{out}$ if $v_{in} = -2.0$ V.

14. If $R_F = 68$ k$\Omega$ and $R_1 = 15$ k$\Omega$ in the circuit of Figure 28–48, determine the voltage gain, input impedance, and output impedance of the amplifier. Solve for $v_{out}$ if $v_{in} = +0.5$ V.

15. Design the amplifier circuit of Figure 28–48 to have a voltage gain of magnitude 5.

16. Design the amplifier circuit of Figure 28–48 to have a voltage gain of magnitude 4.

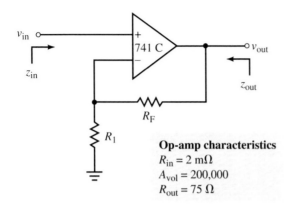

FIGURE 28–48

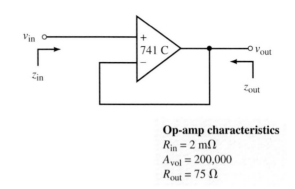

FIGURE 28–49

17. Determine the voltage gain, input impedance, and output impedance of the circuit shown in Figure 28–49.

18. The circuit of Figure 28–50(a) shows the loading effect when a low-resistance load is connected to a high-resistance source. Figure 28–50(b) shows how a voltage-follower (buffer) circuit is used to prevent loading effect.

    a. Calculate $v_{out}$ for the circuit in Figure 28–50(a).

    b. Using the input impedance determined in Problem 17, find $v_{in}$ for the circuit of Figure 28–50(b). Calculate $v_{out}$ for the circuit.

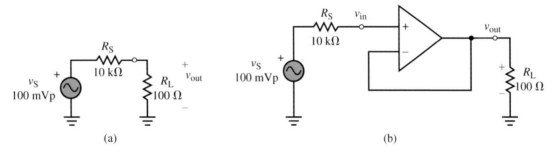

(a)                                                          (b)

FIGURE 28–50

## 28.6    Op-Amp Specifications

19. Given that $R_F = 10$ k$\Omega$ and $R_1 = 10$ $\Omega$ in the circuit of Figure 28–51, calculate the value of output voltage that you would expect if the manufacturer of the op-amp gives a typical value of input offset voltage, $V_{io} = 2$ mV.

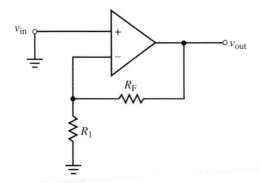

FIGURE 28–51

20. What value of output voltage would you expect for a voltage follower using the op-amp having input offset voltage, $V_{io} = 2$ mV?

21. An op-amp is measured to have $I_{B(+)} = 60$ nA and $I_{B(-)} = 40$ nA. Calculate the values of the input bias current, $I_B$ and the input offset current, $I_{os}$.

22. An op-amp is measured to have $I_{B(+)} = 65$ nA and $I_{B(-)} = 45$ nA. Calculate the values of the input bias current, $I_B$ and the input offset current, $I_{os}$.

23. If the output voltage in the circuit of Figure 28–52 is measured with a digital voltmeter and is found to be 0.5 V, determine the value of the input offset current, $I_{os}$.

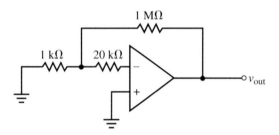

**FIGURE 28–52**

24. Repeat the calculation of Problem 23 if $v_{out} = 0.7$ V.

25. Determine the bandwidth for the inverting amplifier of Problem 9.

26. Determine the bandwidth for the inverting amplifier of Problem 10.

27. Determine the bandwidth for the non-inverting amplifier of Problem 15.

28. Determine the bandwidth for the non-inverting amplifier of Problem 16.

29. Using the slew rate for the 741C op-amp, calculate the maximum sinusoidal frequency that can be applied to the non-inverting amplifier of Problem 15 if the amplitude of the input is 1.0 $V_p$.

30. Using the slew rate for the 741C op-amp, calculate the maximum signal (amplitude) that can be applied to the input of the non-inverting amplifier of Problem 16.

31. Solve for the value of compensating resistor that would be required for the inverting amplifier of Problem 9. Sketch the resulting circuit, showing all resistor values.

32. Solve for the value of compensating resistor that would be required for the inverting amplifier of Problem 10. Sketch the resulting circuit, showing all resistor values.

## 28.7 Troubleshooting an Op-Amp Circuit

33. An inverting op-amp circuit has been operating properly for a long time. Given two failures that could result an output voltage of $v_{out} = 0$ V.

34. An inverting op-amp circuit has been operating properly for a long time. Given two failures that could result an output voltage of $v_{out} = \pm V_{SAT}$.

## 28.8 Computer Analysis of Op-Amp Circuits

◀ MULTISIM

35. Use MultiSIM to input the circuit of Problem 9 using a 741C op-amp. Apply a signal of 100 $mV_p$ to the input of the amplifier and use the oscilloscope tool to simultaneously display the waveforms for $v_{in}$ and $v_{out}$. Use the oscilloscope display to determine the voltage gain, $A_v = v_{out}/v_{in}$ of the circuit.

36. Use MultiSIM to input the circuit of Problem 10 using a 741C op-amp. Apply a signal of 100 mV$_p$ to the input of the amplifier and use the oscilloscope tool to simultaneously display the waveforms for $v_{in}$ and $v_{out}$. Use the oscilloscope display to determine the voltage gain, $A_v = v_{out}/v_{in}$ of the circuit.

◀ MULTISIM

37. Use MultiSIM to input the circuit of Problem 15 using a 741C op-amp. Apply a signal of 100 mV$_p$ to the input of the amplifier and use the oscilloscope tool to simultaneously display the waveforms for $v_{in}$ and $v_{out}$. Use the oscilloscope display to determine the voltage gain, $A_v = v_{out}/v_{in}$ of the circuit.

◀ MULTISIM

38. Use MultiSIM to input the circuit of Problem 16 using a 741C op-amp. Apply a signal of 100 mV$_p$ to the input of the amplifier and use the oscilloscope tool to simultaneously display the waveforms for $v_{in}$ and $v_{out}$. Use the oscilloscope display to determine the voltage gain, $A_v = v_{out}/v_{in}$ of the circuit.

◀ MULTISIM

39. Use PSpice to input the equivalent circuit model of 741C op-amp. Using this model and the resistor values calculated in Problem 9, determine the input impedance and output impedance of circuit of the amplifier.

◀ CADENCE

40. Use PSpice to input the equivalent circuit model of 741C op-amp. Using this model and the resistor values calculated in Problem 10, determine the input impedance and output impedance of circuit of the amplifier.

◀ CADENCE

41. Use PSpice to input the equivalent circuit model of 741C op-amp. Using this model and the resistor values calculated in Problem 15, determine the input impedance and output impedance of circuit of the amplifier.

◀ CADENCE

42. Use PSpice to input the equivalent circuit model of 741C op-amp. Using this model and the resistor values calculated in Problem 16, determine the input impedance and output impedance of circuit of the amplifier.

◀ CADENCE

## ■ OBJECTIVES

On completion of this chapter, you will be able to

- analyze a comparator circuit and determine the circuit operation,
- analyze and design a voltage summing amplifier circuit,
- analyze the operation and determine the output waveform for an integrator circuit,
- analyze the operation and determine the output waveform for a differentiator circuit,
- analyze the operation of an instrumentation amplifier and be able to solve for the output of an unbalanced resistor bridge circuit,
- determine cutoff frequencies of low- and high-pass active filters and be able to sketch the frequency response of these filters,
- analyze and design wideband and narrowband bandpass filters for desired bandwidths,
- design an active notch filter circuit using a narrowband bandpass filter combined with a summing amplifier,
- analyze and design voltage regulator circuits using zener diodes, op-amps, and three-terminal voltage regulator ICs,
- calculate line regulation, load regulation, and ripple rejection ratio for given conditions in a regulator circuit,
- describe the operation of a voltage regulator circuit using an op-amp,
- use computer software to simulate the operation of op-amp circuits.

# Applications of Op-Amps

# 29

In the previous chapter, you learned that operational amplifiers can be used to provide inverting and non-inverting amplifiers. In this chapter we examine how op-amps can be used in both linear and non-linear applications. We begin by examining the comparator, which as the name implies, provides an output based on the result of voltage comparison at the input. We then examine the operation of op-amps in instrumentation amplifiers, where the signals are generally very small and often occur in environments that are electrically noisy. We then examine the operation of active filter circuits, which use the op-amp to provide additional gain and prevent loading effect that would occur if we used R-L-C components alone. Finally, the chapter is concluded by examining the operation of voltage regulators. ■

ALTHOUGH MOST PEOPLE THINK OF the computer as an invention that occurred in the late twentieth century, computers were in fact used much earlier. The first computers were not digital computers, as are modern computers, but rather were **analog computers,** constructed using mechanical components such as levers, gears, wheels, and springs to predict tides, positions of the planets and to measure and emulate the occurrence of other physical events.

William Thomson, 1824–1907 (who is better known as Lord Kelvin), was convinced that most mechanical events could be analyzed and predicted by using analogous mathematical models. Thomson invented and built devices called **planimeters** that used disk and wheel arrangements to solve mathematical integrals of harmonic motion such as tides. Similar analog computers are still in use today. For example, the mechanical odometer/speedometer converts the speed of tire rotation into an analogous distance traveled. (Remember from your physics course that the integral of speed is distance.)

The invention of the operational amplifier has made it possible to simplify analog computations without the necessity of using often-large, inefficient mechanical devices. By using operational amplifiers, it is possible to design and build electronic circuits that will add, subtract, and perform differentiation and integration.

Although the analog computer has been largely overshadowed by the much faster and smaller digital computer, it is highly unlikely that the operational amplifier will become obsolete anytime soon. ■

## 29.1 Comparators

In the previous chapter you learned that the operational amplifier has a very large open-loop gain, which results in the device becoming saturated even when a very small differential input voltage is applied between the input terminals. In order to have an op-amp work as a linear device, where output is proportional to the input, you learned that it was necessary to implement negative feedback. Thus, the gain of the amplifier became much more stable with the addition of a few external resistors.

In this section, you will find that we will use the op-amp as a **comparator,** which is a non-linear device having an output voltage that is one of two values. If the voltage at the non-inverting $(+)$ input is greater than the voltage at the inverting $(-)$ input, the output will be $+V_{SAT}$, and if the opposite occurs the output will be $-V_{SAT}$. This occurs since even a very small difference will be amplified by the op-amp's very large open-loop voltage gain. Consider the circuit of Figure 29–1(a). Here we see that the inverting terminal of the op-amp is connected to ground, giving a reference voltage of $V_{REF} = 0$ V. Figure 29–1(b) shows that if a sine-wave is applied to the input, the output of the op-amp will be a square wave.

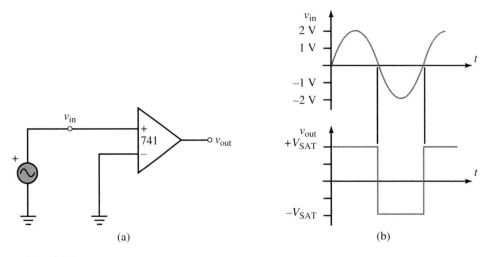

**FIGURE 29–1**   Comparator circuit.

Now, if we were to apply a dc reference voltage, $V_{REF} = 1$ V, as shown in Figure 29–2(a) to the inverting terminal, the output would be equal to $+V_{SAT}$ only when the input voltage exceeds $+1$ V. The resultant is shown in Figure 29–2(b).

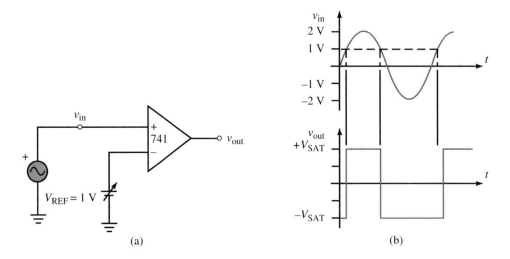

**FIGURE 29–2**

Although we have been connecting a reference voltage to the inverting terminal, it is often useful to connect the reference to the non-inverting terminal as illustrated in Figure 29–3.

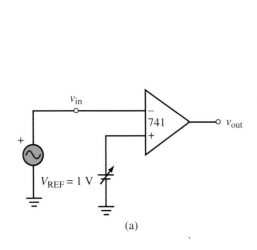
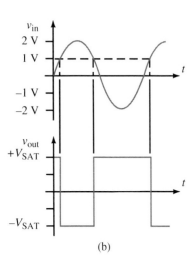

(a)          (b)

**FIGURE 29–3**

In this circuit, $v_{out} = -V_{SAT}$ whenever the input voltage is greater than $V_{REF}$ as illustrated in Figure 29–3(b).

The comparator circuit has many applications in electronics. We will examine two possible applications. Remember, whenever you see a comparator used in any electronic circuit, the output will be either $-V_{SAT}$ or $+V_{SAT}$, depending on difference between the two input terminals of the op-amp.

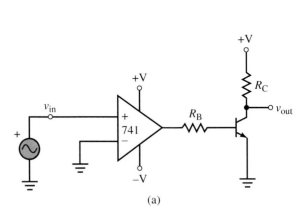
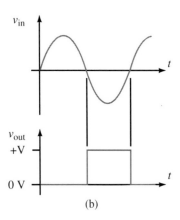

(a)          (b)

**FIGURE 29–4**    Zero-crossing detector.

## Zero-Crossing Detector

In the zero-crossing detector circuit shown in Figure 29–4(a), the output of the comparator will go from $-V_{SAT}$ to $+V_{SAT}$ as the input signal goes from a negative value to a positive value (zero crossing). If the value of $R_B$ is sufficiently small, the base current will saturate the transistor and result in $v_{out} = 0$ V. When the input voltage falls below 0 V, the output of the comparator goes to $-V_{SAT}$, reverse-biasing the base-emitter junction of the transistor and forcing the transistor into cutoff. The output will now be $+V$. Figure 29–4(b) shows the output of a zero-crossing detector for a sinusoidal input.

### LED Voltage Level Indicator

The circuit of Figure 29–5 shows how comparators can be used to turn on progressively more LEDs as the input voltage increases. Such a circuit can be used in stereo amplifiers to show the relative signal strength at the input of a power amplifier. As the signal increases, more LEDs will turn on. (Normally, the top few LEDs in the stack will be red to indicate that the signal level is too large.) In the circuit of Figure 29–5, the four resistors, $R_1$, $R_2$, $R_3$, and $R_4$, establish a voltage divider network. By applying the voltage divider rule, we determine the reference voltage at the inverting input of the bottom comparator to be 1 V, while the reference voltages at the other two comparators will be 2 V and 3 V respectively. If the input voltage goes above 1 V, the output of the bottom comparator will go to $+V_{SAT} \approx 8$ V, causing current through LED1. If $v_{in}$ is between 1 V and 2 V, the output of the top two comparators will be $- V_{SAT}$, resulting in no current through LED2 and LED3.

If $v_{in}$ becomes greater than 2 V, the second comparator will have an output voltage of $+V_{SAT}$, resulting in current through LED2. Note that the output of comparator 1 remains at $+V_{SAT}$, and so diode LED1 will be on as well. Although the circuit of Figure 29–5 shows only three LEDs, it is possible to select any number of diodes by choosing appropriate resistors in the voltage divider network.

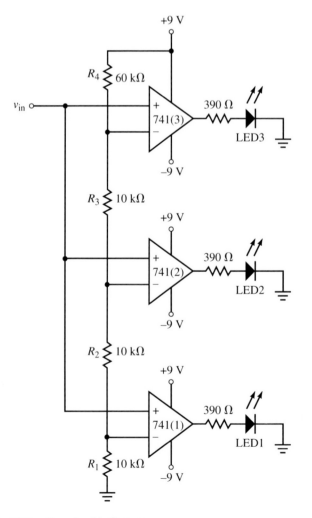

**FIGURE 29–5** LED voltage level indicator.

As the name implies, the summing amplifier shown in Figure 29–6 has an output that is determined as the sum of the input voltages, each multiplied by some gain. If we examine the circuit of Figure 29–6 and assume that the input voltages, $V_1$, $V_2$, and $V_3$ are all positive with respect to ground, then we are able to determine the current through each of the input resistances as $I_1 = \dfrac{V_1}{R_1}$, $I_2 = \dfrac{V_2}{R_2}$,

and $I_3 = \dfrac{V_3}{R_3}$. (Remember that the inverting terminal of the op-amp is at virtual ground.) Now, by applying Kirchhoff's current law at the summing junction, we determine that the current through the feedback resistor is

$$I_F = I_1 + I_2 + I_2$$

and the output voltage as

$$V_{out} = -I_F R_F$$

which gives

$$V_{out} = -\left( \frac{R_F}{R_1} V_1 + \frac{R_F}{R_2} V_2 + \frac{R_F}{R_3} V_3 \right) \tag{29–1}$$

## 29.2 Voltage Summing Amplifier

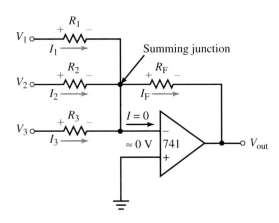

**FIGURE 29–6**   Op-amp used as a summing amplifier.

Given that the circuit of Figure 29–7 has the following resistor values:
$R_1 = 20 \text{ k}\Omega$, $R_2 = 10 \text{ k}\Omega$, $R_3 = 40 \text{ k}\Omega$, and $R_F = 100 \text{ k}\Omega$.
Solve for $v_{out}$ if $V_1 = -0.8 \text{ V}$, $V_2 = 1.2 \text{ V}$, and $V_3 = -2.5 \text{ V}$.

**Solution**

$$V_{out} = -\left[ \frac{100 \text{ k}\Omega}{20 \text{ k}\Omega} (-0.8 \text{ V}) + \frac{100 \text{ k}\Omega}{10 \text{ k}\Omega} (1.2 \text{ V}) + \frac{100 \text{ k}\Omega}{40 \text{ k}\Omega} (-2.5 \text{ V}) \right]$$

$$= -\left[ -4.0 \text{ V} + 12 \text{ V} + (-6.25 \text{ V}) \right]$$

$$= -1.75 \text{ V}$$

**EXAMPLE 29–1**

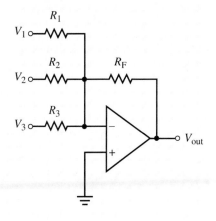

**FIGURE 29–7**

Solve for $v_{out}$ in the circuit of Figure 29–7 if $R_1 = 75$ k$\Omega$, $R_2 = 75$ k$\Omega$, $R_3 = 75$ k$\Omega$, and $R_F = 75$ k$\Omega$. Let $V_1 = 1.5$ V, $V_2 = 2.2$ V, and $V_3 = -2.5$ V.

*Answer*
$-1.2$ V

IN-PROCESS
LEARNING CHECK 1

*(Answers are at the end of the chapter.)*

For the circuit shown in Figure 29–8, solve for the voltages at points *A*, *B*, and *C*. Determine the output voltage, $v_{out}$.

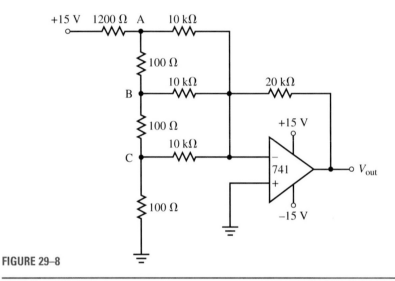

**FIGURE 29–8**

Many of the op-amp circuits that we have examined so far have used negative feedback as shown in Figure 29–9, with all impedances being resistive. However, this is not always the case. Indeed, many op-amp circuits use combinations of resistors and capacitors in the blocks labeled $Z_1$ and $Z_2$ to provide interesting filter circuits. We will limit our analysis to two simple circuits: the integrator and the differentiator.

## 29.3 Integrators and Differentiators

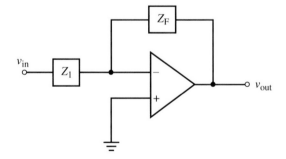

**FIGURE 29–9**

### The Integrator

Figure 29–10 shows a simple integrator circuit. If we assume that $v_{in}$ is positive with respect to ground, then the current through $R_1$ is determined as $i = \dfrac{v_{in}}{R_1}$. Due to the very high input impedance of the op-amp, there cannot be any current into the non-inverting input. Consequently, the current $i$ must enter the feedback loop and charge the capacitor. Recall that the voltage across a capacitor is given by the expression:

$$v_C(t) = \frac{1}{C} \int_0^t i(t)dt + V_o \qquad (29–2)$$

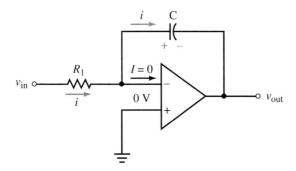

**FIGURE 29–10**   Op-amp integrator.

When we substitute the expression for current into this expression, we have

$$v_c(t) = \frac{1}{R_1 C} \int_0^t v_{in}(t)dt + V_o \qquad \text{(29–3)}$$

Now, if we assume that the capacitor is initially uncharged ($V_o = 0$ V), then we can write the expression for the output as

$$v_{out}(t) = -\frac{1}{R_1 C} \int_0^t v_{in}(t)dt \qquad \text{(29–4)}$$

The following example illustrates the operation of the integrator.

Given the circuit of Figure 29–11, sketch the output of the integrator for the given input waveform.

**EXAMPLE 29–2**

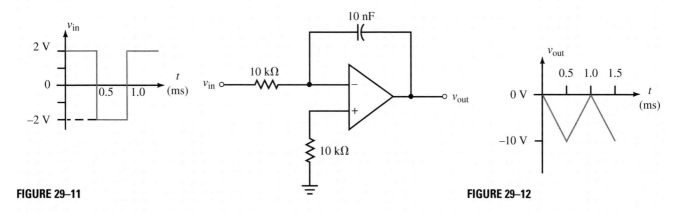

**FIGURE 29–11**

**FIGURE 29–12**

**Solution**
In the interval between $t = 0$ and $t = 0.5$ ms, the input voltage is a constant value of 2 V. Consequently, we determine that the voltage in this region is expressed as

$$v_{out}(t) = -\frac{1}{(10 \text{ k}\Omega)(10 \text{ nF})} \int 2\text{ V}dt$$

$$= -20,000t \, \frac{\text{V}}{\text{s}}$$

If we were to assume that at $t = 0$, the capacitor is initially uncharged, then in 0.5 ms the voltage at the output will go from 0 V to $-10$ V. From $t = 0.5$ ms to $t = 1.0$ ms, the voltage across the capacitor will increase at a rate of 20,000 V/s. The resulting output waveform is shown in Figure 29–12.

**PRACTICAL NOTES . . .**

Due to offset voltage and current in the op-amp in Figure 29–11, the initial voltage across the capacitor will normally be $\pm V_{SAT}$. To cancel the output offset voltage, a large resistor ($R_F = 1$ M$\Omega$) is generally placed across the capacitor in the feedback loop.

## The Differentiator

The op-amp differentiator, shown in Figure 29–13 is less common than the integrator. Just as was the case with the integrator, the operation of the differentiator is easily explained by applying a few of the basic principles of capacitor operation. If we were to apply an input voltage to the circuit of Figure 29–13, this voltage appears across the capacitor. The current through the capacitor is therefore

$$i(t) = C\frac{dv_{in}}{dt} \tag{29-5}$$

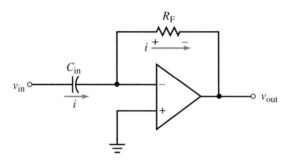

**FIGURE 29–13**   Op-amp differentiator.

Lastly, the voltage appearing at the output of the differentiator is easily determined to be

$$v_{out}(t) = -R_{F}C\frac{dv_{in}}{dt} \tag{29-6}$$

The differentiator circuit that is shown in Figure 29–13 is inherently unstable and tends to have high frequency oscillations. The stability of the differentiator can be improved by adding a small resistor in series with $C_{in}$ and a small capacitor in parallel with the feedback resistor, $R_{F}$. Although the analysis of the improved circuit is outside the scope of this textbook, the resulting circuit appears in Figure 29–14. Students who are interested will find many good reference textbooks that deal exclusively with the topic of op-amps.

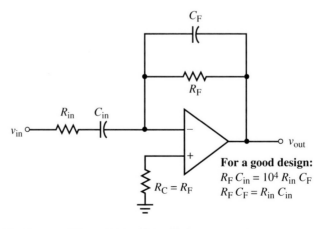

**For a good design:**
$R_{F}C_{in} = 10^{4}R_{in}C_{F}$
$R_{F}C_{F} = R_{in}C_{in}$

**FIGURE 29–14**   Op-amp differentiator with oscillation suppression.

Instrumentation amplifiers are op-amp circuits that are designed to operate in environments that would normally result in excessive noise. By using the op-amp as a differential amplifier, any common-mode signal (noise) will be cancelled, while at the same time permitting the amplification of the desired difference voltage. The instrumentation amplifier shown in Figure 29–15 offers a very good common-mode rejection ratio, while at the same time providing a reasonable gain for a differential signal.

## 29.4 Instrumentation Amplifiers

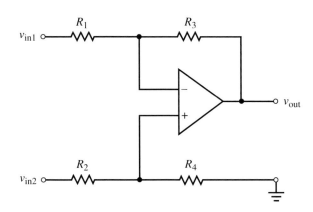

**FIGURE 29–15**    Instrumentation amplifier.

The following example shows the analysis of an instrumentation amplifier.

Given the instrumentation amplifier shown in Figure 29–16:

**EXAMPLE 29–3**

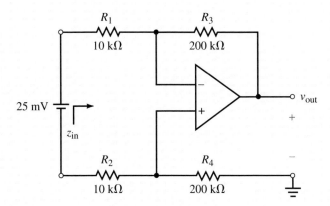

**FIGURE 29–16**

a. Determine the current through each resistor.
b. Solve for the output voltage, $v_{out}$.
c. Calculate the differential voltage gain of the amplifier.
d. Solve for the input impedance of the amplifier, $z_{in}$.

**Solution**

a. We begin by using the approximation that the voltage between the inverting and non-inverting terminals is zero. By examining the input loop, of the op-amp, we determine the currents

$$I_1 = I_2 = \frac{25 \text{ mV}}{10 \text{ k}\Omega + 10 \text{ k}\Omega} = 1.25 \text{ }\mu\text{A}$$

Now, due to the very high input impedance of the op-amp, there can be no current entering or leaving the input terminals of the op-amp and so applying Kirchhoff's current law, we have $I_3 = I_4 = 1.25$ $\mu$A. Figure 29–17 shows the currents and corresponding voltage drops.

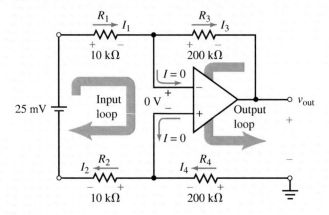

**FIGURE 29–17**

b. By applying Kirchhoff's voltage law to the output loop, we determine that the output voltage is

$$v_{out} = -I_3R_3 - I_4R_4 = -0.50 \text{ V}$$

c. The differential voltage gain of the amplifier is determined to be

$$A_{vd} = \frac{v_{out}}{v_{in}} = \frac{-0.50 \text{ V}}{0.025 \text{ V}} = -20$$

d. The input impedance of the amplifier is

$$z_{in} = \frac{v_{in}}{i_{in}} = \frac{24 \text{ mV}}{1.25 \text{ }\mu\text{A}} = 20 \text{ k}\Omega$$

A practical application of an instrumentation amplifier is for measuring very small voltages associated with sensitive transducers such as strain gages. In Chapter 3 you learned that a **transducer** is simply defined as any device that converts a physical change into an electrical change. A **strain gage** is a device that converts force into a change in electrical resistance. Figure 29–18 shows one application of a strain gage.

By applying an external force to a metal bar, the length of the bar (and hence the length of conductor of the strain gage) changes. Although the change in resistance is in the order of a few milliohms, this change can be measured by placing the strain gage into a bridge circuit and using an instrumentation amplifier to measure the resulting difference in potential. It is then possible to convert the voltage into a corresponding value of force (in newtons, pounds, or tons).

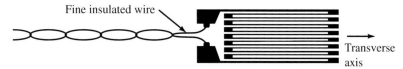

Fine insulated wire

Transverse
axis

(a) A strain gage is constructed of very thin metal foil mounted on a plastic backing.

(b) The strain gage is glued onto a metal bar, which is subjected to tension and compression. Here we have the strain gage in equilibrium. The resistance of the gage is equal to the equilibrium resistance, $R$.

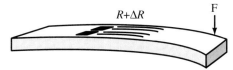

$R+\Delta R$          F

(c) Strain gage under tension. The strain gage is stretched in the direction of its transverse axis resulting in an increase in resistance due to the extra length and decrease in cross-sectional area. The resistance is now $R+\Delta R$.

$R-\Delta R$

F

(d) Strain gage under compression. The strain gage is compressed in the direction of its transverse axis resulting in a decrease in resistance due to the reduction in length and increase in cross-sectional area. The resistance is now $R-\Delta R$.

**FIGURE 29–18**

An instrumentation amplifier and strain gage are used in the circuit shown in Figure 29–19. Determine the value of output voltage if the equilibrium resistance of the strain gage is 100 Ω, and the resistance, $R_4$ increases by 5 mΩ when a force is applied to the strain gage.

**EXAMPLE 29–4**

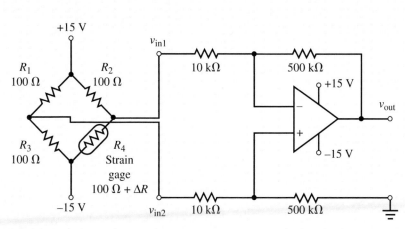

**FIGURE 29–19**

## Solution

We begin by examining the bridge circuit. The voltage applied to $v_{in2}$ is determined by voltage divider as

$$v_{in2} = \left(\frac{100\ \Omega}{100\ \Omega + 100\ \Omega}\right)30\ V - 15.00V = 0.00\ V$$

and similarly $v_{in1}$ is found as

$$v_{in1} = \left(\frac{100.005\ \Omega}{100\ \Omega + 100.005\ \Omega}\right)30\ V - 15.0\ V = 0.000375\ V$$

Notice that we use all the significant digits in solving for the voltages. This is important, since there will normally be only a very small change in voltage in the bridge circuit. The difference in potential applied to the instrumentation amplifier is now easily seen to be $\Delta V = 375\ \mu V$. It is this value that will be amplified by the closed-loop gain, $A_v = -\dfrac{500\ k\Omega}{10\ k\Omega} = -50$ of the op-amp.

As a result, we have an output voltage of $V_{out} = (-50)(375\ \mu V) = -18.75\ mV$

This example clearly illustrates the need for having an amplifier with a high common-mode rejection ratio. With an output voltage in the order of a few millivolts, it would be very easy for the signal to be lost in a large noise voltage.

---

PRACTICE PROBLEMS 2

If the strain gage resistance in the circuit of Figure 29–19 was to decrease by 18 m$\Omega$, calculate the corresponding output voltage of the instrumentation amplifier.

*Answer*
+0.135 V

---

## 29.5 Active Filters

In Chapter 22, we studied four basic types of passive filters: low-pass, high-pass, bandpass and band reject. The same types of filters are easily built with op-amps and may be designed to provide a gain. Another advantage of using an op-amp filter is that this circuit has minimal loading effect due to the load resistor. Although outside the scope of this textbook, other types of specialty filters can be designed and built with op-amps so that the resulting filter has a response that more closely approaches the ideal frequency response. The student is encouraged to examine some of the many excellent texts dealing with the design and analysis of Bessel, Chebyshev, and Butterworth filters.

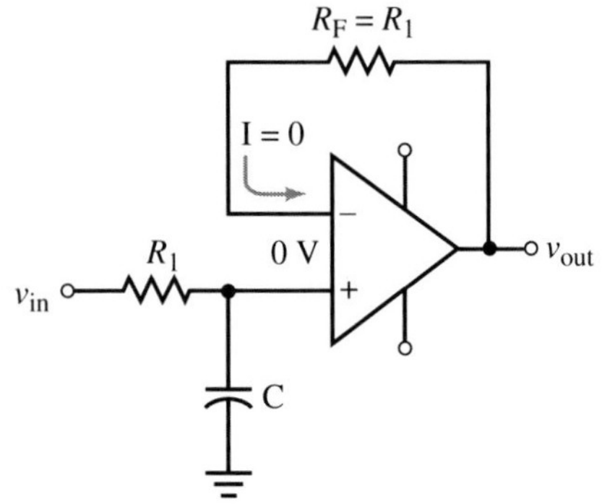

### Low-Pass Active Filter

The simple low-pass op-amp filter is illustrated in Figure 29–20. You will recognize that the input resistance, $R_1$, and capacitor, $C$, form a passive low-pass filter. Since the differential voltage at the input of the op-amp is effectively zero, and since the current through the feedback resistor must be zero, we conclude that output voltage must be

**FIGURE 29–20** Low-pass op-amp filter.

$$V_{out} = v_C = \frac{Z_C}{R_1 + Z_C}V_{in} = \frac{\dfrac{1}{j\omega C}}{R_1 + \dfrac{1}{j\omega C}}V_{in}$$

and so we see that the transfer function of the low-pass op-amp filter is the same as that for a passive low-pass $RC$ filter, namely

$$\mathbf{TF}(j\omega) = \frac{1}{1 + j\omega R_1 C} \qquad (29\text{–}7)$$

Notice that the feedback resistor has the same value as $R_1$. Because the capacitor is an open circuit at dc, setting $R_F = R_1$ ensures that the dc resistance to ground at both the inverting and the non-inverting terminals is the same. This helps to prevent a dc offset at the output of the op-amp. Figure 29–21 shows that the amplifier may also be modified to provide low-frequency gain.

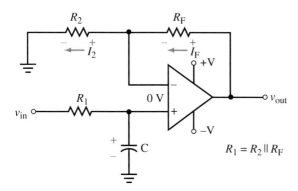

**FIGURE 29–21**    Low-pass op-amp filter with gain.

In Figure 29–21, we see that the voltage across the resistor $R_2$ must be the same as the voltage across the capacitor, $C$. Now since there is no current into or out of the non-inverting terminal, we have $I_F = I_2$. We see therefore that this amplifier has a dc gain of

$$A_v = 1 + \frac{R_F}{R_2} \qquad (29\text{–}8)$$

Given the filter circuit of Figure 29–22:

**EXAMPLE 29–5**

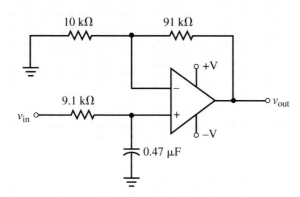

**FIGURE 29–22**

a. Determine the dc gain of the filter.

b. Calculate the cutoff frequency of the filter.

c. Sketch the straight-line approximation of the voltage gain (in dB) as a function of the frequency.

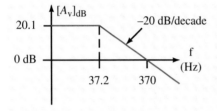

**FIGURE 29–23**

**Solution**

a. The dc voltage gain of the filter is

$$A_v = 1 + \frac{91\ k\Omega}{10\ k\Omega} = 10.1$$

which gives

$$[A_v]_{dB} = 20 \log(10.1) = 20.1\ dB$$

b. The cutoff frequency (in Hz) of the filter is

$$f_c = \frac{1}{2\pi R_1 C} = \frac{1}{2\pi(9.1\ k\Omega)(0.47\ \mu F)} = 37.2\ Hz$$

c. The straight-line approximation of the voltage gain (in dB) as a function of the frequency is shown in Figure 29–23.

## High-Pass Active Filter

As one might expect, the high-pass filter can be constructed as illustrated in Figure 29–24. In this circuit, the output voltage will be the same as the voltage across $R_1$, namely,

$$V_{out} = v_R = \frac{R_1}{R_1 + Z_C}\,V_{in} = \frac{R_1}{R_1 + \dfrac{1}{j\omega C}}\,V_{in}$$

and so the transfer function for the circuit is

$$\mathbf{TF}(j\omega) = \frac{R_1 C}{1 + j\omega R_1 C} \tag{29–9}$$

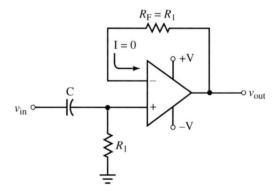

**FIGURE 29–24**    High-pass op-amp filter.

Although it is possible to design the circuit with a dc gain, in practice this is not generally done, since the op-amp has a high-frequency cutoff as determined by the gain-bandwidth product of the op-amp. The circuit would therefore result in a bandpass filter. For example, if an op-amp having a gain-bandwidth product of 1 MHz were designed to have a dc gain of 10, the resultant upper cutoff frequency of the filter circuit would be 100 kHz. If the gain were 100, the upper cutoff frequency would be 10 kHz, and so on.

You will notice that in this circuit, the feedback resistor once again has the same value as $R_1$, ensuring that the dc resistance to ground at both input terminals is the same.

Given that the filter circuit of Figure 29–24 has $R_1 = R_F = 9.1\ k\Omega$ and $C = 0.47\ \mu F$:

**EXAMPLE 29–6**

a. Determine the dc gain of the filter.

b. Calculate the cutoff frequency of the filter.

c. Sketch the straight-line approximation of the voltage gain (in dB) as a function of the frequency. Assume that the op-amp has a gain-bandwidth product of 1 MHz.

**Solution**

a. The dc voltage gain of the filter is $A_v = 1$, which is equivalent to $[A_v]_{dB} = 0$ db. (A gain of 1 results in an upper cutoff frequency for the circuit of 1 MHz.)

b. The cutoff frequency (in Hz) of the filter is

$$f_c = \frac{1}{2\pi R_1 C} = \frac{1}{2\pi(9.1\ k\Omega)(0.47\ \mu F)} = 37.2\ Hz$$

c. The frequency response of the circuit is shown in Figure 29–25. Notice that the sketch shows the upper cutoff frequency due to the gain-bandwidth product of the op-amp. In any design, it is important to consider the effects of this quantity.

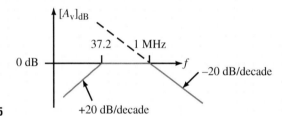

**FIGURE 29–25**

## Active Wideband Bandpass Filter

It is possible to design a bandpass filter by cascading a low-pass op-amp filter with a high-pass filter. Each active filter is similar to the filters examined previously. Since the input impedance of the second filter does not affect the operation of the first, the filters can be cascaded in any order. Figure 29–26 shows

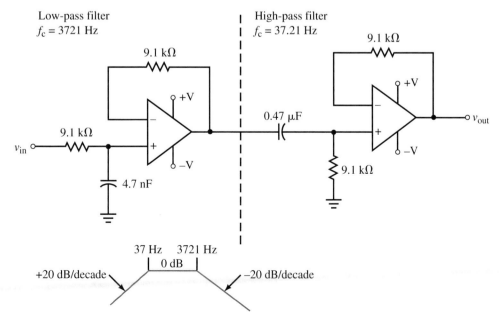

**FIGURE 29–26**   Wideband bandpass filter and frequency response.

a low-pass filter followed by a high-pass filter. The low-pass filter must have the higher cutoff frequency, in this case $f_c = 3721$ Hz. The high-pass filter must provide the lower cutoff frequency, in this case $f_c = 37$ Hz.

### Active Narrowband Bandpass Filter

It is possible to construct a narrowband bandpass filter by using a single op-amp as illustrated in Figure 29–27.

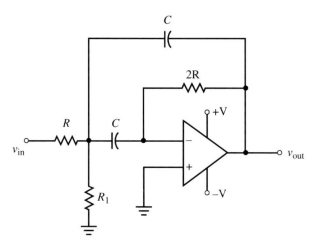

**FIGURE 29-27** Narrowband bandpass filter.

This filter has a resonant frequency (in Hz) given as

$$f_0 = \frac{0.1125}{RC}\sqrt{1 + \frac{R}{R_1}} \qquad (29\text{--}10)$$

and a bandwidth of

$$\text{BW} = \frac{0.1591}{RC} \qquad (29\text{--}11)$$

**EXAMPLE 29–7**

Design a narrowband bandpass filter having a resonant frequency of 400 Hz and a bandwidth of 100 Hz.

**Solution**
We begin our design by selecting an appropriate value of capacitance. Let $C = 0.01$ μF. Next, we use the bandwidth value to determine the value of resistance, $R$ from Equation 29–10.

$$R = \frac{0.1591}{\text{BW } C} = \frac{0.1591}{(100 \text{ Hz})(0.01 \, \mu\text{F})} = 159.1 \text{ k}\Omega$$

Now, we solve for the value of $R_1$ by applying Equation 29–10.

$$R_1 = \frac{(0.1125)^2 R}{f_0^2 R^2 C^2 - 0.1125^2}$$

$$= \frac{(0.1125)^2 (159.1 \text{ k}\Omega)}{(400 \text{ Hz})^2 (159.1 \text{ k}\Omega)^2 (0.01 \, \mu\text{F})^2 - 0.1125^2}$$

$$= 5.132 \text{ k}\Omega$$

The resulting design is shown in Figure 29–28. The results of this design are easily verified by using MultiSIM to simulate the operation. At the resonant frequency, the output of the bandpass filter is equal in magnitude and 180° out-of-phase with respect to the input signal.

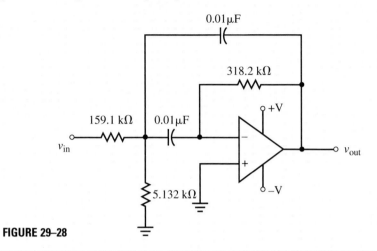

**FIGURE 29–28**

## Active Notch Filter

The notch filter is easily constructed by cascading the narrowband bandpass filter with an adder circuit as illustrated in Figure 29–29. The output of the adder will have the same magnitude for all frequencies except at the resonant frequency of the bandpass filter. At the resonant frequency, both inputs to the adder will be equal but 180° out-of-phase. Consequently, the signal at the resonant frequency will be eliminated.

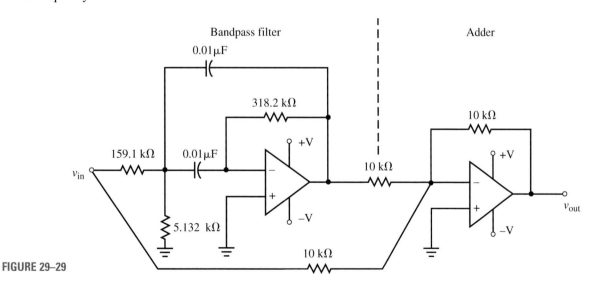

**FIGURE 29–29**

As the name implies a **voltage regulator** is a circuit or component that regulates the voltage of a circuit. Normally as more current is demanded from a voltage source, the voltage of the source drops due to internal losses of the source. Also, if the input voltage were to increase, the voltage across the load will similarly increase. A voltage regulator ensures that the voltage delivered to a load remains constant for a specified range of load currents and within a specified input voltage. You were introduced to the zener diode regulator in Chapter 25, which is shown again in Figure 29–30.

## 29.6 Voltage Regulation

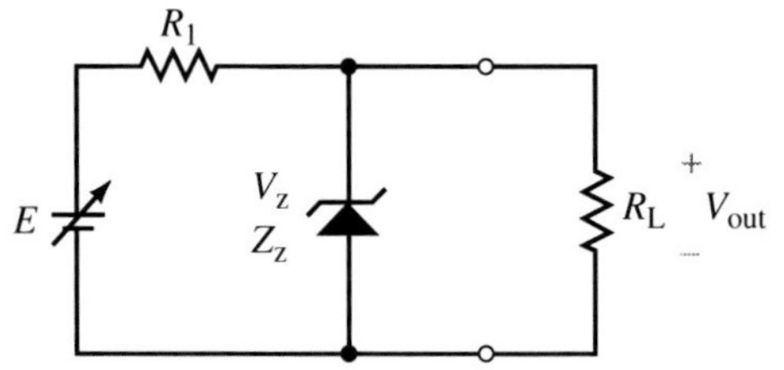

**FIGURE 29–30**

Recall that the zener diode regulator had the disadvantage of being ineffi-cient, since the diode dissipates a significant amount of power, especially when the load resistor is quite large. Many types of regulators are used in the elec-tronics industry. Some of the different types of voltage regulators that you are likely to encounter include the fixed voltage regulator, the variable voltage reg-ulator, and the switching regulator. Although there are many types of regula-tors, they all have some common characteristics. In this section, we examine some of the characteristics of regulators and apply these characteristics to actual circuits.

### Line Regulation

Consider the simplified regulator circuit shown in Figure 29–31. In the ideal regulator, there will be no change in output voltage even if the voltage at the input of the regulator were to change. This, however, will seldom be the case. We define **percent line regulation** as the following:

$$\% \text{ line regulation} = \frac{\Delta V_{\text{out}}}{\Delta V_{\text{in}}} \times 100\% \qquad \textbf{(29–12)}$$

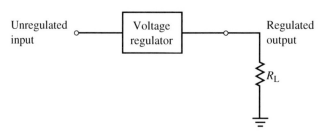

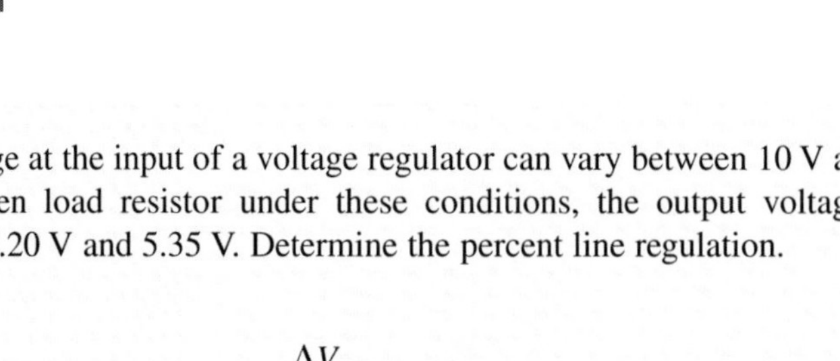

**FIGURE 29–31**

EXAMPLE 29–8

The voltage at the input of a voltage regulator can vary between 10 V and 30 V. For a given load resistor under these conditions, the output voltage varies between 5.20 V and 5.35 V. Determine the percent line regulation.

**Solution**

$$\% \text{ line regulation} = \frac{\Delta V_{\text{out}}}{\Delta V_{\text{in}}} \times 100\%$$

$$= \frac{5.35 \text{ V} - 5.20 \text{ V}}{30 \text{ V} - 10 \text{ V}} \times 100\% = 0.75\%$$

Occasionally, the line regulation is simply expressed as a ratio; in this case 7.5 mV/V. This means that for every volt that the input increases, there will be a corresponding 7.5 mV increase in output voltage.

The zener diode in the circuit shown in Figure 29–32a) has the characteristic shown in Figure 29–32b). Here we see that the voltage across the zener diode will not be constant, but rather will increase as the current through the diode increases.

**EXAMPLE 29–9**

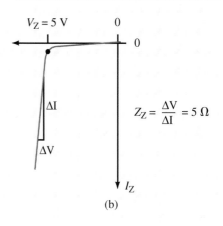

$Z_Z = \dfrac{\Delta V}{\Delta I} = 5\ \Omega$

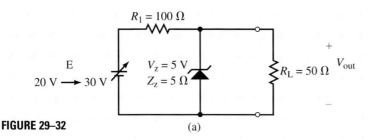

**FIGURE 29–32**                     (a)                                                        (b)

a. Determine the variation in output voltage as the unregulated input goes from 20 V to 30 V.

b. Solve for the line regulation of the circuit.

**Solution**

a. The analysis of this circuit is simplified when we determine the Thévenin equivalent circuit external to the zener diode. We begin by letting $E = 20$ V.

$$R_{Th} = 100\ \Omega \parallel 50\ \Omega = 33.33\ \Omega$$

and

$$E_{Th} = \left(\frac{50\ \Omega}{50\ \Omega + 100\ \Omega}\right)20\ V = 6.667\ V$$

The resulting circuit is shown in Figure 29–33.

Here we see that the current through the zener diode is

$$I_Z = \frac{6.667\ V - 5.0\ V}{33.33\ \Omega + 5\ \Omega} = 0.04348\ A$$

and the resulting output voltage is

$$V_{out} = 5\ V + (0.043448\ A)5\ \Omega = 5.217\ V$$

Next, if we let $E = 30$ V, we have $R_{Th} = 33.33\ \Omega$

and

$$E_{Th} = \left(\frac{50\ \Omega}{50\ \Omega + 100\ \Omega}\right)30\ V = 10.00\ V$$

which results in

$$I_Z = \frac{10.0\ V - 5.0\ V}{33.33\ \Omega + 5\ \Omega} = 0.1304\ A$$

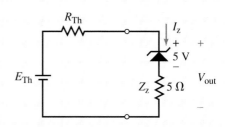

**FIGUR.E 29–33**

and

$$V_{out} = 5\ V + (0.1304\ A)5\ \Omega = 5.652\ V$$

b. The line regulation is solved as

$$\% \text{ line regulation} = \frac{\Delta V_{out}}{\Delta V_{in}} \times 100\%$$

$$= \frac{5.652\ V - 5.217\ V}{30\ V - 20\ V} \times 100\% = 4.35\%$$

(or simply, line regulation $= 43.5$ mV/V)

If the load resistance in the circuit of Figure 29–32 has a value of $R_L = 80 \, \Omega$,

a. Determine the variation in output voltage as the unregulated input goes from 20 V to 30 V.

b. Solve for the line regulation of the circuit.

*Answers*
a.  5.39 V to 5.84 V;  b.  4.50 %

## Load Regulation

Refer to the regulator diagram shown in Figure 29–31. As mentioned previously, the output voltage of the ideal regulator will remain constant for all conditions. However, in a real voltage regulator, if we were to decrease the value of load resistance, the output voltage will decrease as the current demand increases. The **percent load regulation** is defined as follows:

$$\% \text{ load regulation} = \frac{V_{NL} - V_{FL}}{V_{FL}} \times 100\% \qquad \textbf{(29–13)}$$

In the Equation of 29–12, $V_{NL}$ is the "no-load" voltage and $V_{FL}$ is the "full-load" voltage. All regulated voltage sources provide a relatively constant voltage until the load current reaches some maximum value. This maximum value will always be specified by a manufacturer and represents the full-load condition. The load regulation may be expressed as maximum variation of output voltage from the nominal output voltage of the regulator.

**EXAMPLE 29–10**

The manufacturer of a 12-V regulator specifies that the output regulation of the device has a typical value of 4 mV. Determine the percent load regulation.

**Solution**
Since the difference in the load voltage is 4 mV, we solve the load regulation as

$$\% \text{ load regulation} = \frac{V_{NL} - V_{FL}}{V_{FL}} \times 100\%$$

$$= \frac{4 \text{ mV}}{12 \text{ V}} \times 100\% = 0.033\%$$

**EXAMPLE 29–11**

Given the zener diode regulator circuit shown in Figure 29–34, determine the load regulation if the load resistance varies between 50 $\Omega$ and 100 $\Omega$. Since the minimum load current occurs when $R_L = 100 \, \Omega$, let this be the no-load condition.

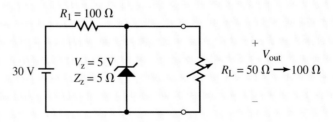

**FIGURE 29–34**

**Solution**

As in the previous example, we solve for the Thévenin equivalent circuit external to the zener diode as follows:

When $R_L = 100\ \Omega$, we have $R_{Th} = 50\ \Omega$
and

$$E_{Th} = \left(\frac{100\ \Omega}{100\ \Omega + 100\ \Omega}\right)30\ V = 15.00\ V$$

which results in

$$I_Z = \frac{15.0\ V - 5.0\ V}{50\ \Omega + 5\ \Omega} = 0.1818\ A$$

and

$$V_{out} = 5\ V + (0.1818\ A)5\ \Omega = 5.909\ V$$

When $R_L = 50\ \Omega$, we have $R_{Th} = 33.33\ \Omega$
and

$$E_{Th} = \left(\frac{50\ \Omega}{50\ \Omega + 100\ \Omega}\right)30\ V = 10.00\ V$$

which results in

$$I_Z = \frac{10.0\ V - 5.0\ V}{33.33\ \Omega + 5\ \Omega} = 0.1304\ A$$

and

$$V_{out} = 5\ V + (0.1304\ A)5\ \Omega = 5.652\ V$$

The load regulation is solved as

$$\% \text{ load regulation} = \frac{5.909\ V - 5.652\ V}{5.652\ V} \times 100\% = 4.55\%$$

---

Besides being inefficient, the zener diode has the added disadvantage of allowing for regulation over only a narrow range of output load resistance. Both of these disadvantages can be largely overcome by using a series regulator as illustrated in Figure 29–35.

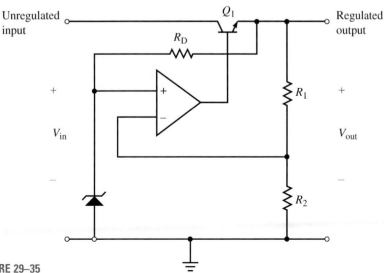

**FIGURE 29–35**

In the regulator circuit, we use a zener diode only as a means of providing a reference voltage rather than directly providing the voltage regulation. The current through the zener diode remains constant, since it is connected to the regulated output voltage. The op-amp comparator is used to detect feedback voltage and to provide a signal at the base of the power transistor, which in turn provides the necessary current for the load. The operation of the series regulator is really quite simple, and is outlined as follows:

1. When it is first turned on, power is provided to the op-amp by the unregulated input.

2. The output of the op-amp will go to some positive voltage, forward-biasing the B-E junction of transistor, $Q_1$.

3. As the transistor begins to conduct the emitter becomes increasingly positive.

4. The increase in output voltage causes the current through the zener diode to also increase, until the knee of the diode is reached. At this point the voltage across the zener diode (and at the non-inverting terminal of the op-amp) remains constant at $V_Z$.

5. The voltage divider that is set up by resistors $R_1$ and $R_2$ provides the feedback for the op-amp. If the voltage at the inverting input starts to increase, the differential voltage at input of the op-amp decreases, which in turn decreases the base bias current for $Q_1$, resulting in less output current, and correspondingly less output voltage.

6. At this point the circuit has reached equilibrium and the output voltage will remain constant.

The output voltage of the circuit is dependent on three quantities: the zener voltage and the values of the resistors $R_1$ and $R_2$. Since the voltage appearing at both the inverting and the non-inverting inputs of the op-amp are approximately the same, and since the current into the input terminals of the op-amp is essentially zero, we conclude that the voltage across $R_2$ must also be $V_Z$. Applying the voltage divider rule to $R_1$ and $R_2$ gives us the following:

$$V_{R_2} = V_Z = \frac{R_2}{R_1 + R_2} V_{out}$$

and so we are able to write the expression for output voltage as

$$V_{out} = \frac{R_1 + R_2}{R_2} V_Z \qquad \text{(29–14)}$$

When designing the regulator circuit of Figure 29–35, there are a few design considerations that will help to make the circuit more functional. Firstly, the transistor will generally dissipate a fair amount of power ($P_D \approx I_C V_{CE}$) and so it is generally a good design practice to used a power transistor. Secondly, the current through the zener should be sufficient to ensure that the zener diode is operating in its breakover region. Generally a current of $I_Z = 10$ mA is sufficient. Lastly, the values of the voltage divider resistors, $R_1$ and $R_2$, are designed to have a current of approximately 1 mA. The following circuit shows a typical design.

Refer to the circuit of the series regulator shown in Figure 29–35.

a. Determine all resistor values, given the following conditions:

Unregulated input voltage, $v_{in}$ = 40 V

Regulated output voltage, $v_{out}$ = 20 V

Zener diode has $V_Z$ = 5.0 V

b. Solve for the approximate power dissipated by the power transistor if a load resistance of $R_L$ = 50 Ω is place across the regulated output voltage.

**Solution**

a. For an output voltage of 20 V, the voltage across $R_D$ must be $V_{RD}$ = 15 V. If we let $I_Z$ = 10 mA, we have

$$R_D = \frac{15\ V}{10\ mA} = 1.5\ k\Omega$$

Similarly, we solve for the resistance $R_1 + R_2$

$$R_1 + R_2 = \frac{20\ V}{1\ mA} = 20\ k\Omega$$

Now, using Equation 29–13, we determine $R_2$ as

$$R_2 = \frac{(R_1 + R_2)V_Z}{v_{out}}$$

$$= \frac{(20\ k\Omega)(5.0\ V)}{20\ V} = 5\ k\Omega$$

And so $R_2$ = 15 kΩ.

The resulting design is shown in Figure 29–36.

**EXAMPLE 29–12**

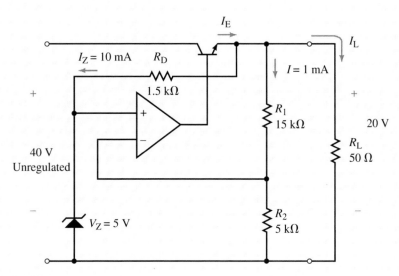

**FIGURE 29–36**

b. For a load resistor of $R_L = 50\ \Omega$, the load current is determined to be

$$I_L = \frac{20\text{ V}}{50\ \Omega} = 400\text{ mA}$$

The total emitter current is simply the sum

$$I_E = I_Z + I + I_L = 10\text{ mA} + 1\text{ mA} + 400\text{ mA} = 411\text{ mA}$$

The collector-emitter voltage of the transistor must be

$$V_{CE} = 40\text{ V} - 20\text{ V} = 20\text{ V}$$

Finally, the power dissipated by the transistor is simply as $P_D = (0.411\text{ A})$ $(20\text{ V}) = 8.22$ W. This example clearly demonstrates that the transistor must be capable of dissipating a large amount of power.

Although the previous circuit is easily built in a lab, it does involve using a substantial number of components. The circuit also has no short circuit protection, with the result that a shorted output will result in excessive current through the transistor. Although the circuit can be modified to provide additional protection, the extra effort is generally not practical. Many types of IC regulators are available to simplify and improve on the design of the series regulator. The μA7800 and μA 7900 series regulators allow the engineer, technologist, or technician to design and build voltage regulators for one of several possible output voltage values. The 7800 series are positive voltage regulators, while the μA 7900 series are negative regulators. Figure 29–37(a) shows the pinout of the μA 7800 series positive-voltage regulators, while Figure 29–37(b) gives typical

**KC PACKAGE**
**(TOP VIEW)**

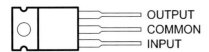

OUTPUT
COMMON
INPUT

The COMMON terminal is in electrical contact with the mounting base.

**TO-220AB**

(a)

**recommended operating conditions**

|  |  |  | MIN | MAX | UNIT |
|---|---|---|---|---|---|
| $V_I$ | Input voltage | μA7805C | 7 | 25 | V |
|  |  | μA7808C | 10.5 | 25 |  |
|  |  | μA7810C | 12.5 | 28 |  |
|  |  | μA7812C | 14.5 | 30 |  |
|  |  | μA7815C | 17.5 | 30 |  |
|  |  | μA7824C | 27 | 38 |  |
| $I_O$ | Output current |  |  | 1.5 | A |
| $T_J$ | Operating virtual junction temperature | μA7800C series | 0 | 125 | °C |

(b)

**electrical characteristics at specified virtual junction temperature, $V_I$ = 19 V, $I_O$ = 500 mA (unless otherwise noted)**

| PARAMETER | TEST CONDITIONS | $T_J$† | μA7808C MIN | μA7808C TYP | μA7808C MAX | UNIT |
|---|---|---|---|---|---|---|
| Output voltage | $I_O$ = 5 mA to 1 A,   $V_I$ = 10.5 V to 23 V, $P_D \le 15$ W | 25°C | 7.7 | 8 | 8.3 | V |
|  |  | 0°C to 125°C | 7.6 |  | 8.4 |  |
| Input voltage regulation | $V_I$ = 10.5 V to 25 V | 25°C |  | 6 | 160 | mV |
|  | $V_I$ = 11 V to 17 V |  |  | 2 | 80 |  |
| Ripple rejection | $V_I$ = 11.5 V to 21.5 V,   f = 120 Hz | 0°C to 125°C | 55 | 72 |  | dB |
| Output voltage regulation | $I_O$ = 5 mA to 1.5 A | 25°C |  | 12 | 160 | mV |
|  | $I_O$ = 250 mA to 750 mA |  |  | 4 | 80 |  |
| Output resistance | f = 1 kHz | 0°C to 125°C |  | 0.016 |  | Ω |
| Temperature coefficient of output voltage | $I_O$ = 5 mA | 0°C to 125°C |  | −0.8 |  | mV/°C |
| Output noise voltage | f = 10 Hz to 100 kHz | 25°C |  | 52 |  | μV |
| Dropout voltage | $I_O$ = 1 A | 25°C |  | 2 |  | V |
| Bias current |  | 25°C |  | 4.3 | 8 | mA |
| Bias current change | $V_I$ = 10.5 V to 25 V | 0°C to 125°C |  |  | 1 | mA |
|  | $I_O$ = 5 mA to 1 A |  |  |  | 0.5 |  |
| Short-circuit output current |  | 25°C |  | 450 |  | mA |
| Peak output current |  | 25°C |  | 2.2 |  | A |

† Pulse-testing techniques maintain the junction temperature as close to the ambient temperature as possible. Thermal effects must be taken into account separately. All characteristics are measured with a 0.33-μF capacitor across the input and a 0.1-μF capacitor across the output.

(c)

**FIGURE 29–37** μA7800 Series Positive Voltage Regulators. *(Courtesy of Texas Instruments)*

input voltage limits. The output voltage for each regulator is determined by the last two numbers in the part number For example the μA7805 is a 5-V regulator, while the μA7812 is a 12-V regulator. Figure 29–37(c) shows the electrical characteristics of the μA7812 regulator. The complete set of specifications sheets for the regulators is available at the Texas Instruments web site, http://www.ti.com/.

Figure 29–38 shows the connection of a μA7812 regulator.

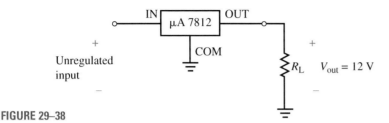

**FIGURE 29–38**

---

Refer to the manufacturer's specifications for the μA7800 series of voltage regulators. Answer the following questions relating to the specifications.

a. What is the range of input voltage that is permitted for the μA7805? The μA7824?

b. What is the typical ripple rejection ratio for the μA7812?

c. If the output terminals of the μA7812 were shorted, how much current would there be?

✓ IN-PROCESS
LEARNING CHECK 2

*(Answers are at the end of the chapter.)*

## Ripple Rejection

In Chapter 25 you examined the operation of rectifier circuits and were introduced to the concept of capacitor filtering. Recall that as the current in the load increased, two important changes occurred in the circuit. The ripple voltage increased since the capacitor discharged more quickly through the smaller resistance of the load. Secondly, the dc voltage delivered to the load was decreased. As you have already observed, a voltage regulator corrects for the variation in load voltage. Another characteristic of an IC regulator is its ability to greatly reduce the ripple voltage that appears across the load. The degree to which a voltage regulator is able to reject ripple is **ripple rejection,** which is calculated in decibels as

$$[\text{ripple rejection}]_{dB} = 20 \log \frac{V_{r(in)}}{V_{r(out)}} \qquad (29\text{--}15)$$

**EXAMPLE 29–13**

A manufacturer specifies that a three-terminal regulator has a ripple rejection greater than 75 dB. If the ripple at the output of a capacitor filtered full-wave rectifier is measured to be 400 mV$_{p\text{-}p}$, calculate the maximum ripple voltage that can be expected at the output of the three-terminal regulator.

**Solution**
Since we know that ripple rejection for a regulated power supply is expressed as

$$[\text{ripple rejection}]_{dB} = 20 \log \frac{V_{r(in)}}{V_{r(out)}}$$

we may rewrite the expression to solve for the output ripple voltage as

$$V_{r(out)} = \left(400 \text{ mV}_{p\text{-}p}\right) 10^{-\frac{75}{20}} = 0.071 \text{ mV}_{p\text{-}p}$$

A ripple voltage of 0.071 mV$_{p\text{-}p}$ will be barely perceptible.

**PRACTICE PROBLEMS 4**

The input of a three-terminal regulator has a dc voltage of 24 V and a 2 $V_{p\text{-}p}$ ripple as illustrated in Figure 29–39. If the output of the regulator is 12 $V_{dc}$ with a 0.5 m$V_{p\text{-}p}$ ripple, determine the following:

a. What is the ripple factor at the input of the regulator?

b. What is the ripple factor at the output of the regulator?

c. What is the ripple rejection (in dB) of the regulator?

d. If the manufacturer specifies that the regulator has a minimum ripple rejection of 55 dB, does this regulator meet the specification?

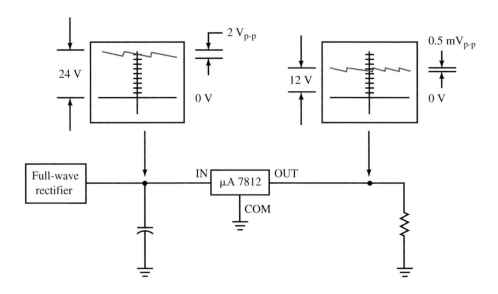

**FIGURE 29–39**

**Solution**

a. Recall (from Chapter 25) that ripple rejection is defined as

$$r = \frac{V_{r(rms)}}{V_{dc}} \times 100\%$$

and so at the input of the regulator, the ripple factor is found to be

$$r = \frac{\dfrac{2\ V_{p\text{-}p}}{2\sqrt{3}}}{24\ V} \times 100\% = 2.41\%$$

b. The ripple factor at the output of the regulator is

$$r = \frac{\dfrac{0.5\ mV_{p\text{-}p}}{2\sqrt{3}}}{12\ V} \times 100\% = 0.0012\%$$

c. The ripple rejection of the regulator is

$$[\text{ripple rejection}]_{dB} = 20\log\frac{2\ V_{p\text{-}p}}{0.5\ mV_{p\text{-}p}} = 72.0\ dB$$

d. The ripple rejection of 72 dB is greater than the minimum specified and so the regulator meets the specification.

In Chapter 22, we used PSpice and MultiSIM software to predict frequency response of passive filters consisting of R-L-C elements. These software packages are equally adept at analyzing active filters. You will also find the software to be very useful in predicting other circuit operations involving op-amps used as comparators, voltage regulators, and amplifiers. The software calculations will easily predict whether a design is likely to work in a laboratory situation and allows us to quickly and easily adjust component values.

## 29.7 Computer Analysis

### PSpice

In Example 29–7, we designed a narrowband bandpass filter to have a center frequency of 400 Hz and a bandwidth of 100 Hz. Use the PSpice Capture to input the circuit of Figure 29–28. Run the Probe postprocessor to view the frequency response (in dB) from 10 Hz to 10 kHz. Use the cursor tool to determine the actual center frequency of the design and solve for the bandwidth by evaluating the frequencies at which the output is 3 dB down from the value at the center frequency.

**EXAMPLE 29–14**

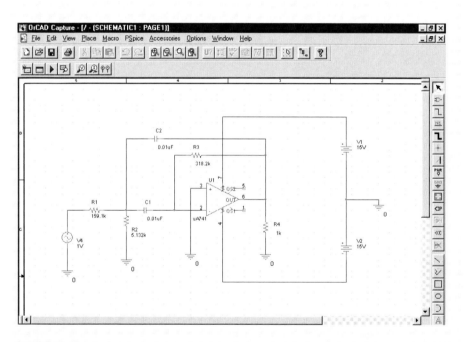

**FIGURE 29–40**

### Solution

The circuit is constructed as shown in Figure 29–40. As in previous problems, we use the VAC part from the SOURCE library as the ac voltage source. After clicking on the part, we change the voltage to **1V.** The 741 op-amp is found in the EVAL library and is found by scrolling down or simple entering uA741 in the Part: box. The ac sweep settings are selected, and the scan is set to go from 10 Hz to 10 kHz. Refer to Chapter 22 if you need a review of how to use PSpice to provide a frequency scan of a filter. The desired display is obtained by selecting the Trace menu and clicking on Add Trace. . . . The output voltage is taken across the load resistor, $R_4 = 1k\Omega$. By using the cursor, we find that the center frequency is 400 Hz and that the bandwidth of the filter is 100 Hz as desired. The resulting voltage gain frequency response is shown in Figure 29–41.

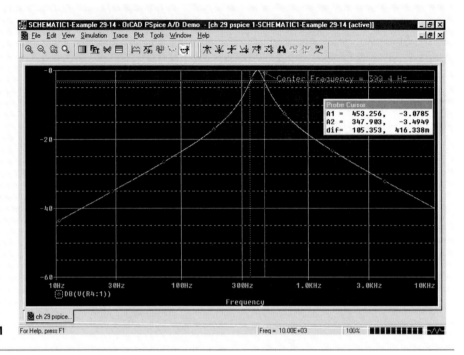

**FIGURE 29–41**

## MultiSIM

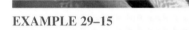

**EXAMPLE 29–15**

a. Use MultiSIM to model the wideband bandpass circuit of Figure 29–26.

b. Use the spectrum analyzer tool to obtain the frequency response of the voltage gain from 1 Hz to 100 kHz.

c. Use the cursor to determine the 3-dB down frequencies. Compare the results to the theoretical values predicted by the component values.

**Solution**

a. Figure 29–42 shows the resultant circuit when MultiSIM is used to generate the circuit.

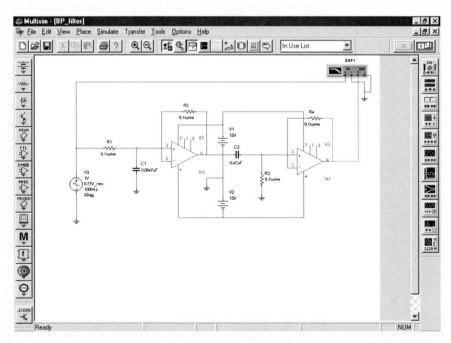

**MULTISIM**    **FIGURE 29–42**

b. By clicking on the Bode Plotter instrument, we obtain the display shown in Figure 29–43.

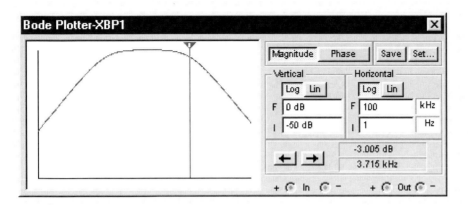

**FIGURE 29–43**

c. By dragging the cursor through the frequency axis, we determine the lower cutoff frequency of the filter (due to the high-pass section) to be 37 Hz, while the upper cutoff frequency (due to the low-pass section) is 3.7 kHz. These results are exactly the same as those predicted theoretically.

## PUTTING IT INTO PRACTICE

Notch filters (also known as band reject filters) can be used to eliminate unwanted frequency components from a signal. As part of an engineering team for an aircraft manufacturer, you have been given the task of designing a notch filter to remove a 400–Hz signal from a monitoring system. You have decided to use two op-amps as shown in Section 29–5. Since you would like to remove only a very narrow band of frequencies, you select a fairly high $Q = 40$. Although you have many capacitors from which to choose, you select a fairly common value of $C = 0.022 \ \mu F$. Show the design of your filter and use Mult-SIM or PSpice to simulate the operation of your design.

## PROBLEMS

### 29.1  Comparators

1. Refer to the circuit and input waveform shown in Figure 29–44. Sketch the corresponding waveform that will be observed at the output of the comparator. Label the resultant waveform, showing the correct amplitude and transition times if the reference voltage is $V_{REF} = +3$ V.

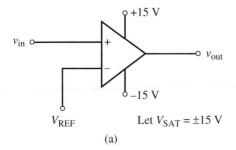

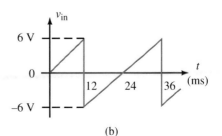

**FIGURE 29–44**    (a)    (b)

2. Repeat Problem 1 for $V_{REF} = +2$ V.

3. Repeat Problem 1 for $V_{REF} = -4$ V.

4. Repeat Problem 1 for $V_{REF} = +2$ V.

5. Refer to the circuit and input waveform shown in Figure 29–45. Sketch the corresponding waveform that will be observed at the output of the comparator. Label the resultant waveform, showing the correct amplitude and transition times if the reference voltage is $V_{REF} = +5$ V.

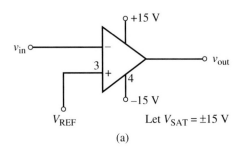

(a)

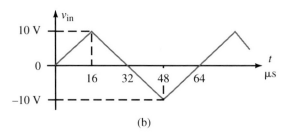

(b)

**FIGURE 29–45**

◀ MULTISIM

6. Repeat Problem 5 for $V_{REF} = +8$ V.

7. Repeat Problem 5 for $V_{REF} = -2$ V.

8. Repeat Problem 5 for $V_{REF} = -6$ V.

9. For the circuit of Figure 29–46:

    a. For what range of input voltage, $v_{in}$, will LED1 be on?

    b. For what range of input voltage, $v_{in}$, will LED2 be on?

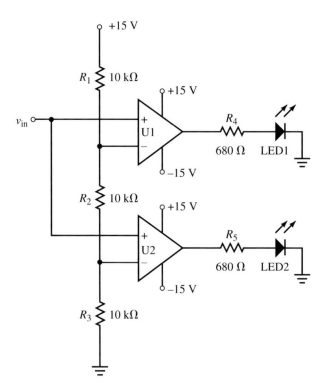

**FIGURE 29–46**

10. Refer to the circuit shown in Figure 29–47. If the indicated waveform is applied to the input of the op-amp comparators, sketch the output waveforms for $v_{out1}$ and $v_{out2}$. Label the resultant waveforms, showing the correct amplitude and transition times.

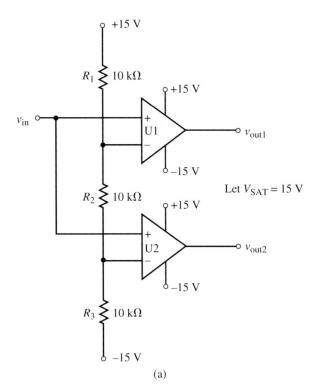

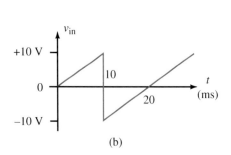

(a)                                                (b)

**FIGURE 29–47**

## 29.2   Voltage Summing Amplifier

11. Refer to the circuit of Figure 29–48, letting $R_1 = 10$ kΩ, $R_2 = 10$ kΩ, $R_3 = 10$ kΩ, and $R_F = 20$ kΩ. Let $V_1 = -2$ V, $V_2 = +4.5$ V, and $V_3 = -1.5$ V.

a. Solve for the currents $I_1$, $I_2$, $I_3$, and $I_F$. (Note the reference directions.)

b. Determine the output voltage, $V_{out}$.

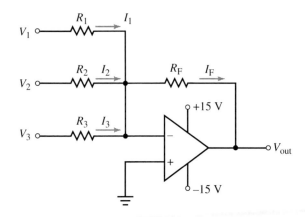

**FIGURE 29–48**                                                    ◀ MULTISIM

12. Repeat Problem 11 by letting $R_1 = 10$ k$\Omega$, $R_2 = 20$ k$\Omega$, $R_3 = 30$ k$\Omega$, and $R_F = 20$ k$\Omega$. Let $V_1 = +2$ V, $V_2 = +1.5$ V, and $V_3 = -2.5$ V.

    a. Solve for the currents $I_1$, $I_2$, $I_3$, and $I_F$.

    b. Determine the output voltage, $V_{out}$.

13. Figure 29–49 shows a summing amplifier that can be used as a "mixer" to algebraically combine two input signals. Given the two waveforms shown in Figure 29–50, sketch the corresponding output waveform, showing the correct amplitude and transition times.

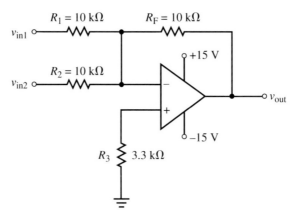

◀ MULTISIM

**FIGURE 29–49**

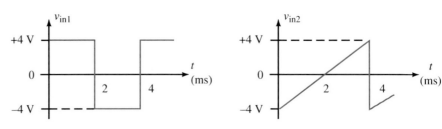

**FIGURE 29–50**

14. Repeat Problem 13 for the waveforms of Figure 29–51.

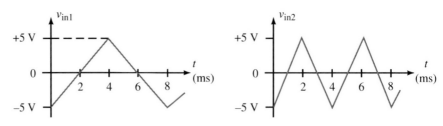

**FIGURE 29–51**

### 29.3   Integrators and Differentiators

15. Given that the integrator circuit of Figure 29–52 has $C = 0.05$ $\mu$F and a square wave input as shown.

    a. Determine the peak-to-peak value of the waveform that will appear at the output of the integrator if the applied square wave has amplitude of 2.0 V and frequency of 500 Hz.

    b. Sketch the corresponding output waveform. (Recall that the purpose of the feedback resistor, $R_F = 1$ M$\Omega$ is to remove the dc offset from the output voltage.)

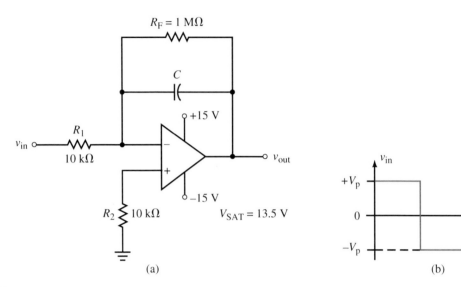

**FIGURE 29–52**

16. Repeat Problem 15 if the square wave has amplitude of 4.0 V and frequency of 500 Hz.

17. For the circuit of Figure 29–52, what is the maximum voltage peak voltage level that a 500 Hz signal can have before the output voltage goes into saturation?

18. If a square wave signal having amplitude of 2.0 V and frequency of 500 Hz is applied to the circuit of Figure 29–52, what is the minimum capacitor value that can be used before the output voltage goes into saturation?

19. Given that the differentiator circuit of Figure 29–53 has a sawtooth input wave as shown.

    a. Determine the expected waveform that will appear at the output of the integrator.

    b. Sketch the corresponding output waveform, showing the correct amplitude and transition times.

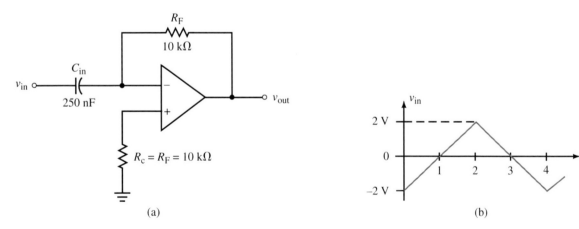

**FIGURE 29–53**

20. Repeat Problem 19 if the value of the capacitor were to be decreased to 100 nF.

21. The circuit of Figure 29–53 is prone to oscillation, due to bias currents. The operation of the circuit is improved by adding extra components into the circuit as illustrated previously in Figure 29–14. Redesign the circuit of Figure 29–53 by letting $R_F C_{in} = 10^4 R_{in} C_F$ and $R_F C_F = R_{in} C_{in}$. Sketch the new design.

22. Repeat Problem 20 using $C_{in} = 100$ nF.

### 29.4  Instrumentation Amplifiers

23. Determine the current (magnitude and direction) through each resistor in the circuit of Figure 29–54 and solve for the output voltage, $v_{out}$.

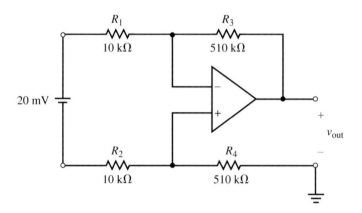

**FIGURE 29–54**

24. Determine the current (magnitude and direction) through each resistor in the circuit of Figure 29–55 and solve for the output voltage, $v_{out}$.

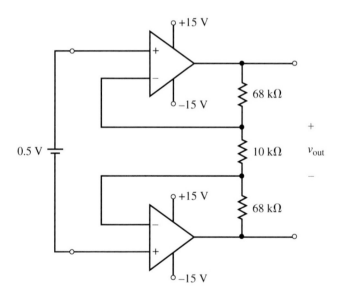

**FIGURE 29–55**

25. Two strain gages are bonded to a mounting beam that is subjected to an external force. When an external force is applied normal to the surface of the beam, the value of resistance in each strain gage increases by 2.0 mΩ. If the gages are connected as illustrated in Figure 29–56, determine the voltages, $v_{in1}$ and $v_{in2}$. Calculate the corresponding output voltage, $v_{out}$ of the instrumentation amplifier.

26. Repeat problem 25 if $R_1$ of the resistance bridge is replaced by a resistor having a constant value of 100 Ω.

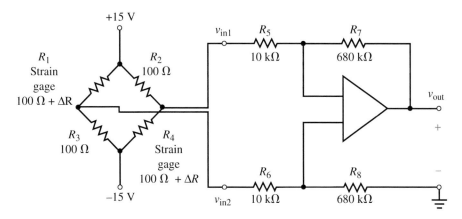

**FIGURE 29–56**

## 29.5   Active Filters

27. Given that $C = 0.01$ μF, design the low-pass filter of Figure 29–57 to have a low-frequency gain, $A_{v(dc)} = 10$ and a cutoff frequency of 10 kHz. Sketch the voltage gain frequency response (in dB) of the filter.

28. Repeat the design of Problem 27 if $C = 0.002$ μF, $A_{v(dc)} = 20$ and the cutoff frequency of the filter is 5 kHz.

29. Determine the low frequency cutoff of the op-amp circuit of Figure 29–58 due to the $R$-$C$ network. Calculate the upper cutoff frequency of the op-amp due to the gain-bandwidth product of $10^6$ Hz. Sketch the voltage gain frequency response (in dB) of the filter.

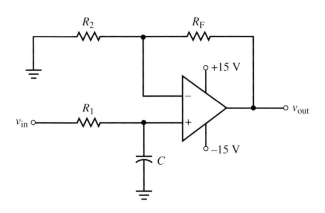

**FIGURE 29–57**

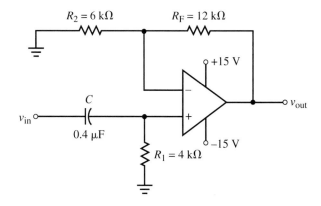

**FIGURE 29–58**

30. Using the same capacitor value, redesign the filter of Figure 29–58 to have a cutoff frequency of 250 Hz and a mid-frequency gain of 10. Calculate the upper cutoff frequency of the op-amp due to the gain-bandwidth product of $10^6$ Hz. Sketch the voltage gain frequency response (in dB) of the filter.

31. Use a capacitor of 0.1 μF to design a narrowband bandpass filter to have a center frequency of 800 Hz and a bandwidth of 80 Hz.

32. Modify the design of Problem 31 to result in a notch filter at 800 Hz.

## 29.6   Voltage Regulation

33. If the voltage source in the circuit of Figure 29–59 varies between $E = 40$ V and $E = 60$ V, determine the corresponding variation in $v_{out}$ for a load resistor, $R_L = 50$ Ω. Calculate the percent line regulation.

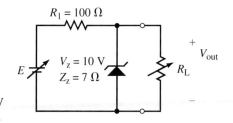

**FIGURE 29–59**

34. If the voltage source in the circuit of Figure 29–59 varies between $E = 40$ V and $E = 60$ V, determine the corresponding variation in $V_{out}$ for a load resistor, $R_L = 100$ Ω. Calculate the percent line regulation.

35. If the load resistor in the circuit of Figure 29–59 varies between 50 Ω and 100 Ω, determine the corresponding variation in $V_{out}$ for a voltage source, $E = 60$ V. Calculate the percent load regulation.

36. If the load resistor in the circuit of Figure 29–59 varies between 50 Ω and 100 Ω, determine the corresponding variation in $V_{out}$ for a voltage source, $E = 40$ V. Calculate the percent load regulation.

37. Refer to the series regulator shown in Figure 29–60.

    a. Determine the range of output voltage over which the regulator provides a constant voltage. (Note: Assume that regulation is assured if $V_{CE}$ of the transistor is maintained above 3 V.)

    b. If a 50-Ω load is connected across the output terminals, what is the maximum power that the transistor will dissipate?

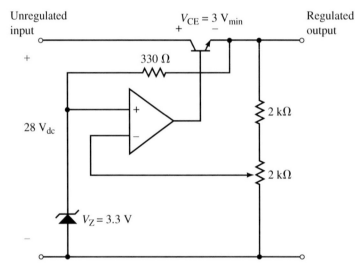

**FIGURE 29–60**

38. Repeat Problem 37 if the 3.3-V zener diode is replaced by a 6.2-V zener diode.

39. A three-terminal 20-V voltage regulator is measured to have a dc output voltage of 12 V with a 4.0 mV$_{p-p}$ ripple when it is under maximum load. If the input voltage of the regulator is measured to have a 2.0 V$_{p-p}$ ripple, calculate the ripple rejection ratio of the regulator (in dB).

40. A three-terminal 5-V voltage regulator is measured to have a dc input voltage of 26 V with a 4 V$_{p-p}$ ripple. If the manufacturer specifies that the voltage regulator has a ripple rejection ratio better than 58 dB, what is the maximum ripple voltage that you would expect to measure at the output of the regulator when it is under maximum load?

## 29.7 Computer Analysis

41. Use MultiSIM to input the circuit of Figure 29–45 using a 741C op-amp. Apply the indicated sawtooth signal to the input of the amplifier and a reference voltage of $V_{REF} = +5$ V. Use the oscilloscope tool to simultaneously display the waveforms for $v_{in}$ and $v_{out}$. ◀ MULTISIM

42. Use MultiSIM to input the circuit of Figure 29–45 using a 741C op-amp. Apply the indicated sawtooth signal to the input of the amplifier and a reference voltage of $V_{REF} = +8$ V. Use the oscilloscope tool to simultaneously display the waveforms for $v_{in}$ and $v_{out}$. ◀ MULTISIM

43. Use MultiSIM to input the circuit of Figure 29–45 using a 741C op-amp. Apply the voltages and resistor values of Problem 11 to the circuit and observe the output voltage with the multimeter tool. ◀ MULTISIM

44. Use MultiSIM to input the circuit of Figure 29–45 using a 741C op-amp. Apply the voltages and resistor values of Problem 11 to the circuit and observe the output voltage with the multimeter tool. ◀ MULTISIM

45. Use MutiSIM to input the circuit of Figure 29–49 using a 741C op-amp. Apply the voltages of Figure 29–50 to the circuit and observe the output voltage with the oscilloscope tool. ◀ MULTISIM

46. Use MultiSIM to input the circuit of Figure 29–49 using a 741C op-amp. Apply the voltages of Figure 29–51 to the circuit and observe the output voltage with the oscilloscope tool. ◀ MULTISIM

47. Use PSpice Capture to input the circuit of Figure 29–54 using a 741C op-amp. Apply a 20-mV input signal and determine the output voltage of the op-amp. Compare your result to the value determined in Problem 23. ◀ CADENCE

48. Use PSpice to input the circuit of Figure 29–55 using a 741C op-amp. Apply a 20-mV input signal and determine the output voltage of the op-amp. Compare your result to the value determined in Problem 24. ◀ CADENCE

49. Use PSpice to input the circuit of Figure 29–57 using a 741C op-amp and the component values of Problem 27. Let the input voltage equal 1 V. Use the Probe postprocessor to obtain a voltage gain frequency response (in dB) from 10 Hz to 10 MHz. ◀ CADENCE

50. Repeat Problem 49 using the component values of Problem 28. ◀ CADENCE

---

✓  ANSWERS TO IN-PROCESS LEARNING CHECKS

---

**In-Process Learning Check 1**

$V_A = +3.0$ V, $V_B = +2.0$ V, $V_C = +1.0$ V, $V_{out} = -12.0$ V

**In-Process Learning Check 2**

a. 7 V to 25 V,  27 V to 38 V

b. 71 dB

c. 350 mA

## ■ KEY TERMS

Astable Operation

Bounding Circuit

Frequency Deviation

Frequency Modulation

Lower Trip Point

Monostable Operation

Negative Feedback

Piezoelectric Effect

Positive Feedback

Relaxation Oscillator

R-S Flip-Flop Circuit

Schmitt Trigger

Upper Trip Point

## ■ OUTLINE

Basics of Feedback

The Relaxation Oscillator

The Wien Bridge Oscillator

The Phase-Shift Oscillator

LC Oscillators

Crystal Oscillators

The 555 Timer

The Voltage Controlled Oscillator—VCO

Computer Analysis

## ■ OBJECTIVES

On completion of this chapter, you will be able to

- use the control system equivalent of an amplifier to explain the principles of negative and positive feedback,

- calculate the closed loop of a non-inverting amplifier given the open-loop gain and the feedback ratio,

- analyze the operation of a Schmitt trigger,

- calculate the frequency of a relaxation oscillator that uses a Schmitt trigger as the active component,

- identify the two conditions required for oscillations to be sustained,

- analyze and design a Wien bridge oscillator,

- analyze and design a phase-shift oscillator,

- analyze a Colpitts oscillator,

- analyze a Hartley oscillator,

- explain the piezoelectric effect and sketch the electrical equivalent circuit of a quartz crystal,

- explain the operation of the 555 timer and be able to analyze and design circuits using monostable and astable operation,

- explain the basic operation of a voltage controlled oscillator and be able to design a voltage controlled oscillator circuit using an LM566 integrated circuit,

- use MutiSIM and PSpice software to simulate the operation of oscillator circuits.

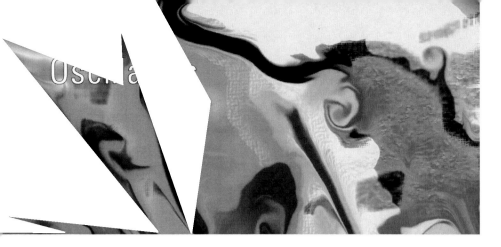

Oscilla...

# 30

Apart from the filter circuit, the oscillator circuit is perhaps one of the most important circuits in electronics. Without the oscillator, it would be impossible to have any radio transmission. AM (amplitude modulation) and FM (frequency modulation) would be impossible since both modulation techniques rely on oscillator circuits to provide the *carrier frequency.* The oscillator circuit is also an integral part of the demodulation process in both AM and FM. Computers use crystal oscillators to ensure that data is sent the appropriate time and provide synchronization. A piezoelectric crystal is used in watches and cellular telephones to provide alarms and ringing. Despite the theoretical simplicity of the oscillator circuit, it is often one of the most difficult circuits to design. A common complaint of the designer is that if she designs an amplifier, the circuit will oscillate. Conversely, if she tries to design an oscillator, she often ends up with an amplifier. In fact, you will discover that there is very little difference between an amplifier and an oscillator circuit. In this chapter you will learn the principles of oscillator operation and examine several oscillator circuits. Some circuits use only resistors and capacitors to induce oscillations while others use the inherent characteristic of inductors and capacitors to oscillate. You will find that crystal oscillators, which are constructed from quartz (crystallized silicon dioxide), are used if a very stable oscillator frequency is desired. ∎

IN ORDER TO BE ABLE to transmit an audio signal (or any other type of signal) using radio waves, it is necessary to first **modulate** this signal. The modulation process takes the low-frequency signal and combines it with a high-frequency carrier signal in a circuit called a **mixer.** In order to be useful, the high-frequency carrier signal must be a very pure sinusoidal waveform that is generated in a circuit called an **oscillator.** All oscillators use the principle of positive feedback in order to generate an alternating waveform. Early oscillators used vacuum tubes, together with inductors and capacitors, to result in the required positive feedback needed to sustain oscillations. With tunable capacitors, the frequency of oscillation can be adjusted until the desired frequency is obtained. It was very difficult to control the frequency of these early oscillators, since the frequency would vary with aging of components, and with variation in the ambient temperature. By using **piezoelectric crystals** such as quartz, the frequency of oscillation can be controlled to within a few parts per million.

Once a signal is modulated and transmitted, it must be converted back into the original signal. Once again, a very stable oscillator is used to down-convert the original signal to a lower frequency called the **intermediate frequency.** This principle called **super heterodyning** was invented by Edwin Armstrong (see Chapter 21—Putting It in Perspective) and allows for better selectivity within the receiver. Improved selectivity means that any station within a band of frequencies can be isolated and amplified without interference from adjacent stations.

Besides being an integral part of communications circuits, oscillators provide the technician or technologist with an indispensable tool for measuring circuit parameters such as voltage gain and bandwidth. ∎

## 30.1  Basics of Feedback

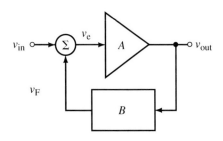

**FIGURE 30–1**

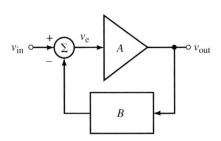

**FIGURE 30–2**

Figure 30–1 shows the control system equivalent of a feedback amplifier. This representation of the amplifier shows three main components: the forward gain element *(A)*, the feedback network *(B)*, and the summing junction (Σ).

The representation of Figure 30–1 can be used to explain the operation of oscillators as well as to derive the expressions for both the inverting and the non-inverting amplifier. For the amplifier circuits that we have studied to this point, the feedback voltage, $v_f$ was always 180° out-of-phase with respect to the input voltage. This **negative feedback** gave rise to many of the desirable characteristics of the op-amp: high input impedance, low output impedance, wide bandwidth, and stable operation. We will briefly consider the feedback amplifiers using the principles of the control systems equivalent. These same principles will then be used to examine several oscillator circuits that use **positive feedback.**

Consider the diagram shown in Figure 30–2, which represents the non-inverting amplifier. The signal applied to the forward gain element, $v_e$ (referred to as the error voltage in control systems) is determined by combining the signals entering the summing junction, as follows:

$$v_e = v_{in} - v_f \tag{30-1}$$

This voltage is then amplified by the high gain of the forward gain element, and so we express the output voltage as

$$v_{out} = A(v_{in} - v_f) \tag{30-2}$$

Now, since the feedback voltage represents that portion of the output voltage that is returned to the input, we have

$$v_f = Bv_{out} \tag{30-3}$$

By combining Equation 30–3 with the expression of Equation 30–2, we get

$$v_{out} = A(v_{in} - Bv_{out})$$

and so,

$$v_{out} = Av_{in} - ABv_{out}$$

or

$$v_{out} + ABv_{out} = Av_{in}$$

Finally, we see that the closed-loop gain of the non-inverting amplifier is determined as

$$\frac{v_{out}}{v_{in}} = \frac{A}{1 + AB} \tag{30-4}$$

Given the non-inverting amplifier shown in Figure 30–3, determine the feedback ratio, $B$, and solve for the closed loop gain using Equation 30–4.

**EXAMPLE 30–1**

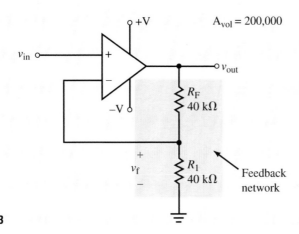

**FIGURE 30–3**

**Solution**

In the circuit of Figure 30–3, we see that the feedback voltage is calculated by applying the voltage divider rule to $R_1$ and $R_F$.

$$v_f = \frac{R_1}{R_1 + R_F} v_{out}$$

$$= \left( \frac{10 \text{ k}\Omega}{10 \text{ k}\Omega + 40 \text{ k}\Omega} \right) v_{out}$$

$$= 0.2 v_{out}$$

From the above calculation, the feedback ratio is simply determined from the resistor values, as $B = 0.2$. Now applying Equation 30–4, we solve for the closed-loop gain of the amplifier as

$$\frac{v_{out}}{v_{in}} = \frac{A}{1 + AB} = \frac{200,000}{1 + (0.2)(200,000)} = 5.00$$

As expected, the above result is consistent with the calculations that we used to find the gain of non-inverting amplifiers in previous chapters. Notice that if the open-loop gain of the op-amp is very large, the feedback ratio is simply the reciprocal of the closed loop gain; in other words, $B = \dfrac{1}{A_{vcl}}$ .

---

The analysis of the inverting amplifier is equally easy. Consider the control system diagram of the inverting amplifier shown in Figure 30–4. The error voltage in this case is determined as

$$v_e = -v_{in} - v_f \qquad \textbf{(30–5)}$$

This voltage is then amplified by the high gain of the forward gain element, which gives the output voltage as

$$v_{out} = A(-v_{in} - v_f) \qquad \textbf{(30–6)}$$

As before, the feedback voltage represents that portion of the output voltage that is returned to the input. We have

$$v_f = Bv_{out} \qquad \textbf{(30–7)}$$

Now, by combining Equation 30–6 with the expression of Equation 30–5, we get

$$v_{out} = A(-v_{in} - Bv_{out})$$

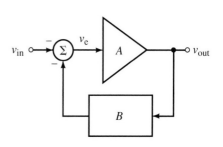

**FIGURE 30–4**

and so,

$$v_{out} = -Av_{in} - ABv_{out}$$

When simplified, the previous expression allows us to solve for closed-loop voltage of the inverting amplifier as

$$\frac{v_{out}}{v_{in}} = -\frac{A}{1 + AB} \qquad (30\text{–}8)$$

which can also be written as

$$\frac{v_{out}}{v_{in}} = -\frac{1}{\dfrac{1}{A} + B}$$

If the open-loop gain of the op-amp is very high, and the feedback ratio kept relatively low, we approximate the closed-loop gain as

$$\frac{v_{out}}{v_{in}} \approx -\frac{1}{B} \qquad (30\text{–}9)$$

From the result of Equation 30–9, we see that the feedback ratio of the inverting amplifier may be determined from the component values, as

$$B = \frac{R_1}{R_F} \qquad (30\text{–}10)$$

---

**EXAMPLE 30–2**

A non-inverting amplifier has $R_1 = 10\ k\Omega$ and $R_F = 68\ k\Omega$. The op-amp has open–loop gain of 100.

a. Solve for the ideal closed-loop gain of the amplifier.

b. Determine the actual closed-loop gain.

c. Solve for the percent error between the two values.

**Solution**

a. The ideal closed-loop gain of the amplifier is

$$A_v = \frac{R_F}{R_1} + 1 = \frac{68\ k\Omega}{10\ k\Omega} + 1 = 7.8$$

b. The actual voltage gain of the amplifier is

$$A_v = \frac{v_{out}}{v_{in}} = \frac{A}{1 + B} = \frac{100}{1 + \left(\dfrac{1}{7.8}\right)(100)} = 7.24$$

c. The error is  percent error $= \dfrac{7.24 - 7.8}{7.24} \times 100\% = -7.8\%$

---

PRACTICE PROBLEMS 1

A non-inverting amplifier uses an op-amp with an open-loop gain of 250 and has $R_1 = 10\ k\Omega$ and $R_F = 68\ k\Omega$.

a. Solve for the ideal closed-loop gain of the amplifier.

b. Determine the actual closed loop gain.

c. Solve for the percent error between the two values.

*Answers*

a. 6.8; b. 6.62; c. $-2.7\%$

In this section we will examine the operation of a simple circuit used to generate a square wave. By applying the knowledge learned in the previous chapter, we will integrate the square wave to obtain a triangular wave. Finally, we use a suitable filter to remove unwanted high-frequency components from the triangular wave to result in a relatively pure sine wave.

## 30.2 The Relaxation Oscillator

The **relaxation oscillator** uses a comparator to produce an output waveform that oscillates between the saturation voltages of the op-amp. In order to understand the operation of the relaxation oscillator, we begin by first considering the Schmitt trigger.

### The Schmitt Trigger

The **Schmitt trigger** shown in Figure 30–5 is commonly used to generate a square wave from a periodic (or any other varying) waveform. A similar circuit is used to generate triggering pulses that provide synchronized scanning of the electron beam across the CRT of an analog oscilloscope.

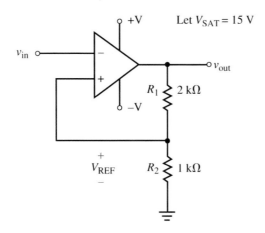

**FIGURE 30–5**    The Schmitt trigger.

The Schmitt trigger circuit is an op-amp circuit that uses positive feedback to generate a reference voltage on the non-inverting input terminal. (Recall that all amplifiers that we analyzed up to now used negative feedback.) As you learned in the previous chapter, if the voltage at the non-inverting ($+$) input terminal of a comparator is greater than the voltage at the inverting ($-$) terminal, the output will be forced to $+V_{SAT}$ due to the very high open-loop gain of the op-amp. Conversely, if the voltage at the ($+$) terminal is less that the voltage at the ($-$) terminal, then the output will be forced to $-V_{SAT}$.

If we examine the circuit of Figure 30–5, we see that the reference voltage (found by applying the voltage divider rule on $R_1$ and $R_2$) will be either $+5$ V or $-5$ V, depending on the input signal. No other values are possible.

Imagine that the input voltage, $v_{in} = +10$ V, in the circuit of Figure 30–5. Since $V_{REF} = \pm 5$ V, the voltage at the ($+$) terminal must be less than the input, and so the output will be forced to $v_{out} = -V_{SAT} = -15$ V. Now if we were to gradually decrease the input voltage from $v_{in} = +10$ V, the output will not change its value until $v_{in}$ is just less than $-5$ V. At this point, the output of the comparator would change to $v_{out} = +V_{SAT} = +15$ V ($V_{REF} = +5$ V). If the input were decreased still further, the output would necessarily remain at the same value, namely $v_{out} = +V_{SAT} = +15$ V.

Now, if the input voltage were to start at $v_{in} = -10$ V, the opposite effect would occur. The transfer characteristic, showing the relationship between the input and the output, is illustrated in Figure 30–6. The overlap between the conditions is called *hysteresis*. Here we see that the output is not only dependent on the input, but also on the previous value of the input. The value of the reference voltage, which results in the output switching from $-V_{SAT}$ to $+V_{SAT}$ is called the **lower trip point** (LTP), while the reference voltage which results in the output switching from $+V_{SAT}$ to $-V_{SAT}$ is called the **upper trip point** (UTP).

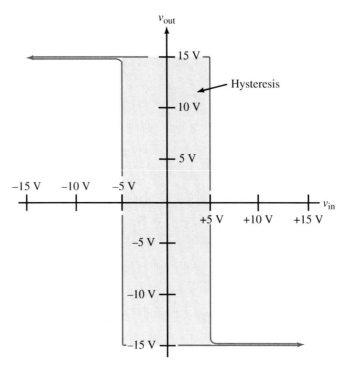

**FIGURE 30–6**

The following example shows the output of a Schmitt trigger for a given input signal.

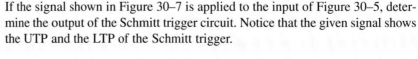

**EXAMPLE 30–3**

If the signal shown in Figure 30–7 is applied to the input of Figure 30–5, determine the output of the Schmitt trigger circuit. Notice that the given signal shows the UTP and the LTP of the Schmitt trigger.

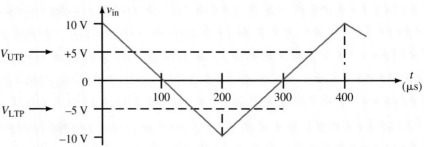

**FIGURE 30–7**

**Solution**

The Schmitt trigger will start at $v_{out} = -V_{SAT}$, since the input voltage is greater than the reference voltage. The output will change its state to $v_{out} = +V_{SAT}$ when the input signal goes to $v_{in} = V_{LTP} = -5$ V (at $t = 150$ μs). The next state change occurs at $t = 350$ μs, when the input signal goes above $v_{in} = V_{UTP} = +5$ V. At this point, the output will once again go to $-V_{SAT}$. The resulting output signal is shown in Figure 30–8.

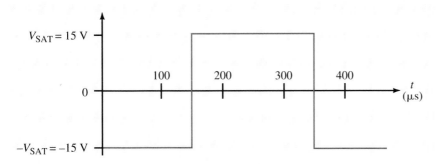

**FIGURE 30–8**

The Schmitt trigger circuit of Figure 30–5 has upper and lower trip points that have the same magnitude. The circuit shown in Figure 30–9 illustrates that the upper and lower trip points can be made adjustable with the addition of an op-amp buffer and through the selection of suitable resistor values.

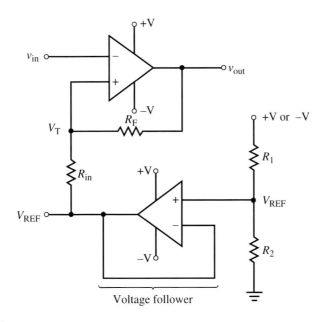

**FIGURE 30–9**

The reference voltage can be either positive or negative and has a magnitude determined by the values of resistors $R_1$ and $R_2$. In either case, the reference voltage will be

$$V_{REF} = \frac{R_2}{R_1 + R_2}(\pm V) \qquad (30\text{–}11)$$

The upper and lower trip points will be determined as

$$V_{UTP} = \frac{R_{in}(V_{SAT} - V_{REF})}{R_{in} + R_F} + V_{REF} \qquad (30\text{--}12)$$

and

$$V_{LTP} = \frac{R_{in}(-V_{SAT} - V_{REF})}{R_{in} + R_F} + V_{REF} \qquad (30\text{--}13)$$

**EXAMPLE 30–4**

Given the circuit and input signal shown in Figure 30–10:

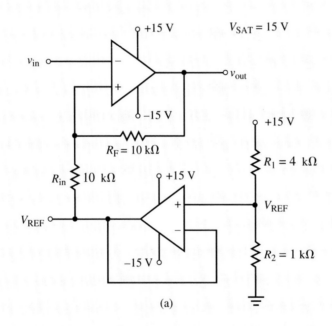

(a)

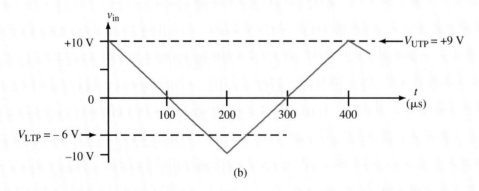

(b)

**FIGURE 30–10**

a. Determine the reference voltage and the values of the UTP and LTP voltages.

b. Sketch the corresponding output voltage of the Schmitt trigger circuit.

## Solution

a. Applying the voltage divider rule gives us the reference voltage as

$$V_{REF} = \left( \frac{1 \text{ k}\Omega}{4 \text{ k}\Omega + 1 \text{ k}\Omega} \right)(+15 \text{ V}) = 3.0 \text{ V}$$

The upper trip point is determined as

$$V_{UTP} = \frac{10 \text{ k}\Omega(+15 \text{ V} - 3 \text{ V})}{10 \text{ k}\Omega + 10 \text{ k}\Omega} + 3.0 \text{ V} = 9.0 \text{ V}$$

and the lower trip point is

$$V_{LTP} = \frac{10 \text{ k}\Omega(-15 \text{ V} - 3 \text{ V})}{10 \text{ k}\Omega + 10 \text{ k}\Omega} + 3.0 \text{ V} = -6.0 \text{ V}$$

The Schmitt trigger will start at $v_{out} = -V_{SAT}$. Once the input voltage reaches the lower trip point, the output voltage will change to $v_{out} = +V_{SAT} = +15$ V. The output remains at this level until the input voltage reaches the upper trip point. The corresponding output signal is shown in Figure 30–11.

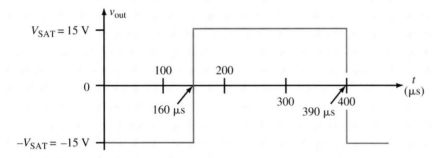

**FIGURE 30–11**

## Schmitt Trigger Relaxation Oscillator

A relaxation oscillator is a circuit that has a frequency of oscillation determined by the alternate charging and discharging of a capacitor. Although there are many types of relaxation oscillators, the Schmitt trigger is perhaps the simplest to understand. Figure 30–12 shows that the Schmitt trigger circuit is easily converted into a relaxation oscillator by adding an extra capacitor and resistor into the circuit.

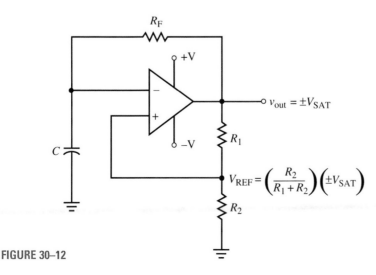

**FIGURE 30–12**

The circuit operation is explained as follows:

1. Resistors $R_1$ and $R_2$ are a voltage divider network that set the reference voltage of the Schmitt trigger. The reference voltage is determined as

$$V_{REF} = \frac{R_2}{R_1 + R_2}\left(\pm V_{SAT}\right) \qquad (30\text{--}14)$$

2. If we assume for a moment that the voltage across the capacitor (voltage applied to the inverting input of the op-amp) is less than the reference voltage, then the capacitor will charge through $R_F$, attempting to reach a value of $+V_{SAT}$. Once the voltage across the capacitor reaches $V_C = V_{REF}$, the output of the Schmitt trigger will change states to $v_{out} = -V_{SAT}$. At this point the reference voltage will be negative.

3. The capacitor will now attempt to charge to $-V_{SAT}$.

4. Once again, when the voltage across the capacitor reaches the reference value, the output of the Schmitt trigger will change and the process repeats.

**EXAMPLE 30–5**

Given the circuit of Figure 30–13:

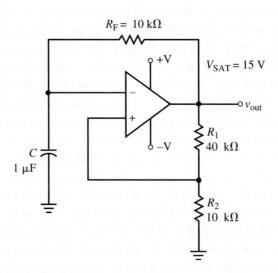

**FIGURE 30–13**

a. Determine the frequency of the relaxation oscillator.

b. Sketch the waveform that would appear at the inverting input terminal of the op-amp.

c. Sketch the waveform that would appear at the output of the Schmitt trigger.

**Solution**

a. We begin by finding the reference voltage determined by the voltage divider of $R_1$ and $R_2$. From Equation 30–14, we have

$$V_{REF} = \frac{10\ k\Omega}{40\ k\Omega + 10\ k\Omega}(\pm 15V) = \pm 3.00\ V$$

Now, if we assume that the capacitor has an initial charge of $-3.00$ V, we can set up the charging equation of a capacitor to determine the length of time needed to charge to $+3.00$ V. Remember that the voltage to which the capacitor will attempt to charge is $+V_{SAT} = +15$ V.

$$v_C(t) = V_0 + \left(V_F - V_0\right)\left(1 - e^{-\frac{t}{RC}}\right)$$

$$+3.00 \text{ V} = -3.00 \text{ V} + \left(15 \text{ V} + 3 \text{ V}\right)\left(1 - e^{-\frac{t}{10 \text{ ms}}}\right)$$

Solving for the charging time, $t$, we have:

$$t = -(10 \text{ ms})(\ln 0.6667) = 4.055 \text{ ms}$$

Therefore, the period of oscillation will be $T = 2(4.055 \text{ ms}) = 8.11$ ms.

b. Figure 30–14 shows the voltage appearing at the input terminal of the op-amp, which is the same as the voltage across the capacitor.

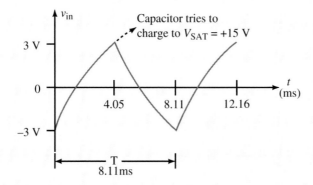

**FIGURE 30–14**

c. Figure 30–15 shows the corresponding output voltage.

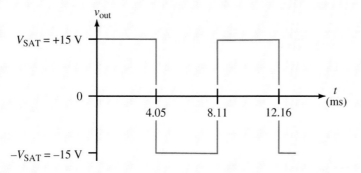

**FIGURE 30–15**

PRACTICE PROBLEMS 2

Solve for the period of the relaxation oscillator of Figure 30–13 if the voltage divider has resistor values of $R_1 = 10$ kΩ and $R_2 = 40$ kΩ.

*Answer*
$T = 43.94$ ms

For the relaxation oscillator of Figure 30–13, it can be shown that the general expression for the period of oscillation is determined as

$$T = 2R_F C \ln\left(1 + \frac{2R_2}{R_1}\right) \tag{30–15}$$

As mentioned previously, adding an integrator and a filter circuit as shown in Figure 30–16, will result in further improvement in the operation of the relaxation oscillator. The modified circuit now has a square wave, a triangular wave, and a sinusoidal output.

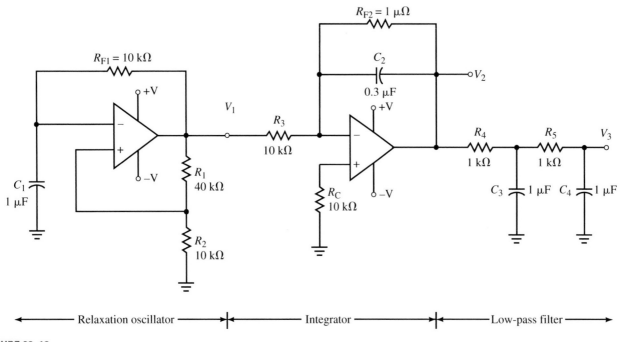

**FIGURE 30–16**

## 30.3 The Wien Bridge Oscillator

In order for any oscillator to provide a sinusoidal output, two conditions must be met:

1. the closed loop gain must be greater than or equal to unity (1), and
2. the phase shift between the input and the output must be equal to 0° at the frequency of oscillation.

Once the above conditions have been met, the circuit will oscillate even though no external signal is applied to the amplifier. Positive feedback (also called *regenerative feedback*) will return a portion of the output signal back to the input where this signal is further amplified together with other noise components at the same frequency. The cumulative effect of returning a portion of the output in phase with the input results in an oscillator very quickly reaching its steady state output at its resonant frequency. Figure 30–17 shows the output

Initial noise voltage                                          Steady-state oscillations

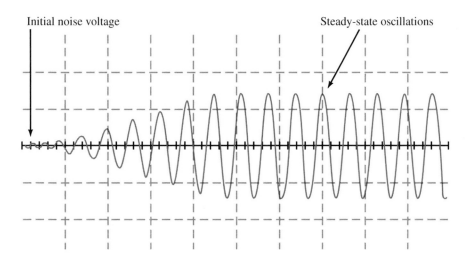

**FIGURE 30–17**

of an oscillator building from a small noise voltage to its steady state value. The origin of the noise that causes the oscillation to begin is primarily due to thermal effects within the amplifier as well as external random noise.

Figure 30–18 shows the Wien bridge oscillator, a circuit that uses positive feedback to provide sinusoidal oscillations. The bridge consists of two separate arms. The *R-C* network in the right arm of the bridge provides the positive feedback while the resistors in the left arm help to establish the required amplifier gain.

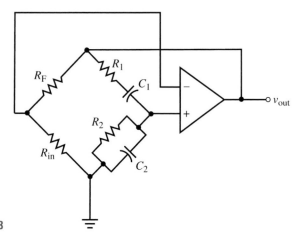

**FIGURE 30–18**

Figure 30–19 shows the isolated *R-C* network that provides the necessary positive feedback. In order to ensure that oscillations are maintained, it is necessary that the circuit provides 0° phase-shift at the resonant frequency. It can be shown that for the network of Figure 30–19, the frequency at which the output is in phase with the input occurs at

$$ f_0 = \frac{1}{2\pi\sqrt{R_1 R_2 C_1 C_2}} \qquad \textbf{(30–16)} $$

Further, it can also be shown that if the transfer function, $\textbf{TF} = v_{out}/v_{in}$ is evaluated at the frequency evaluated by Equation 30–16, the feedback gain of the *R-C* network is a real value (phase angle, $\theta = 0°$) determined as

$$ B = \frac{R_2 C_1}{R_1 C_1 + R_2 C_2 + R_2 C_1} \qquad \textbf{(30–17)} $$

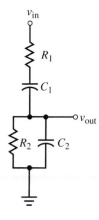

**FIGURE 30–19**

Since the components are generally selected so that $R_1 = R_2$ and $C_1 = C_2$, Equations 30–16 and 30–17 are simplified as follows:

$$f_0 = \frac{1}{2\pi RC} \tag{30–18}$$

and

$$B = \frac{1}{3} \tag{30–19}$$

In order to ensure that the oscillator has a closed-loop gain, $AB = 1$ (unity), the op-amp must provide the circuit with a gain of at least 3. Figure 30–20 shows the resultant circuit of the Wien bridge oscillator. Although the circuit does not show the bridge circuit in an easily recognized form, this circuit better illustrates both the positive feedback path ($A = 3$) and the negative feedback path ($B = \frac{1}{3}$).

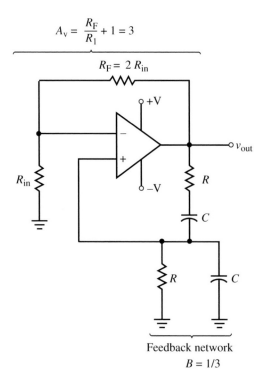

**FIGURE 30–20**

The operation of the circuit is further improved by separating the feedback resistor, $R_F$ into two resistors, one variable and one fixed. The variable resistor is then adjusted to minimize the distortion on the output signal. Zener diodes are placed across the fixed resistor to form part of the **bounding circuit** to limit the range of the output voltage. When low-voltage zener diodes are used in the circuit, the variable resistor not only adjusts for distortion, but also provides better control of the output amplitude. The modified circuit is shown in Figure 30–21.

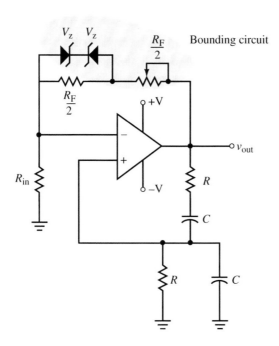

**FIGURE 30–21**

Design a Wien bridge oscillator having a resonant frequency of 1 kHz. Assume that you are given capacitors having values of $C = 0.01\ \mu F$.

**EXAMPLE 30–6**

**Solution**
By applying Equation 30–18, we solve for the required resistance in the $R$-$C$ feedback network as

$$R = \frac{1}{2\pi f_0 C}$$

$$= \frac{1}{2\pi(1000\ \text{Hz})(0.01\ \mu F)} = 15.9\ k\Omega$$

If we let $R = 16\ k\Omega$, our design would have a frequency variation of less than 1% from the desired value of 1 kHz. To minimize the effect of bias voltage and currents, we select $R_{in} = R = 24\ k\Omega$. Now the value of $R_F$ is easily determined to be $R_F = 2R_{in} = 48\ k\Omega$. A 47-k$\Omega$ resistor would not be suitable for this circuit, since its value may not result in sufficient gain for the amplifier to oscillate. Therefore, in order to sustain the oscillations, it is better to use a larger resistor such as $R_F = 51\ k\Omega$, even though the output signal may have excessive distortion. Figure 30–22 shows the resulting design.

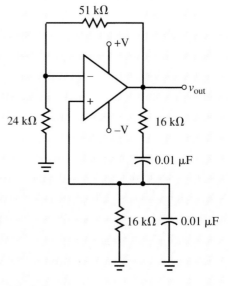

**FIGURE 30–22**

Refer to the $R$-$C$ feedback network of Figure 30–19. If $R_1 = R$, $R_2 = 2R$ and $C_1 = C_2 = C$, determine the feedback gain of this network. What must be the value of the amplifier gain in order for the oscillator to provide a sinusoidal output?

IN-PROCESS
LEARNING CHECK 1

*(Answers are at the end of the chapter.)*

## 30.4 The Phase-Shift Oscillator

The phase-shift oscillator, shown in Figure 30–23, uses a three-section $R$-$C$ network to provide the required feedback to allow the amplifier to oscillate. At resonance, the $R$-$C$ network provides a total phase shift of 180°. Although one might expect that each of the three sections contributes 60° of the total, the actual phase-shift of each section is determined by the loading effect of adjacent components. Since the oscillator circuit requires 360° ($\equiv$ 0°) of phase shift, the other 180° is obtained by applying the feedback to the inverting input of the op-amp.

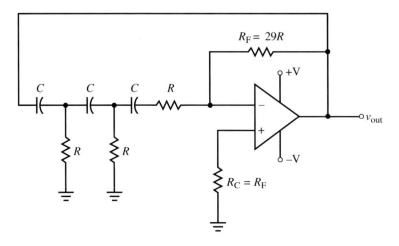

**FIGURE 30–23**

It can be shown that the output of the three-section $R$-$C$ network provides exactly 180° of phase shift at a frequency determined as

$$f_0 = \frac{1}{2\pi\sqrt{6}RC} \tag{30–20}$$

At this frequency, the phase-shift feedback network has a gain of $B = 1/29$, returning 1/29 of the output magnitude back to the input. Therefore, in order to ensure oscillations, it is necessary for the amplifier to provide a voltage gain of

$$A = 29 \tag{30–21}$$

The following example illustrates the operation of the phase-shift oscillator.

**EXAMPLE 30–7**

Given the circuit shown in Figure 30–24:

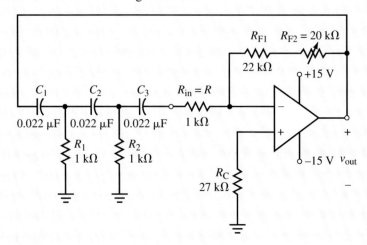

**FIGURE 30–24**

a) Determine the frequency of oscillation.

b) What is the minimum value of $R_{F2}$ to ensure that oscillation will occur?

c) At the required amplifier gain, what is the bandwidth of the amplifier if the gain-bandwidth product for the op-amp is $10^6$ Hz.

**Solution**

a. The frequency of oscillation is

$$f_0 = \frac{1}{2\pi\sqrt{6}RC} = \frac{1}{2\pi\sqrt{6}(1\text{ k}\Omega)(0.022\text{ }\mu\text{F})} = 2953\text{ Hz}$$

b. In order for oscillations to be sustained, the value of the feedback resistor must be

$$R_F = 29R = 29\text{ k}\Omega \text{ and so } R_{F2} = 7\text{ k}\Omega$$

c. At a gain of $A = 29$, the bandwidth of the amplifier will be

$$BW = \frac{10^6}{29} = 34.49\text{ kHz}$$

The above calculation implies that the cutoff frequency of the amplifier is 34.49 kHz, illustrating that the amplifier will no longer be able to provide sufficient gain above this frequency to sustain oscillation. This example clearly illustrates that the gain-bandwidth product of an op-amp limits the oscillator frequency. If a high-frequency oscillator is desired, it is necessary to use an active component that is able to provide enough gain at the required frequency. Very often, high-frequency junction transistors or field-effect transistors are used for these applications.

---

Using the same capacitor values, redesign the phase-shift oscillator of Figure 20–24 to have a resonant frequency of 5.0 kHz.

**PRACTICE PROBLEMS 3**

*Answers*
$R_1 = R_2 = R_{in} = 591\text{ }\Omega$; $R_F = R_C = 17.13\text{ k}\Omega$

---

As we have already seen in previous chapters, inductor-capacitor circuits are inherently well-suited to produce sinusoidal oscillations. There are several types of *L-C* oscillators that have been used for many decades to provide desired output frequencies for applications including radio transmission and reception and test and measurement circuits. Many of these designs have been named for pioneer engineers who developed the designs, the most common being the Colpitts, Hartley, Clapp, and Armstrong oscillators. In this section we will examine the basic operation of the Colpitts and Hartley oscillators.

## 30.5 LC Oscillators

### Colpitts Oscillator

The basic circuit of the Colpitts oscillator is shown in Figure 30–25. In this circuit, the feedback network consists of $C_1$, $L$, and $C_2$. It can be shown the impedance of this network (between the input and the output) is dependent on the frequency and is given as

$$\mathbf{Z}(j\omega) = \frac{1 + (j\omega)^2 LC_2}{j\omega(C_1 + C_2)\left(1 + \frac{(j\omega)^2 LC_1C_2}{C_1 + C_2}\right)} \qquad (30\text{–}22)$$

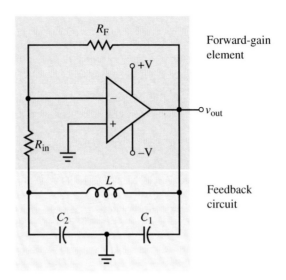

**FIGURE 30–25**   The Colpitts Oscillator.

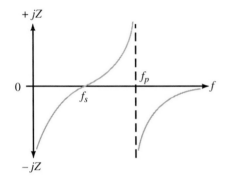

**FIGURE 30–26**   Impedance as a function of frequency for the feedback network of the Colpitts oscillator.

Figure 30–26 shows this impedance plotted as a function of frequency.

Notice that there are two frequencies of importance: $f_s$ is the series resonant frequency determined when the numerator of Equation 30–22 is zero and $f_p$ is the parallel resonant frequency (also referred to as *antiresonance*) found when the denominator is zero (called a *pole*). For the circuit shown, the L-C network provides 180° of phase shift at the parallel resonant frequency, which we see is determined by the expression,

$$f_0 = \frac{1}{2\pi\sqrt{L\dfrac{C_1 C_2}{C_1 + C_2}}} \qquad (30\text{–}23)$$

---

**EXAMPLE 30–8**

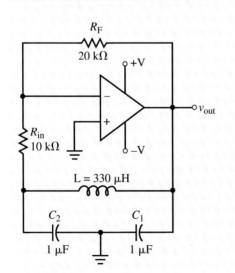

**FIGURE 30–27**

Determine the resonant frequency for the Colpitts oscillator shown in Figure 30–27.

**Solution**
By applying Equation 30–23, we determine the resonant frequency of this circuit to be

$$f_0 = \frac{1}{2\pi\sqrt{L\dfrac{C_1 C_2}{C_1 + C_2}}} = \frac{1}{2\pi\sqrt{(330\ \mu H)(0.5\ \mu F)}} = 12.39\ \text{kHz}$$

This circuit will be later examined using computer simulation.

## Hartley Oscillator

Figure 30–28 shows the Hartley oscillator, which is similar to the Colpitts oscillator except that the locations of capacitors and inductors are interchanged. As expected, the impedance of this network is frequency dependent and can be shown to be

$$\mathbf{Z}(j\omega) = \frac{j\omega L_1\left(1 + (j\omega)^2 L_2 C\right)}{1 + (j\omega)^2\left(L_1 + L_2\right)C} \tag{30–24}$$

Figure 30–29 shows this impedance plotted as a function of frequency.

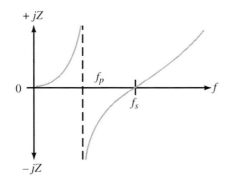

FIGURE 30–28   The Hartley oscillator.

**FIGURE 30–29**   Impedance as a function of frequency for the feedback network of the Hartley oscillator.

As before, there are two frequencies of importance: $f_s$, which is the series resonant frequency, and $f_p$, the parallel resonant frequency, which is found when the denominator is zero. Once again, the *L-C* network provides 180° of phase shift at the parallel resonant frequency, which from the expression for impedance (Equation 30–24) is determined as,

$$f_0 = \frac{1}{2\pi\sqrt{\left(L_1 + L_2\right)C}} \tag{30–25}$$

---

Determine the resonant frequency for the Hartley oscillator shown in Figure 30–30.

**PRACTICE PROBLEMS 4**

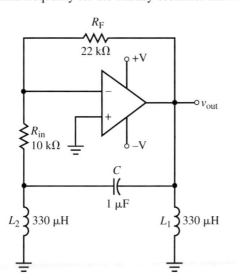

**FIGURE 30–30**

*Answer*
6195 Hz

As mentioned previously, the Colpitts and Hartley sinusoidal oscillators may also be constructed by using either bipolar junction transistors or junction field effect transistors. Figure 30–31 shows the transistor equivalent forms of the Colpitts oscillator, while Figure 30–32 shows the Hartley oscillator. The operation of these circuits is similar to the operation of op-amp oscillators. As is the case with the op-amp oscillators, each transistor must provide not only the required 180° of phase shift, but must also have sufficient forward gain to ensure oscillations can be sustained. The frequency of oscillation for each of

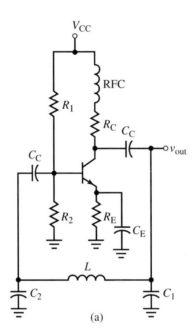
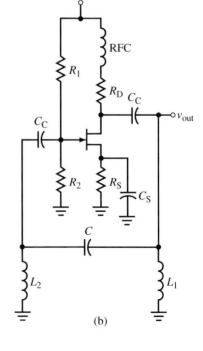

(a)

(b)

**FIGURE 30–31**

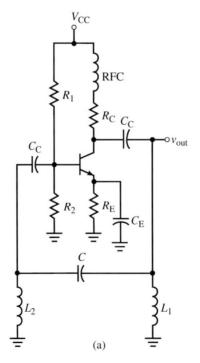

(a)

(b)

**FIGURE 30–32**

the circuits will be very nearly the same as those for op-amps, with the exception that stray capacitance due to the terminals of the transistors will result in slight variation. The RF choke (RFC) in each circuit helps to remove unwanted high-frequency (radio frequency) components from the output.

## 30.6 Crystal Oscillators

Although inductors, capacitors, and resistors are used to set oscillator frequencies for low-frequency requirements (less than 1 MHz), these components are not stable enough or accurate enough to provide the required feedback circuits for high-frequency oscillators. Quartz crystals offer improved stability, accuracy, and reliability for the high-frequency oscillators that are used in transmitters, receivers, computers, and watches. If a circuit requires lower (or higher) operating frequencies, the clock frequency can be applied to a divider or multiplier network.

The quartz crystal is a crystal of silicon dioxide, $SiO_2$, the same material that is used to provide insulation in an integrated circuit. The property that makes this crystal ideal for oscillators is its **piezoelectric effect.** When the crystal is subjected to mechanical pressure, an electric field is developed at right angles to the applied pressure. Conversely, if an electrical field is applied to the crystal, the material will deflect at right angles to the applied field. A quartz crystal that is used for oscillator circuits will be cut from very pure material and have a frequency that is dependent on the thickness of the cut and the angle at which the cut is taken within the base material. The most common crystal used in electronic circuits uses the "AT" cut, which consists of a slab cut so that one side of the crystal is along the x-axis and the main plane is at 35° with respect to the z-axis as illustrated in Figure 30–33.

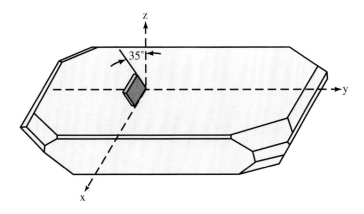

**FIGURE 30–33**  A quartz crystal showing the "AT" cut.

The crystal is mounted between two parallel plates, which are then connected to two external pins. Although the crystal is a mechanical device, the circuit shown in Figure 30–34 is an electrical model its operation. In the diagram shown, the capacitor, $C_0$, is the shunt capacitance between the crystal electrodes. The resistor, $R_1$, represents the bulk resistance between the terminals and gives rise to the losses within the crystal. The capacitance, $C_1$, is the motional capacitance representing the elasticity of the quartz; the inductance, $L_1$, is the motional inductance, which represents the vibrating mass of the crystal.

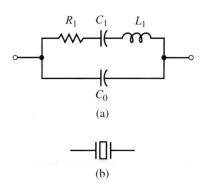

**FIGURE 30–34**  Electrical model and symbol of the quartz crystal.

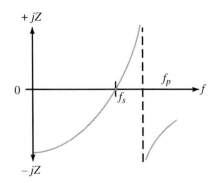

**FIGURE 30–35**
Impedance as a function of frequency for a quartz crystal.

The electrical properties shown in Figure 30–34 result in crystal impedance that varies as a function of frequency. This response is shown in Figure 30–35. You will notice that the response is very similar to that of the feedback circuit in the Colpitts oscillator, which we examined in the previous section. In fact, the crystal is normally connected into the feedback loop with two capacitors as illustrated in Figure 30–36. The active element in this circuit is a CMOS inverter. Since the inverter provides only two outputs ("1" $\approx +5$ V and "0" $\approx 0$ V ), the circuit operates as a square oscillator.

The capacitors in the circuit of Figure 30–36 are selected to result in an equivalent circuit capacitance that will cause the crystal to oscillate at a frequency that falls between the series resonant frequency $f_s$ and the parallel resonant frequency, $f_p$.

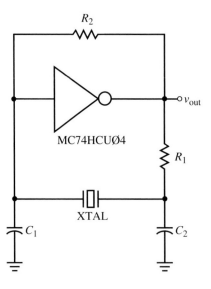

**FIGURE 30–36**

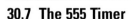

## 30.7 The 555 Timer

The 555 timer is an integrated circuit that allows accurate timing of single-occurrence events (monostable timing) or allows for oscillation in the astable mode. Figure 30–37 shows the simplified internal circuit of a 555 timer.

In the circuit, the 5-k$\Omega$ resistors form a voltage divider network. When connected into a circuit, each resistor will drop a voltage of $V_{CC}/3$. The bottom comparator will have an output of $+V_{SAT}$ when the *trigger* voltage is less than $V_{CC}/3$ and an output of 0 V when the trigger voltage is greater than $V_{CC}/3$. The top comparator will have an output of 0 V when the *threshold* voltage is less than the *control* voltage of $2V_{CC}/3$ and the output will be $+V_{SAT}$ when the *threshold* voltage goes above $2V_{CC}/3$. Notice that it is impossible for the outputs of both comparators to be $+V_{SAT}$ at the same time. (This characteristic becomes important when we consider the operation of the R-S flip-flop circuit.)

The outputs of both comparators are then applied to the input of a logic circuit called the **R-S flip-flop circuit.** This part of the timer circuit is instrumental in determining the output. The R-S flip-flop circuit is a sequential logic circuit, which means that output is not only dependent on the present values of the input, but rather may also be dependent on the previous output condition. (In other words, this device has memory.) Although the actual operation of the

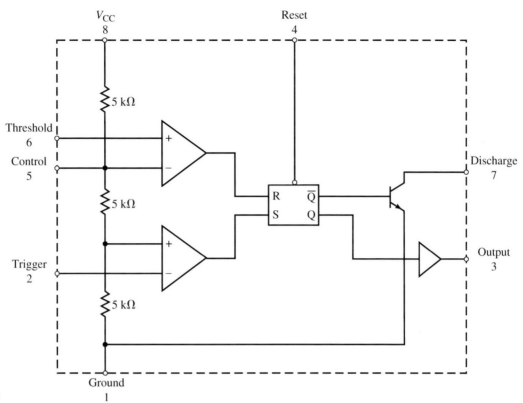

**FIGURE 30–37**

R-S flip-flop is outside the scope of this textbook, its operation can be summarized with a truth table as shown in Table 30–1.

The truth table shows us that the SET-action (S = 1, R = 0) causes the Q-output to go HIGH ($\equiv$1) with the complement, $\overline{Q}$ = 0. Conversely, the RESET-action (R = 1, S = 0) causes the $\overline{Q}$-output to go HIGH and the complement, Q = 0. In the case where S = R = 0, there will no change (N/C) occurring at the output. Consequently, the output of the R-S flip-flop will remain at whatever the previous condition was. Lastly, the case where S = R = 1 is referred to as the "forbidden condition" since this would result in Q = $\overline{Q}$, which is contradictory. If a 555-timer circuit is designed correctly, this condition will not occur.

**TABLE 30–1    Truth Table for an R-S Flip-Flop Circuit**

| S | R | Q | $\overline{Q}$ |
|---|---|-----|-----|
| 0 | 0 | N/C | N/C |
| 0 | 1 | 0 | 1 |
| 1 | 0 | 1 | 0 |
| 1 | 1 | F | F |

## Relaxation Oscillator (Astable Operation)

Figure 30–38 shows the 555 timer used as relaxation oscillator. If we assume that the capacitor is initially uncharged, the capacitor will go through a charge-discharge sequence as outlined below.

1. With the *trigger* voltage less than $V_{CC}/3$, the output of the bottom comparator will be HIGH, causing the R-S flip-flop to *set* (Q = 1 and $\overline{Q}$ = 0). The output of the 555 timer will be $+V_{CC}$ and the discharge transistor will be off.

2. As the voltage across the capacitor increases beyond $V_{CC}/3$, the output of the bottom comparator goes LOW. Since both inputs of the R-S flip-flop are LOW, the outputs will retain the same values as Step 1.

3. When the *threshold* voltage goes above $2 V_{CC}/3$, then the output of the top comparator will go high, causing the R-S flip-flop to *reset* (Q = 0 and $\overline{Q}$ = 1). The output of the 555 timer will be zero volts. The B-E junction of the discharge transistor will be forward biased, allowing the transistor to provide a low-resistance path to discharge a capacitor through $R_B$.

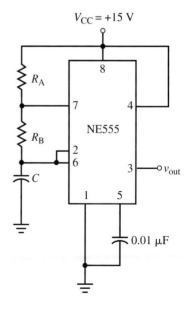

**FIGURE 30–38**

4. The outputs of the R-S flip-flop can also be reset ($Q = 0$ and $\overline{Q} = 1$) by applying a low voltage to the reset input. (The reset pin of the timer shown in Figure 30–38 is disabled by connecting it to $V_{CC}$ to prevent noise pulses from inadvertently resetting the device.)

5. In the circuit of Figure 30–38, the capacitor, $C$, alternately charges from the trigger voltage level ($\approx V_{CC}/3$) to the threshold voltage level ($\approx 2V_{CC}/3$). The resulting waveforms observed across the capacitor and at the output of the 555 timer are shown in Figure 30–39. (In a lab you will not normally see the voltage buildup occurring from $t = 0$.)

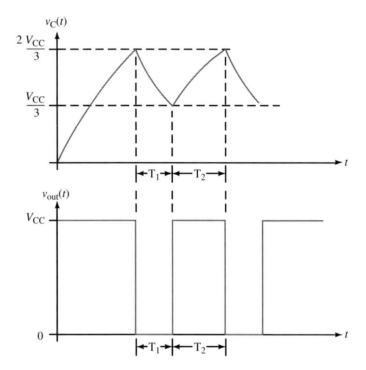

**FIGURE 30–39**

6. By applying discharge and charge equations to the circuit, it can be shown that the following expressions are derived.

$$T_1 = (\ln 2)(R_B C) \tag{30–26}$$

and

$$T_2 = (\ln 2)(R_A + R_B)C \tag{30–27}$$

Therefore, the period of oscillation for the relaxation oscillator is the sum of Equations 30–26 and 30–27, namely

$$T = (\ln 2)(R_A + 2R_B)C \tag{30–28}$$

Finally, the frequency of oscillation is determined as the reciprocal of Equation 30–28:

$$f = \frac{1}{(\ln 2)\left(R_A + 2R_B\right)C} \approx \frac{1.44}{\left(R_A + 2R_B\right)C} \tag{30–29}$$

EXAMPLE 30-9

If $R_A = R_B = 7.5$ k$\Omega$ and $C = 0.1$ $\mu$F in the circuit of Figure 30–38, determine the frequency of oscillation.

**Solution**

$$f \approx \frac{1.44}{(R_A + 2R_B)C} = \frac{1.44}{(7.5 \text{ k}\Omega + 2\{7.5 \text{ k}\Omega\})0.1\,\mu\text{F}} = 640 \text{ Hz}$$

## One-Shot (Monostable) Operation

As well as providing **astable operation** as a relaxation oscillator, the 555 timer can be used as a monostable circuit, which provides a single pulse each time the trigger voltage goes low. The resulting output pulse will have a minimum duration, regardless of how short the trigger pulse was. This condition is ideally suited for alarm circuits, which will continue to provide an alarm, even if the alarm trigger was reset. The duration of the output pulse is determined by the timing circuit and can be adjusted to be active from several seconds up to many minutes. The **monostable circuit** is shown in Figure 30–40.

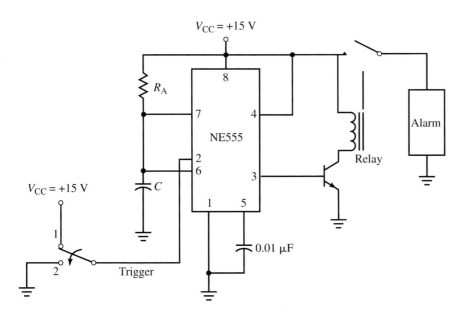

**FIGURE 30–40**

In Figure 30–40, we see that the voltage normally applied to the trigger input of the 555 timer circuit is +15 V. This high voltage will keep the output of the bottom comparator of the 555 timer low, and so the output voltage applied to the external transistor will also be low, keeping this transistor (and the alarm) off. At the same time, the internal discharge transistor will be turned on, preventing the capacitor from charging. When the switch in the trigger circuit is activated, the resulting low voltage at the trigger input will cause the bottom comparator to SET the R-S flip-flop, causing the output to go high. The high voltage forward biases the external transistor, closing the relay, and resulting in an alarm. Simultaneously, the internal transistor is turned off, allowing the capacitor to charge through $R_A$. The alarm will stay on until the capacitor, which is initially uncharged, reaches a voltage of $2\ V_{CC}/3$. Once the capacitor begins charging, the charging will continue even though the input switch may have been reset. The duration of the output pulse is given as

$$T_W = (\ln 3)R_A C \approx 1.10 R_A C \qquad\qquad (30\text{–}30)$$

The diagram of Figure 30–41 shows a typical trigger pulse and the corresponding waveforms that would be observed across the capacitor (threshold) and at the output terminal of the 555 timer.

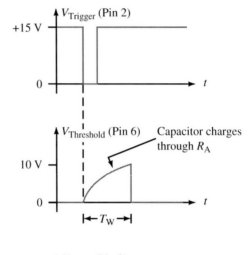

**FIGURE 30–41**

**EXAMPLE 30–10**

Determine component values for the circuit of Figure 30–40 so that the alarm will sound for a minimum of 30 seconds if the switch in the trigger circuit goes from position *1* to position *2*.

**Solution**

We begin by selecting a suitable value of resistance for $R_A$. The manufacturer suggests component values between $R_A = 2\ k\Omega$ to $100\ k\Omega$. We arbitrarily select a value of $R_A = 10\ k\Omega$. The capacitor value is then determined by applying Equation 30–30 as follows:

$$C \approx \frac{T_W}{1.10 R_A} = \frac{30\ s}{1.10(10\ k\Omega)} = 2730\ \mu F$$

If we were to use a larger capacitor, say $C = 3000\ \mu F$, the alarm would be activated for slightly longer than 30 s.

## 30.8 The Voltage Controlled Oscillator—VCO

Voltage controlled oscillators (VCOs) are used in numerous electronic applications to provide an output frequency that changes as the magnitude of input voltage changes. In particular, VCOs are used as both **frequency modulator** (FM) and demodulator circuits. VCO circuits can be constructed using discrete components or by using 555 timers. However, the most common VCO circuits now use an integrated circuit specially designed for the application. The LM566C is a general purpose VCO that uses an external resistor and capacitor to produce both a square wave and a (sawtooth) triangular waveform. The output frequency varies linearly as a function of the input voltage. Figure 30–42 shows both the connection diagram and block diagram of the 8-pin package to help understand the basic circuit operation of the circuit. A 1-nF capacitor connected between pins 5 and 6 prevents unwanted parasitic oscillations that may occur during switching of the VCO.

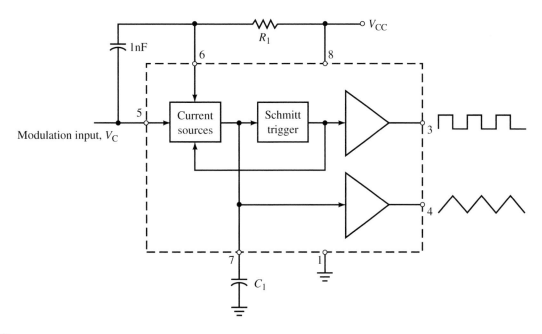

**FIGURE 30–42**

In order for the LM566 VCO to operate, the modulating voltage, $V_C$, must be applied between 0.75 $V_{CC}$ and $V_{CC}$. The output frequency of the VCO is dependent on the supply voltage, $R_1$, $C_1$, and the modulating voltage, $V_C$, according to the relationship of Equation 30–31.

$$f_0 = \frac{2.4(V_{CC} - V_C)}{R_1 C_1 V_{CC}} \qquad (30\text{--}31)$$

The manufacturer recommends that the timing resistor have a value between $R_1 = 2 \ \text{k}\Omega$ to $20 \ \text{k}\Omega$.

**EXAMPLE 30–11**

Refer to the circuit shown in Figure 30–43.

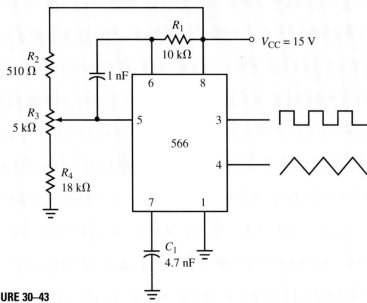

**FIGURE 30–43**

a. Determine the output frequency when the wiper (center terminal of $R_3$) is at 0% (bottom), 25%, 50%, 75%, and 100% (top).

b. Sketch the output frequency (in kHz) as a function of the modulating voltage (V).

**Solution**

a. When the wiper is at 0%, the modulating voltage is

$$V_C = \left( \frac{18\ k\Omega}{18\ k\Omega + 5\ k\Omega + 0.51\ k\Omega} \right)15\ V = 11.5\ V$$

and so the output frequency is

$$f = \frac{2.4}{(10\ k\Omega)(4.7\ nF)}\left( \frac{15\ V - 11.5\ V}{15\ V} \right)$$

$$= (51.06\ kHz)(0.2344) = 12.0\ kHz$$

When the wiper is at 25%, we have

$$V_C = \left( \frac{19.25\ k\Omega}{23.51\ k\Omega} \right)15\ V = 12.3\ V$$

and

$$f = (51.06\ kHz)\left( \frac{15\ V - 12.3\ V}{15\ V} \right) = 9.3\ kHz$$

When the wiper is at 50%, we have $V_C = 13.1$ V and $f = 6.5$ kHz; when the wiper is at 75%, we have $V_C = 13.9$ V and $f = 3.8$ kHz; and when the wiper is at 100%, we have $V_C = 14.7$ V and $f = 1.1$ kHz.

b. Figure 30–44 shows the plot of frequency as a function of modulating voltage. Notice the linearity of this graph. It is this linear relationship that makes the LM566 VCO an ideal circuit for low-frequency FM.

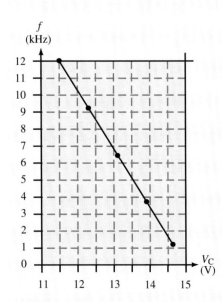

**FIGURE 30–44**

Figure 30–45 shows how the LM566 can be used to provide an FM output waveform. In this circuit, the resistors $R_2$ and $R_3$, establish the center frequency, $f_C$, of the oscillator. The modulating input will cause the VCO frequency to vary around the center frequency. This variation, called the **frequency deviation, δ (delta)** is dependent on the amplitude of the modulating signal.

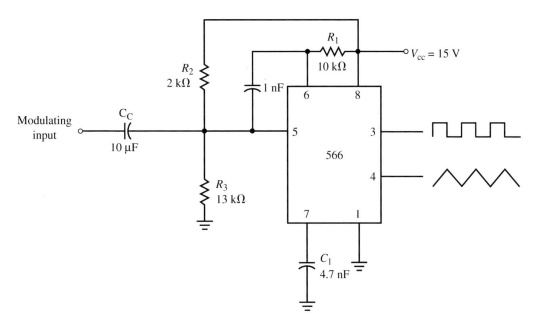

**FIGURE 30–45**

Determine the center frequency in the circuit of Figure 30–45. If the modulating input is 2.0 $V_{p\text{-}p}$, determine the frequency deviation at the output of the VCO.

IN-PROCESS
LEARNING CHECK 2

*(Answers are at the end of the chapter.)*

### MultiSIM

MultiSIM and PSpice are extremely useful tools to analyze oscillator circuits. Oscillator circuits are difficult to design because the conditions required to sustain oscillations do not exist at all frequencies. Using a software package allows very simple modification of a circuit and easily shows the corresponding change in output. In this section, we examine some of the oscillators that were analyzed in previous sections of this chapter. You will find that the results very closely follow the theoretical calculations.

## 30.9 Computer Analysis

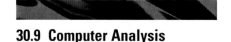

**EXAMPLE 30–12**

Use MultiSIM to observe the output waveform for the circuit of Figure 30–27. Use cursors to find the period of the waveform and compare the frequency to the theoretical frequency determined in Example 30–8.

### Solution

After entering the circuit in MultiSIM, we have the schematic as illustrated in Figure 30–46.

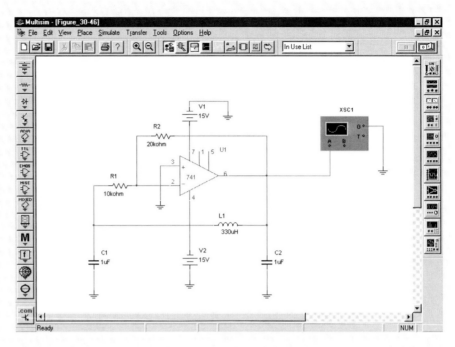

◀ MULTISIM

**FIGURE 30–46**

After the circuit has been entered, we click on the RUN/STOP button to obtain the oscilloscope display shown in Figure 30–47. Occasionally, it is necessary to wait a few seconds for the oscillations to begin.

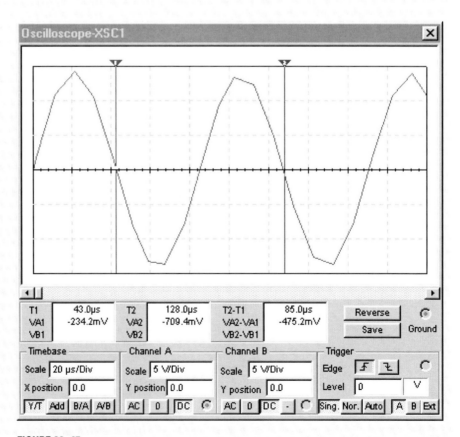

**FIGURE 30–47**

From the waveform observed in Figure 30–47, we see that the period of oscillation is $T = 85$ μs. The corresponding frequency of oscillation is determined as $f = 11.76$ kHz. These values correspond closely to the predicted value of 12.39 kHz. The discrepancy is likely due to the software accounting for parasitic capacitance of the component leads.

---

Use MultiSIM to construct the phase shift oscillator shown in Figure 30–24. Run the simulation to determine the frequency of oscillation and compare the result to the predicted frequency of oscillation in Example 30–7.

PRACTICE PROBLEMS 5

*Answer*
$f = 2878$ Hz compares well to the theoretical value of $f = 2953$ Hz.

## PSpice

Use PSpice to construct the 555-relaxation oscillator circuit shown in Figure 30–38. Let $R_A = R_B = 7.5$ kΩ and $C = 0.1$ μF. Note: Since PSpice does not permit any open or unused terminals, it is necessary to connect a load resistor (say $R_L = 1$ kΩ) between the output terminal and ground. Display the output voltage (pin 3) and the capacitor voltage (pin 6) using the Probe postprocessor. Measure the period and calculate the frequency of oscillation. Compare these values to the theoretical calculations.

EXAMPLE 30–13

### Solution
The resulting PSpice diagram is shown in Figure 30–48, and the display in the Probe postprocessor is shown in Figure 30–49.

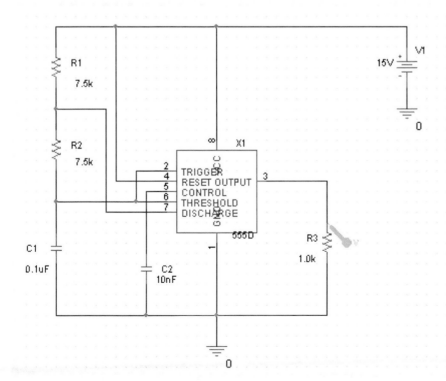

**FIGURE 30–48**

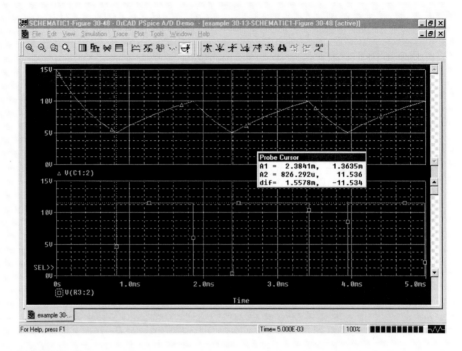

**FIGURE 30–49**

By using the cursors, we determine the period of oscillation to be $T = 1.56$ ms, which results in a frequency, $f = 641$ Hz. This result is same as that found in Example 30–10.

## PUTTING IT INTO PRACTICE

As part of a home laboratory, you would like to have an oscillator that provides a square wave, a triangular wave, and a sine-wave output. You would like the frequency of each waveform to be within a range of 1 kHz to 2 kHz. Use the skills developed in this chapter to design a suitable circuit using commercially available component values. Simulate the operation of the circuit using either MultiSIM or PSpice.

## PROBLEMS

### 30.1  Basics of Feedback

1. Given the non-inverting amplifier shown in Figure 30–50, determine the feedback ratio, $B$, and solve for the closed loop gain if the open-loop gain of the op-amp is 500.

2. Repeat Problem 1 if the open-loop gain of the op-amp is 1000.

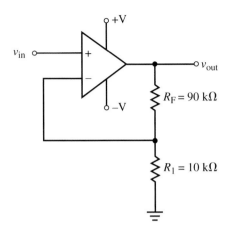

**FIGURE 30–50**

## 30.2   The Relaxation Oscillator

3. Given that $R_1 = 2$ k$\Omega$ and $R_2 = 3$ k$\Omega$ in the Schmitt trigger circuit shown in Figure 30–51:

   a.  Sketch the hysteresis curve for the circuit.

   b.  Sketch the corresponding output for the given input waveform.

4. If $R_1 = 4$ k$\Omega$ and $R_2 = 4$ k$\Omega$ in the Schmitt trigger circuit shown in Figure 30–51:

   a.  Sketch the hysteresis curve for the circuit.

   b.  Sketch the corresponding output for the given input waveform.

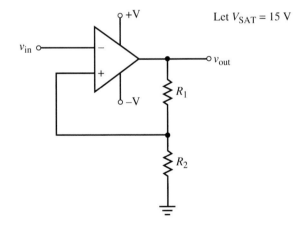

Let $V_{SAT} = 15$ V

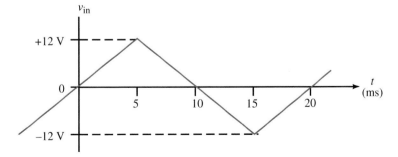

**FIGURE 30–51**

5. If $R_1 = 2$ kΩ, $R_2 = 3$ kΩ, $R_F = 10$ kΩ, and $R_{in} = 10$ kΩ in the Schmitt trigger circuit shown in Figure 30–52.

   a. Sketch the hysteresis curve for the circuit.

   b. Determine the value of the reference voltage, $V_{REF}$.

   c. Sketch the corresponding output for the given input waveform.

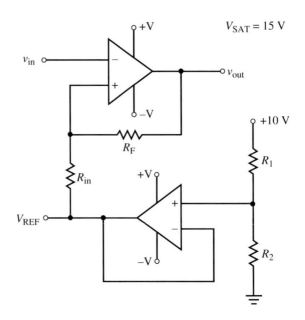

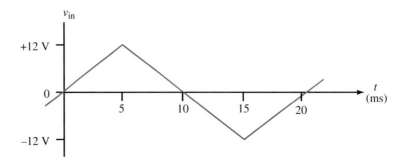

**◀ MULTISIM**    **FIGURE 30–52**

6. If $R_1 = 3$ kΩ, $R_2 = 2$ kΩ, $R_F = 20$ kΩ, and $R_{in} = 10$ kΩ in the Schmitt trigger circuit shown in Figure 30–52.

   a. Sketch the hysteresis curve for the circuit.

   b. Determine the value of the reference voltage, $V_{REF}$.

   c. Sketch the corresponding output for the given input waveform.

7. If $R_1 = 3$ kΩ, $R_2 = 2$ kΩ, $R_F = 20$ kΩ, and $C = 0.20$ μF in the circuit illustrated in Figure 30–53.

   a. Sketch the capacitor voltage, $v_C$.

   b. Sketch the output voltage, $v_{out}$. Label the times and amplitudes correctly.

8. If $R_1 = 10$ kΩ, $R_2 = 20$ kΩ, $R_F = 20$ kΩ, and $C = 0.10$ μF in the circuit illustrated in Figure 30–53.

   a. Sketch the capacitor voltage, $v_C$.

   b. Sketch the output voltage, $v_{out}$. Label the times and amplitudes correctly.

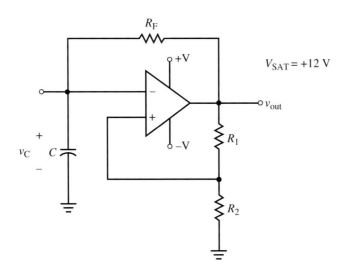

**FIGURE 30–53**

## 30.3    The Wien Bridge Oscillator

9. If $R_{in} = R_1 = R_2 = 10$ kΩ and $C_1 = C_2 = 0.22$ μF in the circuit shown in Figure 30–54:

   a.  What is the minimum value of $R_F$ to ensure that oscillations can begin?

   b.  Determine the frequency of oscillation.

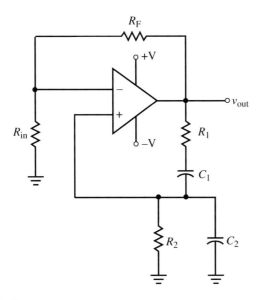

**FIGURE 30–54**

◀ MULTISIM

10. What values of capacitor, $C$ would be needed in the circuit of Problem 9 so that the output frequency is 1 kHz.

11. If $R_1 = 2R_2$ in the circuit of Figure 30–54, what would be the feedback ratio, $B$? How much forward gain would the amplifier need?

12. If $R_2 = 2R_1$ in the circuit of Figure 30–54, what would be the feedback ratio, $B$? How much forward gain would the amplifier need?

## 30.4 The Phase-Shift Oscillator

13. Given that the circuit of Figure 30–55 has component values $C = 0.047$ μF, $R = 1.5$ kΩ, and $R_{F1} = 33$ kΩ:

  a. Determine the frequency of oscillation.

  b. What is the minimum value of $R_{F2}$ to ensure that oscillation will occur?

  c. What should be the value of the compensating resistor, $R_C$?

  d. At the required amplifier gain, what is the bandwidth of the amplifier if the gain-bandwidth product for the op-amp is $2 \times 10^6$ Hz.

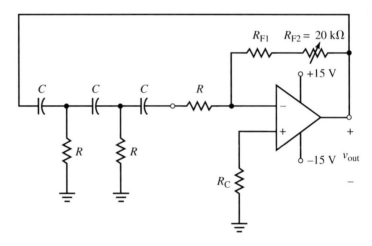

**FIGURE 30–55**

14. Given that the circuit of Figure 30–55 has component values $C = 0.01$ μF, $R = 2.0$ kΩ, and $R_{F1} = 47$ kΩ:

  a. Determine the frequency of oscillation.

  b. What is the minimum value of $R_{F2}$ to ensure that oscillation will occur?

  c. What should be the value of the compensating resistor, $R_C$?

  d. At the required amplifier gain, what is the bandwidth of the amplifier if the gain-bandwidth product for the op-amp is $2 \times 10^6$ Hz.

15. Using the same capacitor values, redesign the phase-shift oscillator of Problem 13 to have a resonant frequency of 4.0 kHz.

16. Using the same capacitor values, redesign the phase-shift oscillator of Problem 14 to have a resonant frequency of 3.0 kHz.

## 30.5 LC Oscillators

17. Identify the type of oscillator that is illustrated in Figure 30–56. Calculate the frequency of oscillation.

18. Identify the type of oscillator that is illustrated in Figure 30–57. Calculate the frequency of oscillation.

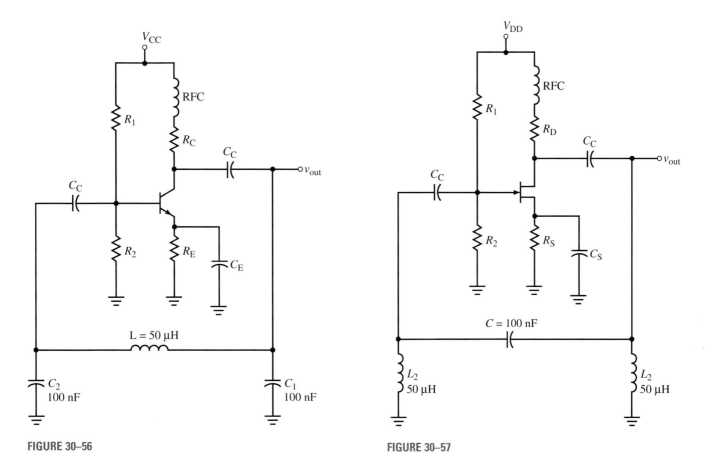

**FIGURE 30–56**                                    **FIGURE 30–57**

### 30.6   Crystal Oscillators

19. What is meant by the term *piezoelectric effect* as it relates to a quartz crystal?

20. Sketch the electrical equivalent circuit of a quartz crystal.

21. Sketch the impedance as a function of frequency for a quartz crystal.

22. When used with a CMOS inverter, a crystal oscillator will normally be tuned to operate in which of the following frequency ranges?
    a. Less than $f_s$?
    b. Between $f_s$ and $f_P$?
    c. Greater than $f_P$?

### 30.7   The 555 Timer

23. Refer to the schematic representation of the 555 timer shown in Figure 30–37. Assume that $V_{CC}$ and Ground have been connected to the timer circuit.
    a. If the trigger voltage is less than $V_{CC}/3$, what will be the value of the output voltage? Will the discharge transistor be ON or OFF?
    b. If the threshold voltage is greater than $2V_{CC}/3$, what will be the value of the output voltage? Will the discharge transistor be ON or OFF?

24. Explain the operation of the 555 timer when it is connected as an astable multivibrator.

25. Design a 555 timer as an astable multivibrator having $T_1 = 0.25$ s and $T_2 = 0.75$ s. As part of your design, let $C = 1.0$ μF.

26. Design a 555 timer as an astable multivibrator having $T_1 = 10$ ms and $T_2 = 90$ ms. As part of your design, let $C = 0.47$ μF.

27. The circuit shown in Figure 30–58 has the indicated input signal. Sketch the corresponding output signal showing expected voltage level and times.

28. Repeat Problem 27 if $R_A = 1.0$ MΩ.

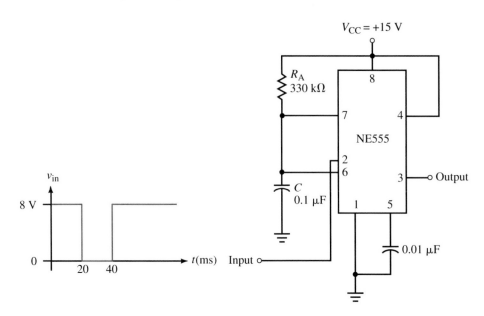

**FIGURE 30–58**

## 30.8 The Voltage Controlled Oscillator—VCO

29. a. Calculate the output frequencies for the VCO circuit shown in Figure 30–59 when the wiper of $R_3$ is at 0% (bottom), 50%, and 100% (top).

   b. Sketch the output frequency (in kHz) as a function of the modulating voltage (V).

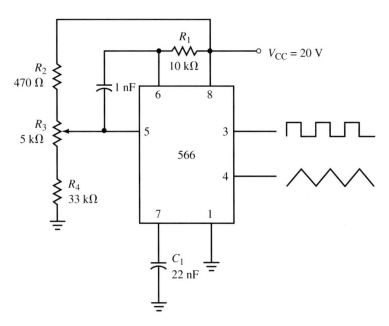

**FIGURE 30–59**

30. Repeat Problem 29 if the timing capacitor is replaced by $C_1 = 1$ nF.

## 30.9 Computer Analysis

31. Use MultiSIM to input the circuit of Figure 30–52, letting $R_1 = 2$ kΩ, $R_2 = 3$ kΩ, $R_F = 10$ kΩ, and $R_{in} = 10$ kΩ. Use 741 op-amps and supply voltages of $\pm 15$ V for the op-amps. Set the signal generator to provide the indicated triangular waveform. Observe the output voltage and compare this result to the predicted output that you determined in Problem 5.   ◀ MULTISIM

32. Use MultiSIM and repeat Problem 31 letting $R_1 = 3$ kΩ, $R_2 = 2$ kΩ, $R_F = 20$ kΩ, and $R_{in} = 10$ kΩ.   ◀ MULTISIM

33. Use MultiSIM to input the circuit of Figure 30–54, letting $R_{in} = R_1 = R_2 = 10$ kΩ, $R_F = 33$ kΩ, and $C_1 = C_2 = 0.22$ μF. Use a 741 op-amp and supply voltages of $\pm 15$ V. Observe the output voltage and compare this result to the predicted output that you determined in Problem 9.   ◀ MULTISIM

34. Use MultiSIM to input the circuit of Figure 30–54, letting $R_{in} = R_1 = R_2 = 10$ kΩ, $R_F = 33$ kΩ. Use the value of $C_1 = C_2 = C$ determined in Problem 10. Observe the output signal. You should observe that the frequency is 1 kHz.   ◀ MULTISIM

35. Use PSpice to input the circuit of Figure 30–53, letting $R_1 = 3$ kΩ, $R_2 = 2$ kΩ, $R_F = 20$ kΩ, and $C = 0.20$ μF. Use 741 op-amps and supply voltages of $\pm 15$ V for the op-amps.   ◀ CADENCE

   a. Use the Probe postprocessor to obtain the capacitor voltage, $v_C$ and the output voltage, $v_{out}$.

   b. Compare the predicted results to those obtained in Problem 7.

36. Use PSpice and repeat Problem 35, $R_1 = 10$ kΩ, $R_2 = 20$ kΩ, $R_F = 20$ kΩ, and $C = 0.10$ μF. Compare the observed results to the predicted results of Problem 8.   ◀ CADENCE

37. Use PSpice to input the astable multivibrator designed in Problem 25. Observe the output waveform at pin 3 of the 555 timer. Compare your results to the required characteristics.   ◀ CADENCE

38. Use PSpice to input the astable multivibrator designed in Problem 26. Observe the output waveform at pin 3 of the 555 timer. Compare your results to the required characteristics.   ◀ CADENCE

 **ANSWERS TO IN-PROCESS LEARNING CHECKS**

**In-Process Learning Check 1**

$B = 0.4$   $A = 2.5$

**In-Process Learning Check 2**

$f_C = 6810$ Hz   $\delta = 3404$ Hz

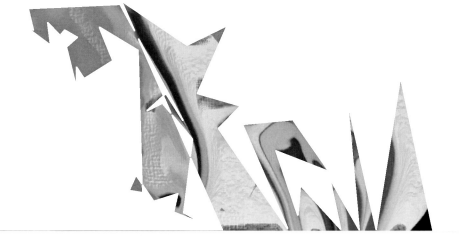

## ■ KEY TERMS

Bilateral Device

Blocking Region

Breakover Voltage

Candela

Conduction Angle

Firing Angle

Impact Ionization

Intrinsic Standoff ratio

Metastable State

Monochromatic, Coherent Light

Peak Point

Unilateral Device

Valley Point

## ■ OUTLINE

Introduction to Thyristors

Triggering Devices

Silicon-Controlled Rectifiers (SCRs)

Triacs

Power Control Fundamentals

Introduction to Optical Devices

Photodetectors

Optocouplers

Semiconductor LASERs

Computer Analysis

## ■ OBJECTIVES

On completion of this chapter, you will be able to

- relate the firing angle to the con-duction angle of a thyristor,

- explain how various triggering devices are used to fire thyristors,

- determine the characteristics of a UJT (unijunction) transistor,

- calculate the frequency (or period) of oscillation of a UJT relaxation oscillator,

- explain the operation of an SCR (sili-con controlled rectifier) circuit,

- explain the operation and be able to analyze a triac circuit,

- identify the modes of operation of a triac and indicate which modes are the most sensitive,

- use power control fundamentals to predict the rms voltage and power delivered to a load for half-wave and full-wave control,

- solve for the frequency or wave-length of a given E/M waveform,

- identify the advantages and disad-vantages of LED displays,

- calculate the current-limiting resis-tor in an LED circuit,

- explain the basic operation of pho-todetectors, such as photodiodes and phototransistors,

- analyze and design circuits using optocouplers,

- describe the basic principle of oper-ation of semiconductor lasers.

and Optical

# 31

In this chapter you will examine several electronic devices that use low-voltage signals to control high-voltage, high-current circuits. Almost everyone has used light dimmers to set the mood at a dinner table or used a potentiometer to control the speed of an electric motor. In this chapter you will learn about thyristors, four-layer devices that are used to perform these functions. You will also examine some of the ways that these devices can be triggered and, more importantly, how they are turned off.

We conclude the chapter by examining optical devices, from the common LED to less common photodiodes and phototransistors. You will discover that optical devices allow us to electrically isolate two circuits, functions that are extremely important in hospitals and anywhere an electrical fault can cause catastrophic results. You will also be introduced to fiber optic transmission that uses a laser as a light source to encode and transmit digital information. ■

## The LASER

LIGHT, WHICH IS SIMPLY MADE up of E/M (electromagnetic) waves, is normally generated when electrons that have been raised to a higher energy level (due to heat or some other external energy) drop from this excited level to their ground state. This process occurs randomly and is therefore called *spontaneous* emission.

In a LASER, electrons are similarly raised to a higher energy level. However, these electrons do not immediately drop to their ground state. Rather, they gather in a semi-stable level called the **metastable state.** When a photon ("particle") of light with exactly the right amount of energy strikes an electron in the metastable state, the electron drops to its ground state. This releases another photon with exactly the same energy (wavelength) and exactly in phase with the originating photon. This amplification process repeats until most of the electrons in the metastable state have dropped to the ground level. Consequently, the acronym LASER stands for *L*ight *A*mplification through *S*timulated *E*mission of *R*adiation.

The principle of laser operation was explained by two American physicists, Charles H. Townes and A. L Schawlow, in 1953. The first operational laser, consisting of a synthetic ruby cylinder, was built and patented in 1960 by Theodore H. Maiman. This laser used a xenon light source to provide the energy to raise the electrons from the ground state to a high energy state. One end of the ruby cylinder was totally silvered to reflect the light, while the other end was partially silvered to allow some of the intense beam to escape in very short duration pulses.

Modern lasers are used in numerous applications, including transmission of data over fiber optic cable, surgery, metal fabrication, surveying, and many other commercial and scientific uses. ■

## 31.1 Introduction to Thyristors

*Thyristors* are electronic devices that behave essentially as switches with two stable states. In the ON-state a thyristor is conducting, while in the OFF-state the device blocks current. Although there are several types of devices that are categorized as thyristors, each of these devices is either a **unilateral (unidirectional) device,** meaning that it conducts in one direction or a **bilateral (bidirectional) device,** which conducts in either direction. All thyristors use internal feedback to provide *latching* (or switching) action. The silicon-controlled rectifier (SCR) and the triac, respectively, are examples of unilateral and bilateral thyristors. In this chapter we will examine the operation of thyristors which, when used in combination with triggering circuits, are used in ac circuits to control the amount of power delivered to a loads such as motors, heaters, or lights. Figure 31–1 illustrates a typical circuit that uses a trigger circuit to control the **firing angle** of a thyristor.

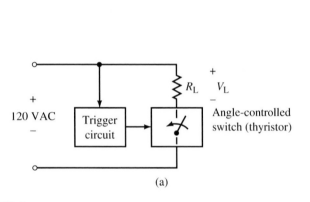

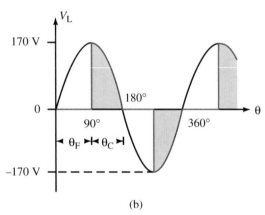

**FIGURE 31–1**

In the illustration of Figure 31–1, the trigger circuit causes the angle-controlled switch (generally a thyristor) to close at an angle of 90°. Since the load receives less than the full 180° of the supply voltage each half period, it stands to reason that the effective (rms) voltage delivered to the load will be significantly less than the rms voltage of the supply. We define the *firing angle,* $\theta_F$ of the circuit as the delay (in degrees) between the zero crossing and the closing of the angle-controlled switch. Conversely, the **conduction angle,** $\theta_C$ is defined as the number of degrees per half-cycle that the source voltage is applied to the load. Note that the following expression always holds:

$$\theta_C = 180° - \theta_F \qquad (31–1)$$

Although we could use calculus to determine the effective (rms) voltage and power applied to a load for a given firing angle, you will find that using graphs conveniently eliminates this tedious work.

## 31.2 Triggering Devices

In order to cause an angle-controlled switch to close at the correct instant, a trigger circuit must provide a suitable pulse to the switching device. Several types of triggering devices are available to provide such signals. Although the 555 timer that you examined in the previous chapter can be used to provide proper timing, the resulting circuit would be more complicated than necessary. In this section, we examine two fairly simple devices that will enable a thyristor to fire at the correct angle.

## The Diac

The diac is a three-layer, bi-directional device, which behaves in a manner similar to having two back-to-back zener diodes. Whenever the voltage across the diac exceeds the breakover voltage, $V_{BR}$ of the device, the diac will conduct. Figure 31–2(a) shows the schematic symbols that are used to represent the diac, and Figure 31–2(b) shows the characteristic curve of the device. In order for the diac to conduct, the voltage across the device must exceed the **breakover voltage,** $V_{BR}$. As long as the voltage across the diac is less than the breakover voltage, the diac is in its **blocking region,** meaning that there is very little current through the device. Once the voltage across the diac is greater than $V_{BR}$, there will be substantial current through the device, along with a reduction in voltage drop across the component. Since the diac operation is essentially the same regardless of the voltage polarity, the device can be connected into a circuit without regard to the terminal polarities.

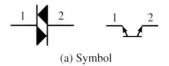

(a) Symbol

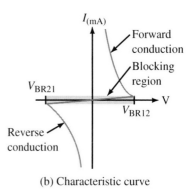

(b) Characteristic curve

**FIGURE 31–2**    The diac.

## The Unijunction Transistor (UJT)

The UJT is a three-terminal device constructed as illustrated in Figure 31–3(a) and having the symbol as illustrated in Figure 31–3(b). The emitter region is heavily doped silicon while the inter-base region is lightly doped material. When the emitter terminal is open, the resistance between the bases, $B_1$ and $B_2$ is relatively high, typically having a total resistance in the order of $R_{BB} = 5$ k$\Omega$ to 10 k$\Omega$. Figure 31–4 shows the electrical equivalent of the UJT and will be used to help explain the operation of this device. As you will discover shortly, the resistance between the emitter connection and the $B_1$ terminal is variable depending on the applied external voltage.

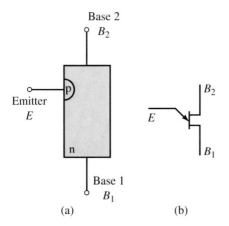

**FIGURE 31–3**    The n-channel unijunction transistor (UJT).

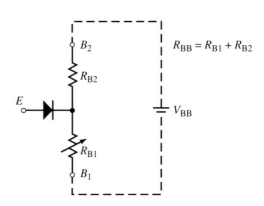

**FIGURE 31–4**    Equivalent circuit of an n-channel UJT.

When an external voltage source, $V_{BB}$, is applied between the base terminals (with the emitter open), an internal voltage will be developed across resistor, $R_{B1}$, in accordance with the voltage divider rule and is expressed as

$$V_1 = \frac{R_{B1}}{R_{B1} + R_{B2}} V_{BB} = \frac{R_{B1}}{R_{BB}} V_{BB} \qquad \textbf{(31–2)}$$

The **intrinsic standoff ratio** of the UJT is defined as the following resistance ratio:

$$\eta = \frac{R_{B1}}{R_{BB}} \qquad \textbf{(31–3)}$$

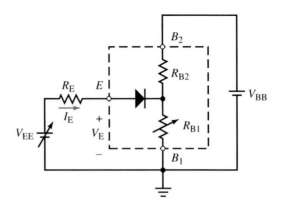

**FIGURE 31–5** UJT test circuit.

Typical values for the intrinsic standoff ratio for UJTs are in the range between $\eta = 0.5$ to 0.9. The operation of a UJT can be examined by placing the device into a test circuit as shown in Figure 31–5.

The circuit operates as follows:

1. When $V_{EE} = 0V$, the p-n junction (represented by the diode) will be reverse-biased. The current in the emitter circuit will be the result of the leakage current through this junction. (Typically in the order of a few microamps.)

2. As the applied emitter voltage is increased to a point where $V_{EE} = V_1$, the diode will begin to conduct. The emitter voltage at this point will represent the *peak voltage* of the UJT and is expressed as

$$V_P = \eta V_{BB} + V_D \qquad\qquad \textbf{(31–4)}$$

3. Since the emitter region of the UJT is heavily doped, the forward-biased p-n junction will allow holes to be injected into the base region of $R_1$, effectively reducing the resistance of this region. Consequently, the value of $V_E$ decreases, while at the same time as the current through the emitter circuit increases.

4. The reduction in resistance causes a further increase in current. The increased current results in the injection of even more carriers into the base region of $R_1$, with a corresponding reduction in the value of $R_1$.

5. Eventually a point is reached where further increase in current does not inject any more holes the lower base region. The resistance, $R_1$, has reached its minimum value. This point is referred to as the **valley point** of the UJT.

6. Further increases in the emitter current, $I_E$, cause $V_E$ to also increase. At this point the UJT is *saturated.*

Figure 31–6 illustrates the typical curve of $V_E$ as a function of $I_E$. Notice that the peak voltage is not a constant for a given transistor, but rather depends on both the intrinsic standoff ratio and the supply voltage, $V_{BB}$.

If a circuit is designed with an emitter resistance, $R_E$, that ensures the UJT operates in the negative resistance region, we can use the UJT as a relaxation oscillator. The frequency of oscillation is dependent on the rate at which an emitter capacitor, $C_E$, charges. Figure 31–7 shows a simple UJT relaxation oscillator and the corresponding emitter voltage.

If we assume that the valley voltage of the UJT is $V_V = 0$ V, that the discharge time of the capacitor is $T_D = 0$, and that the voltage across the internal

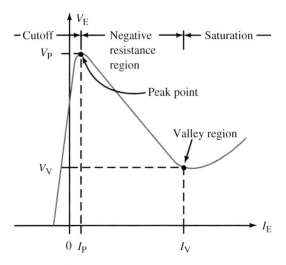

**FIGURE 31–6** Emitter current-voltage characteristics of a UJT.

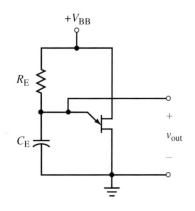

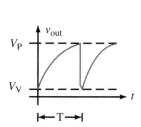

**FIGURE 31–7** UJT relaxation oscillator.

p-n junction (forward-biased diode) is also 0 V, then it can be shown that the period of oscillation for the circuit of Figure 31–7 is approximated as:

$$T \approx R_E C_E \ln\left(\frac{1}{1 - \eta}\right) \qquad \textbf{(31–5)}$$

Consequently, the frequency of oscillation for the UJT relaxation oscillator is approximately

$$f \approx \frac{1}{R_E C_E \ln\left(\dfrac{1}{1 - \eta}\right)} \qquad \textbf{(31–6)}$$

Although the circuit of shown in Figure 31–7 is useful as a relaxation oscillator, it requires an additional resistor between $B_1$ and ground in order to be used as a trigger circuit. By adding a carbon resistor between the voltage supply and $B_2$, the frequency of oscillation will remain more constant despite changes in temperature. The resulting circuit is shown in Figure 31–8. The pulses appearing across $R_1$ can now be applied to trigger thyristor circuits.

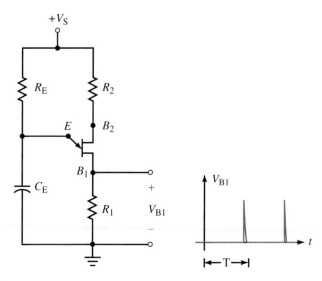

**FIGURE 31–8**

In order for the UJT oscillator to maintain its oscillations, it must operate in the negative resistance region. This means that the operating point must lie between the peak and valley points of the emitter characteristic curve. In order for the circuit to have enough current to cause the UJT to fire, the emitter resistance must have a value that is less than a value $R_{E(max)}$, determined from the peak point voltage and current as

$$R_{E(max)} = \frac{V_S - V_P}{I_P} \qquad (31\text{–}7)$$

Additionally, the value of $R_E$ must be greater than the minimum value $R_{E(min)}$, determined from the valley point as

$$R_{E(min)} = \frac{V_S - V_V}{I_V} \qquad (31\text{–}8)$$

When designing a UJT relaxation oscillator circuit, a good rule of thumb is to select

$$R_E = 3R_{E(min)} \qquad (31\text{–}9)$$

**EXAMPLE 31–1**

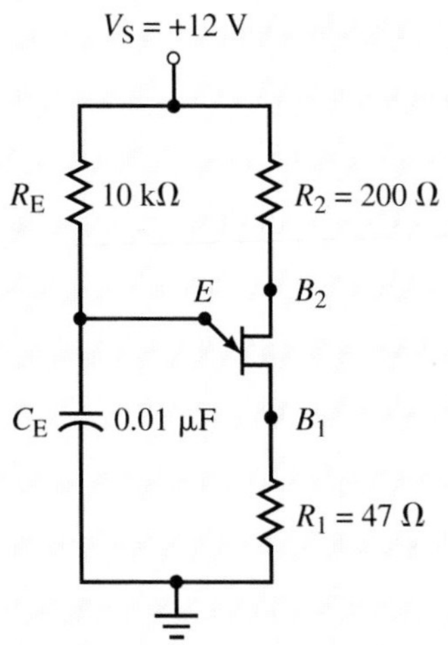

$V_S = +12$ V

$R_E$  10 kΩ    $R_2 = 200$ Ω

$E$    $B_2$

$C_E$  0.01 µF    $B_1$

$R_1 = 47$ Ω

**FIGURE 31–9**

Given that the UJT in the circuit of Figure 31–9 has the following characteristics:

Valley point: $V_V = 1.5$ V        $I_V = 2.0$ mA
Peak point: $V_P = 8.0$ V        $I_P = 2.0$ µA
$V_D = 0.6$ V
$I_{B2} = 1.8$ mA when $I_E = 0$

a. Solve for the frequency of oscillation,
b. Determine the value of $R_{BB}$ of the UJT.
c. Sketch the waveforms that you would expect to observe at $E$, $B_1$, and $B_2$.

**Solution**

a. First we solve for the intrinsic standoff ratio. From Equation 31–4 we have

$$V_P = \eta V_{BB} + V_D$$

and $\eta$ is determined as

$$\eta = \frac{V_P - V_D}{V_{BB}} = \frac{8.0 \text{ V} - 0.6 \text{ V}}{12.0 \text{ V}} = 0.617$$

The frequency of oscillation is now easily determined by applying Equation 31–6 as

$$f \approx \frac{1}{R_E C_E \ln\left(\dfrac{1}{1 - \eta}\right)}$$

$$= \frac{1}{(10 \text{ k}\Omega)(0.01 \text{ µF})\ln\left(\dfrac{1}{1 - 0.617}\right)} = 10.4 \text{ kHz}$$

b. The total resistance in the output loop of the UJT is determined from Ohm's law as

$$R_T = \frac{V_S}{I_{B2}} = \frac{12 \text{ V}}{1.8 \text{ mA}} = 6.67 \text{ k}\Omega$$

and so we solve for $R_{BB}$ as

$$R_{BB} = R_T - R_2 - R_1$$
$$= 6.66 \text{ K}\Omega - 200 \text{ }\Omega - 47 \text{ }\Omega = 6.42 \text{ k}\Omega$$

c. The waveforms that are observed at the three terminals of the UJT appear as shown in Figure 31–10. The voltage spikes appearing across $R_1$ are the result of the capacitor rapidly discharging through the low-resistance path of the forward-biased p-n junction of the emitter.

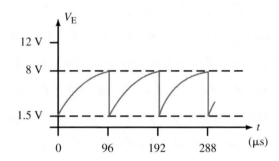

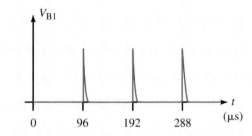

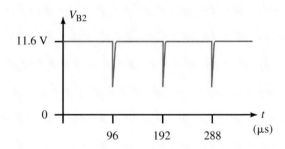

**FIGURE 31–10**

Determine the values of $R_E$ and $C_E$ so the circuit of Figure 31–9 oscillates at a frequency of 5 kHz. Let $R_E = 3R_{E(min)}$.

PRACTICE PROBLEMS 1

*Answers*
$R_E = 11.25 \text{ k}\Omega$,  $C_E = 18.5 \text{ nF}$

## 31.3 Silicon-Controlled Rectifiers (SCRs)

The SCR is a four-layer device that is equivalent to two transistors connected so that once one of the transistors is turned on, the feedback due to the other transistor will keep both transistors on even though the triggering source is removed. Figure 31–11 shows the structure, the symbol, and the electronic

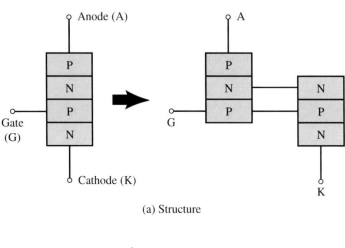

(a) Structure

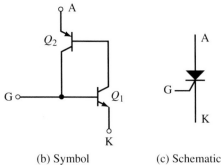

(b) Symbol          (c) Schematic

**FIGURE 31–11**   The silicon-controlled rectifier (SCR).

equivalent of the SCR. As one might expect, current through the SCR can only be in one direction, from the anode (A) to the cathode (K). The SCR can be used to provide phase control of a load for the positive half-cycle of an ac waveform, while preventing current during the negative half-cycle. Although less common, it is possible use an SCR together with a full-wave bridge rectifier to provide phase control during both positive and negative half-cycles of an ac waveform. Figure 31–12 shows the characteristic curve of a typical SCR.

The SCR operates as follows:

1. When the anode to cathode is forward-biased (assuming there is no gate current, $I_G = 0$), there will be no anode current through the device until the forward breakover voltage, $V_{DRM}$, of the device is exceeded. In the *forward blocking region,* the C-B junction of $Q_1$ is reverse-biased, allowing very little leakage current.

2. If a positive voltage is applied to the gate (relative to the cathode), the base-emitter junction of $Q_1$ will be forward-biased, resulting in a large collector current.

3. The large collector current of $Q_1$ will cause an equal amount of base current to be applied to $Q_2$.

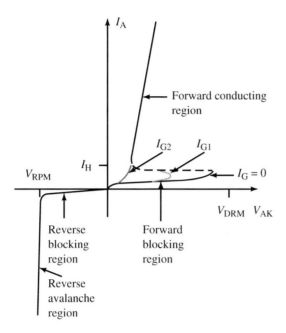

**FIGURE 31–12**   The SCR characteristic curve.

4. The resulting collector current of $Q_2$ will force $Q_1$ to be driven on even further. This regenerative feedback very quickly forces both transistors into saturation. Typical turn-on times for a low-power SCR is in the order of 0.1 to 1 μs. If the forward bias, which was initially applied between the gate and the cathode, is removed now, it will have no effect. The SCR will remain on.

5. The SCR will only turn off if the current through the device drops below the holding current, $I_H$, specified by the manufacturer. Typical holding current is in the order of $I_H = 10$ mA. The usual method to turn an SCR off is to either reverse the applied voltage (as in an ac voltage source) or to have a switch open the anode circuit.

6. Instead of applying a positive gate pulse, an SCR may also be latched on by providing a forward voltage that exceeds the forward breakover voltage, $V_{FOM}$. In this case, both transistors in the equivalent circuit go into saturation. Once again, the only way to turn the device off is by low-current dropout or by anode current interruption.

7. Other less common methods of turning an SCR on include:
   - high temperature, which would result in excessive leakage current, allowing the regenerative feedback to begin,
   - rate effect caused by high $\Delta V/\Delta t$ on the supply voltage due to a noise spike, and
   - radiation, which like an increased temperature will cause excessive charge movement.

The above methods of firing an SCR should be avoided, since they result in unpredictable and sometimes dangerous operation of high-voltage switching.

Figure 31–13 shows some of the specifications for the C106 Series SCR. There are many other SCRs available, each type having specifications that can be applied to a particular application. For example, some SCRs are capable of handling currents up to 2500 A and/or voltages up to 2500 V.

# SCRs
# 4 AMPERES RMS
# 200 thru 600 VOLTS

**MAXIMUM RATINGS** ($T_J$ = 25°C unless otherwise noted)

| Rating | Symbol | Value | Unit |
|---|---|---|---|
| Peak Repetitive Off–State Voltage (Note 1) (Sine Wave, 50–60 Hz, $R_{GK}$ = 1 kΩ, $T_C$ = –40° to 110°C)       C106B       C106D, C106D1       C106M, C106M1 | $V_{DRM}$, $V_{RRM}$ | 200 400 600 | Volts |
| On-State RMS Current (180° Conduction Angles, $T_C$ = 80°C) | $I_{T(RMS)}$ | 4.0 | Amps |
| Average On–State Current (180° Conduction Angles, $T_C$ = 80°C) | $I_{T(AV)}$ | 2.55 | Amps |
| Peak Non-Repetitive Surge Current (1/2 Cycle, Sine Wave, 60 Hz, $T_J$ = +110°C) | $I_{TSM}$ | 20 | Amps |

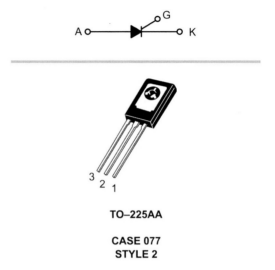

**TO–225AA**

**CASE 077**
**STYLE 2**

| PIN ASSIGNMENT | |
|---|---|
| 1 | Cathode |
| 2 | Anode |
| 3 | Gate |

## ON CHARACTERISTICS

| | | | | | | |
|---|---|---|---|---|---|---|
| Peak Forward On–State Voltage (Note 3) ($I_{TM}$ = 4 A) | | $V_{TM}$ | – | – | 2.2 | Volts |
| Gate Trigger Current (Continuous dc) (Note 4) ($V_{AK}$ = 6 Vdc, $R_L$ = 100 Ohms) | $T_J$ = 25°C $T_J$ = –40°C | $I_{GT}$ | – – | 15 35 | 200 500 | µA |
| Peak Reverse Gate Voltage ($I_{GR}$ = 10 µA) | | $V_{GRM}$ | – | – | 6.0 | Volts |
| Gate Trigger Voltage (Continuous dc) (Note 4) ($V_{AK}$ = 6 Vdc, $R_L$ = 100 Ohms) | $T_J$ = 25°C $T_J$ = –40°C | $V_{GT}$ | 0.4 0.5 | 0.60 0.75 | 0.8 1.0 | Volts |
| Gate Non–Trigger Voltage (Continuous dc) (Note 4) ($V_{AK}$ = 12 V, $R_L$ = 100 Ohms, $T_J$ = 110°C) | | $V_{GD}$ | 0.2 | – | – | Volts |
| Latching Current ($V_{AK}$ = 12 V, $I_G$ = 20 mA) | $T_J$ = 25°C $T_J$ = –40°C | $I_L$ | – – | 0.20 0.35 | 5.0 7.0 | mA |
| Holding Current ($V_D$ = 12 Vdc) (Initiating Current = 20 mA, Gate Open) | $T_J$ = 25°C $T_J$ = –40°C $T_J$ = +110°C | $I_H$ | – – – | 0.19 0.33 0.07 | 3.0 6.0 2.0 | mA |

**FIGURE 31–13** The C106 series silicon-controlled rectifier. *(Courtesy of Semiconductor Components Industries, LLC 2002)*

The circuit shown in Figure 31–14 provides phase control of an SCR with firing angles of 0° to 90°.

As the sinusoidal voltage of the applied voltage source in the circuit of Figure 31–14 increases, a point is reached where there is sufficient forward current through the gate circuit to cause the SCR to fire. Once the SCR fires, it continues to conduct for the balance of the half-cycle, until the voltage of the ac source drops below the value needed to sustain the holding current of the SCR. The diode, $D_1$, protects the SCR gate circuit from excessive voltage during negative half-cycle because the SCR will not conduct during the negative half-cycle. The value of $R_1$ limits the gate current, and, consequently, determines the angle at which the SCR fires. The operation of an SCR can be simply explained by applying circuit theory.

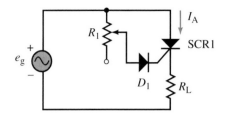

**FIGURE 31–14**  SCR providing $0° \rightarrow 90°$ phase control.

Refer to the circuit of Figure 31–14. Assume that you are given a voltage source having amplitude of 30 V, operating at a frequency of 60 Hz, and load resistance of $R_L = 15\ \Omega$. The SCR has a gate trigger current, $I_{GT} = 100\ \mu A$, and a gate trigger voltage of $V_{GT} = 0.6$ V. Determine the range of values for resistor $R_1$ so that the SCR will trigger between 10° and 90°.

**EXAMPLE 31–2**

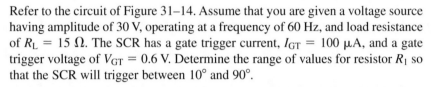

**Solution**

*At $\theta = 10°$ triggering:* The instantaneous voltage is $v(10°) = 30\sin 10° = 5.21$ V. Since the current through the SCR is $I_A = 0$, we write the Kirchhoff voltage law equation as

$$5.21\ V = I_G R_L + I_G R_1 + V_{D1} + V_{GT}$$
$$= (100\ \mu A)(15\ \Omega) + (100\ \mu A)R_1 + 0.7\ V + 0.6\ V$$

and so

$$R_1 = \frac{5.21\ V - 0.0015 - 0.7\ V - 0.6\ V}{100\ \mu A} = 39.1\ k\Omega$$

*At $\theta = 90°$ triggering:* The instantaneous voltage is $v(90°) = 30$ V. Using the same approach as before, we have

$$R_1 = \frac{30\ V - 0.0015 - 0.7\ V - 0.6\ V}{100\ \mu A} = 287\ k\Omega$$

In order for the SCR to have triggering control between 10° and 90°, the value of $R_1$ must be adjustable between 39 k$\Omega$ and 287 k$\Omega$.

The circuit of Figure 31–15 shows an SCR circuit that provides phase angle control between 0° and 180°.

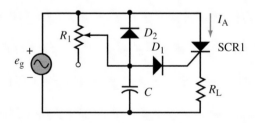

**FIGURE 31–15**  SCR providing $0° \rightarrow 180°$ phase control.

On the negative half-cycle of the input waveform, the SCR will not conduct. The capacitor, $C$, charges to the source voltage through the low forward resistance of diode $D_2$. On the positive half-cycle, the capacitor voltage will initially be negative, keeping the SCR off. As the capacitor charges through $R_1$, a point is reached at which the voltage is sufficiently positive to cause the SCR to fire. If the value of $R_1$ is small, the capacitor will quickly charge to the required positive voltage, allowing the SCR to fire at approximately 0°. Conversely, if the value of $R_1$ is large, the capacitor will slowly charge, allowing the SCR to fire as late as 180°. (If the value of $R_1$ is too large, the capacitor will charge too slowly, with the result that the SCR will not fire at all.)

Figure 31–16 shows that a UJT relaxation oscillator can be used as a source of positive pulses, enabling the SCR to fire at any angle between 0° and 180°. In this circuit, the 100-kΩ potentiometer is adjusted to provide the correct firing angle as observed with an oscilloscope connected across the load. Since the UJT will only operate on the positive half-cycle, full-wave control can be achieved if the circuit is modified with a full-wave rectifier bridge at the input.

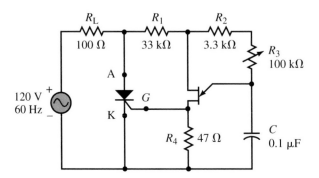

**FIGURE 31–16**   The UJT relaxation oscillator provides timing pulses to trigger the SCR.

Describe the operation of the SCR circuit shown in Figure 31–16.

## 31.4 Triacs

The triac is a three-terminal semiconductor switch, which unlike the SCR, permits current in either direction. Whereas an SCR requires a positive pulse between the gate and the cathode in order to be triggered, a pulse of either polarity can trigger the triac. The symbol and corresponding voltage-current characteristic of a triac is illustrated in Figure 31–17.

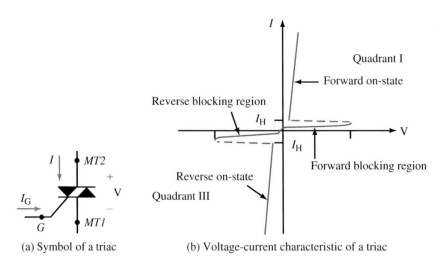

(a) Symbol of a triac      (b) Voltage-current characteristic of a triac

**FIGURE 31–17**

Since the triac is a bi-directional device, the terms *anode* and *cathode,* which are used for uni-directional devices, have no meaning. Rather, the terminals are labeled as main terminal 1, *MT1,* main terminal 2, *MT2,* and gate, *G.* (Some textbooks and data sheets use the term *anode* instead of *main terminal.*) Typical electrical specifications for a triac are shown in Figure 31–18.

## TRIACS
## 4 AMPERES RMS
## 200 thru 600 VOLTS

**MAXIMUM RATINGS** ($T_J$ = 25°C unless otherwise noted)

| Rating | Symbol | Value | Unit |
|---|---|---|---|
| *Peak Repetitive Off-State Voltage(1)<br>($T_J$ = − 40 to 110°C, Sine Wave,<br>50 to 60 Hz, Gate Open)<br>    2N6071A,B<br>    2N6073A,B<br>    2N6075A,B | $V_{DRM}$,<br>$V_{RRM}$ | <br><br><br>200<br>400<br>600 | Volts |
| *On-State RMS Current ($T_C$ = 85°C)<br>Full Cycle Sine Wave 50 to 60 Hz | $I_{T(RMS)}$ | 4.0 | Amps |
| *Peak Non–repetitive Surge Current<br>(One Full cycle, 60 Hz, $T_J$ = +110°C) | $I_{TSM}$ | 30 | Amps |
| Circuit Fusing Considerations<br>(t = 8.3 ms) | $I^2t$ | 3.7 | $A^2s$ |
| *Peak Gate Power<br>(Pulse Width ≤ 1.0 µs, $T_C$ = 85°C) | $P_{GM}$ | 10 | Watts |
| *Average Gate Power<br>(t = 8.3 ms, $T_C$ = 85°C) | $P_{G(AV)}$ | 0.5 | Watt |
| *Peak Gate Voltage<br>(Pulse Width ≤ 1.0 µs, $T_C$ = 85°C) | $V_{GM}$ | 5.0 | Volts |

MT2 ○──────▷|◁──────○ MT1

**TO–225AA**

**CASE 077**
**STYLE 5**

| PIN ASSIGNMENT | |
|---|---|
| 1 | Main Terminal 1 |
| 2 | Main Terminal 2 |
| 3 | Gate |

## ON CHARACTERISTICS

| | Symbol | | | | Unit |
|---|---|---|---|---|---|
| *Peak On-State Voltage(1)<br>($I_{TM}$ = ±6 A Peak) | $V_{TM}$ | — | — | 2 | Volts |
| *Gate Trigger Voltage (Continuous dc)<br>(Main Terminal Voltage = 12 Vdc, $R_L$ = 100 Ohms, $T_J$ = −40°C)<br>All Quadrants | $V_{GT}$ | — | 1.4 | 2.5 | Volts |
| Gate Non–Trigger Voltage<br>(Main Terminal Voltage = 12 Vdc, $R_L$ = 100 Ohms, $T_J$ = 110°C)<br>All Quadrants | $V_{GD}$ | 0.2 | — | — | Volts |
| *Holding Current<br>(Main Terminal Voltage = 12 Vdc, Gate Open,<br>Initiating Current = ±1 Adc)         ($T_J$ = −40°C)<br>                                                                    ($T_J$ = 25°C) | $I_H$ | —<br>— | —<br>— | 30<br>15 | mA |
| Turn-On Time<br>($I_{TM}$ = 14 Adc, $I_{GT}$ = 100 mAdc) | $t_{gt}$ | — | 1.5 | — | µs |

**FIGURE 31–18**  The 2N6071 series triac. *(Courtesy of Semiconductor Components Industries, LLC 2002)*

## Characteristics of the Triac

Triacs may be used to provide direct replacement for ac mechanical relays or may be connected to a trigger circuit to provide full-wave control of an ac load such as a light, heater, or motor. The trigger circuit, which when connected to the gate, provides phase control by turning the triac on for a predetermined conduction angle for each half-cycle of an applied ac source. If no gate signal is applied to the triac, the device will remain in its *blocking region,* providing that the voltage across the main terminals does not exceed the *peak repetitive off-state voltage,* $V_{DRM}$ of the device. In the blocking region, the current through the triac is very small—typically a few microamps.

There are four possible modes that will turn a triac on. When the *MT2* terminal is positive with respect to the *MT1* terminal, the triac is said to operate in Quadrant I as shown in Figure 31–17(b). If a positive gate pulse (with respect to the *MT1* terminal) is applied, the triac is said to operate in Mode I+, and if a negative gate pulse is applied, the triac is in Mode I−.

When the *MT2* terminal is negative with respect to the *MT1* terminal, the triac is said to operate in Quadrant III. If a positive gate pulse (once again, with respect to the *MT1* terminal) is applied, the triac is said to operate in Mode III+, and if a negative gate pulse is applied, the triac is in Mode III−.

A triac is most sensitive in Modes I+ and III−. It is less sensitive in Mode I− and least sensitive in Mode III+, and it should not be operated in this mode. Once a triac has been triggered and operates in its on-state, it will remain on until the current drops below the holding current, $I_H$.

## Applications of Triacs

The circuit of Figure 31–19 shows a triac used as a phase-control light dimmer for an incandescent light bulb. The capacitor in the circuit charges through the load resistor (light bulb) and resistor, $R_1$. If the value of $R_1$ is small, the capacitor will quickly charge to a voltage large enough to cause the diac to breakover. When this happens, the corresponding positive voltage is applied to the gate of the triac, causing it to trigger. The triac, which is now effectively a short circuit, permits a large amount of current to keep the light bulb on for the balance of the half-cycle. The triac is now operating in Quadrant I. As the input sinusoidal voltage reaches the zero-crossing, the current in the circuit drops below the holding current, $I_H$, of the triac, and current ceases. During the negative half-cycle of the applied ac voltage, the capacitor again charges, this time to the opposite polarity. Since the diac is a bi-directional device, a negative gate current is now applied to the triac, causing the triac to operate in Quadrant III. The conduction angle will be essentially the same for

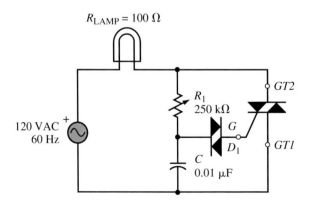

**FIGURE 31–19**

both the positive and negative half-cycles. Figure 31–20(a) shows the applied sinusoidal voltage, while Figure 31–20(b) and Figure 31–20(c) show the waveforms that will appear across the load and the triac respectively for a firing angle of $\theta_F = 90°$. (The conduction angle is $\theta_C = 90°$.) For a firing angle of 90°, the power delivered to the load will be exactly half the power that would be delivered had the full sinusoidal been applied.

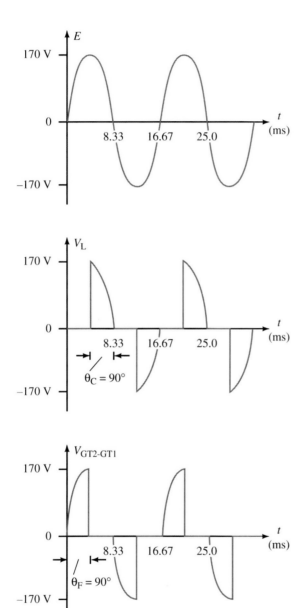

**FIGURE 31–20**

---

In what modes does the triac of Figure 31–19 operate? Explain your answers.

PRACTICE PROBLEMS 2

*Answers*
Mode I+. When the applied voltage is in the positive half-cycle (Quadrant I), the voltage across the capacitor will be positive. Mode III−. When the applied voltage is in the negative half-cycle (Quadrant III), the voltage across the capacitor will be negative.

Figure 31–21 shows how a triac is used to control temperature in a room. Notice that the ac voltage source is applied to the heater through the triac. In order for the heater to turn on, it is necessary to first trigger the triac. The required pulses for the gate of the triac are obtained as follows.

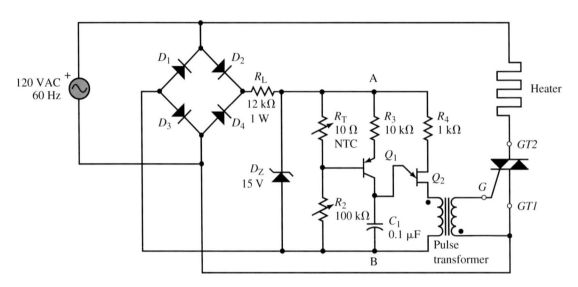

**FIGURE 31–21**    Temperature control circuit using a triac.

The full-wave rectifier bridge, together with $R_1$ and $D_Z$, form a dc supply for the two transistors. As the temperature in the room decreases below some set point determined by $R_2$, the negative temperature coefficient (NTC) of $R_T$ causes an increase in resistance. This results in more voltage drop across $R_T$, which in turn increases the emitter current of $Q_1$. The capacitor charges quickly due to the additional current, causing the UJT transistor to fire early in the half-cycle. When $Q_2$ fires, the current pulse on the primary of the pulse transformer results in a negative-going pulse on the gate of the triac. Although $Q_2$ may produce additional pulses during the same half-cycle, these additional pulses will have no further effect on the triac, which remains on for the balance of the half-cycle.

At the end of each half-cycle, the voltage $V_{AB}$ returns to zero, allowing the transistor circuits of $Q_1$ and $Q_2$ to reset. As the temperature increases, the value of $R_T$ gets smaller, with the result that the feedback stabilizes the temperature of the room.

---

PRACTICE PROBLEMS 3

In what modes does the triac of Figure 31–21 operate? Explain your answers.

*Answers*
Mode I– and Mode III–. Regardless of whether the applied voltage is in the positive or the negative half-cycle, the voltage pulse between the gate and *MT1* of the triac will be negative.

---

## 31.5 Power Control Fundamentals

In the previous sections we observed that by delaying the firing time of thyristors, the power delivered to a load can be substantially less than the peak power that would be delivered if the load received the full cycle of ac voltage. By delaying the firing time of a thyristor, the resulting power can be a fraction of the peak value. The result is a circuit that can control the intensity of a lamp, the amount of heat from a resistive heater, or the speed of a motor. In this section, we examine the relationship between the firing angle and the resulting voltage and power delivered to the load. We will examine the effects of using both unidirectional (SCR) and bi-directional (triac) thyristors.

As a quick review, recall that the power delivered by an ac source to a resistive load is determined from the rms voltage, $V$, of a waveform and is given as

$$P = \frac{V_{rms}^2}{R} \tag{31–10}$$

In Chapter 15, you learned that the rms value of any periodic waveform can be calculated using calculus and is given as

$$V_{rms} = \sqrt{\frac{\int_0^T [V(t)]^2 \, dt}{T}} \tag{31–11}$$

Specifically for a sinusoidal (or a full-wave rectified sinusoidal) having a peak voltage, $V$, the expression becomes

$$
\begin{aligned}
V_{rms(FW)} &= \sqrt{\frac{\int_0^\pi [V \sin\theta]^2 \, d\theta}{\pi}} \\
&= V\sqrt{\frac{1}{\pi}\left[\frac{\theta}{2} - \frac{1}{4}\sin 2\theta\right]_0^\pi} \tag{31–12} \\
&= \frac{V}{\sqrt{2}}
\end{aligned}
$$

Similarly, the rms voltage of a half-wave rectified sinusoidal is reduced to

$$
\begin{aligned}
V_{rms(HW)} &= \sqrt{\frac{\int_0^\pi [V \sin\theta]^2 \, d\theta}{2\pi}} \\
&= V\sqrt{\frac{1}{2\pi}\left[\frac{\theta}{2} - \frac{1}{4}\sin 2\theta\right]_0^\pi} \tag{31–13} \\
&= \frac{V}{2}
\end{aligned}
$$

Now, if the firing angle of the thyristor is delayed, the rms value of the resulting signal delivered to the load will be reduced. For a full-wave signal having a firing angle, $\theta_F$ we have

$$
\begin{aligned}
V_{rms(FW)} &= \sqrt{\frac{\int_{\theta_F}^T [V \sin\theta]^2 \, d\theta}{\pi}} \\
&= V\sqrt{\frac{1}{\pi}\left[\frac{\theta}{2} - \frac{1}{4}\sin 2\theta\right]_{\theta_F}^\pi} \tag{31–14}
\end{aligned}
$$

and for a half-wave rectified signal this becomes

$$
\begin{aligned}
V_{rms(HW)} &= \sqrt{\frac{\int_{\theta_F}^\pi [V \sin\theta]^2 \, d\theta}{2\pi}} \\
&= V\sqrt{\frac{1}{2\pi}\left[\frac{\theta}{2} - \frac{1}{4}\sin 2\theta\right]_{\theta_F}^\pi} \tag{31–15}
\end{aligned}
$$

The following examples show the difference between using an SCR and a triac as angle-controlled switches to control the intensity of an incandescent light bulb.

**EXAMPLE 31–3**

A trigger circuit delays firing of an SCR until the center of each half-cycle, as illustrated in Figure 31–22. Use calculus to determine the rms voltage and the power delivered to a 100-Ω load.

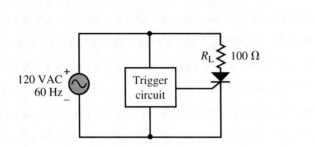

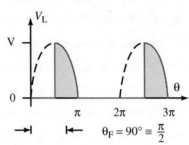

**FIGURE 31–22**

**Solution**

Since each half-cycle represents 180° or π radians, the trigger circuit results in a firing angle of $\theta_F = 90° \equiv \pi/2$ radians. Substituting this value into Equation 31–15 gives us an rms value of

$$V_{rms(HW)} = V \sqrt{\frac{1}{2\pi} \left[ \frac{\theta}{2} - \frac{1}{4} \sin 2\theta \right]_{\frac{\pi}{2}}^{\pi}}$$

$$= 169.7 \text{ V} \sqrt{\frac{1}{2\pi} \left[ \left( \frac{\pi}{2} - \frac{1}{4} \sin 2\pi \right) - \left( \frac{\left( \frac{\pi}{2} \right)}{2} - \frac{1}{4} \sin 2\left( \frac{\pi}{2} \right) \right) \right]}$$

$$= 169.7 \text{ V} \sqrt{\frac{1}{2\pi} \left[ \frac{\pi}{2} - \frac{\pi}{4} \right]}$$

$$= 60.0 \text{ V}$$

The corresponding power delivered to the load is

$$P = \frac{(60.0 \text{ V})^2}{100 \text{ Ω}} = 36.0 \text{ W}$$

(Note that a power of 36.0 W represents exactly ¼ of the 144 W that would have been delivered to the load if the full sinusoidal wave had been applied.)

A trigger circuit delays firing of a triac until the center of each half-cycle, as illustrated in Figure 31–23. Use calculus to determine the rms voltage and the power delivered to a 100-Ω load.

**EXAMPLE 31–4**

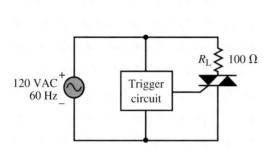

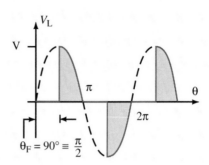

**FIGURE 31–23**

**Solution**
As in the previous example, we have a firing angle of $\theta_F = 90° \equiv \pi/2$ radians. Substituting this value into Equation 31–14 gives us an rms value of

$$V_{\text{rms(FW)}} = V\sqrt{\frac{1}{\pi}\left[\frac{\theta}{2} - \frac{1}{4}\sin 2\theta\right]_{\frac{\pi}{2}}^{\pi}}$$

$$= 169.7 \text{ V}\sqrt{\frac{1}{\pi}\left[\left(\frac{\pi}{2} - \frac{1}{4}\sin 2\pi\right) - \left(\frac{\left(\frac{\pi}{2}\right)}{2} - \frac{1}{4}\sin 2\left(\frac{\pi}{2}\right)\right)\right]}$$

$$= 169.7 \text{ V}\sqrt{\frac{1}{\pi}\left[\frac{\pi}{2} - \frac{\pi}{4}\right]}$$

$$= 84.85 \text{ V}$$

The corresponding power delivered to the load is

$$P = \frac{(84.85 \text{ V})^2}{100 \text{ }\Omega} = 72.0 \text{ W}$$

As expected, since half the waveform appears across the load, we find that the load resistance receives exactly half of the 144 W that would have been delivered to the load if the full sinusoidal wave had been applied.

Although it is possible to use calculus to solve for the rms voltage for any firing angle, it is much more convenient to use a graphical approach when solving for the voltage and power. Figures 31–24 and 31–25 are normalized curves that allow us to solve for the rms voltage and power for any firing angle for half-wave or full-wave angle control.

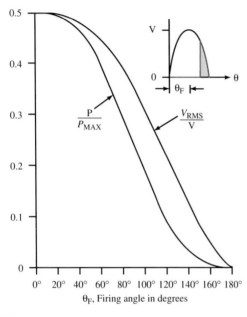

**FIGURE 31–24**   Voltage and power curves for half-wave control.

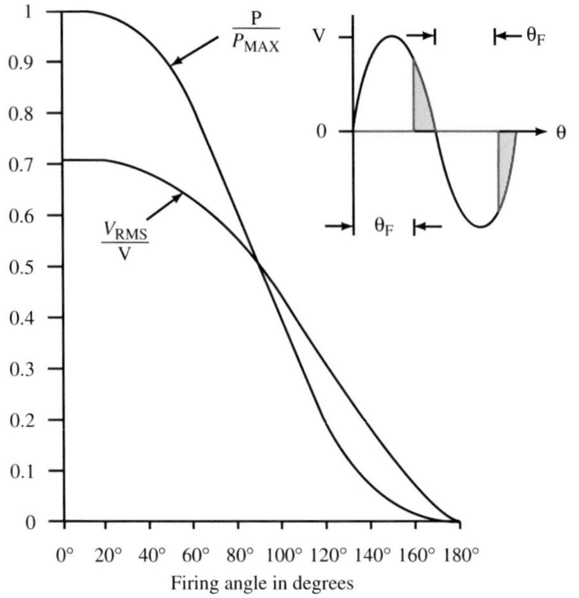

**FIGURE 31–25**   Voltage and power curves for full-wave control.

In order to use the power curves, we need to know three quantities for a given circuit; the peak voltage $V$ (amplitude of the sinusoidal), the firing angle $\theta_F$, and whether the device uses half-wave control (such as an SCR) or full-wave control (such as a triac or an SCR that is preceded by a full-wave rectifier bridge). The maximum power for any resistive load is based on the power that will be delivered to the load if the complete sinusoidal is applied. This value will be the same for both half-wave and full-wave control circuits. The following examples illustrate how the curves are used.

**EXAMPLE 31–5**

A trigger circuit delays firing of an SCR until $\theta_F = 120°$. If the supply voltage is a 120-VAC sinusoidal, determine the rms voltage and the power delivered to a 20-$\Omega$ load.

**Solution**
For a 20-$\Omega$ load, the maximum power that would be delivered is determined as

$$P_{max} = \frac{(120 \text{ V})^2}{20 \text{ }\Omega} = 720 \text{ W}$$

The peak voltage of the sinusoidal source is $V = (120 \text{ V})\sqrt{2} = 169.7$ V. For a firing angle of $\theta_F = 120°$, the normalized voltage ratio is approximately 0.222, and so we determine the rms voltage as

$$V_{rms} = (0.222)(169.7 \text{ V}) = 37.7 \text{ V}$$

The corresponding power can be determined either graphically as

$$P = (0.10)P_{max} = 72.0 \text{ W}$$

or mathematically from the rms voltage as

$$P = \frac{(37.7 \text{ V})^2}{20 \text{ }\Omega} = 71.0 \text{ W}$$

A trigger circuit fires a triac at $\theta_F = 130°$. If the supply voltage is a 240-VAC sinusoidal, determine the rms voltage and the power delivered to a 12–$\Omega$ load.

*Answers*
81.5 V,  576 W

PRACTICE PROBLEMS 4

## 31.6 Introduction to Optical Devices

Opto-electronic devices fall into two categories: devices that convert electric current into light and devices that convert light into electric current. Although we normally associate light with the visible spectrum, many optical devices operate in the infrared region of the electromagnetic (E/M spectrum). Figure 31–26 shows the electromagnetic frequency spectrum, together with various applications of the frequencies. Each horizontal division represents a decade (10-fold increase in frequency). Notice that the visible spectrum is a very narrow portion between $10^{14}$ Hz and $10^{15}$ Hz. Since all E/M waves propagate through free space (in a vacuum or in air) at a speed $c = 3.00 \times 10^8$ m/s, we relate wavelength and frequency as follows:

$$\lambda = \frac{c}{f} \qquad \textbf{(31–16)}$$

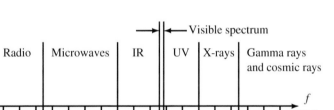

FIGURE 31–26   The electromagnetic frequency spectrum.

The wavelength of visible and near-visible light (which includes infrared—IR and ultraviolet—UV) is often measured in either nm (nanometers) or angstroms (Å), where

$$1 \text{ Å} \equiv 1 \times 10^{-10} \text{ m} \qquad \textbf{(31–17)}$$

Red light (at approximately 750 nm) and violet light (at approximately 380 nm) bound the visible light spectrum. All other colors have wavelengths between these values.

Determine the frequencies that correspond to red light and violet light.

**EXAMPLE 31–6**

**Solution**
From Equation 31–16, we have

$$f_{\text{red}} = \frac{c}{\lambda} = \frac{3.00 \times 10^8 \text{ m/s}}{750 \times 10^{-9} \text{ m}} = 4.0 \times 10^{14} \text{ Hz}$$

and

$$f_{\text{violet}} = \frac{3.00 \times 10^8 \text{ m/s}}{380 \times 10^{-9} \text{ m}} = 7.9 \times 10^{14} \text{ Hz}$$

### Light Emitting Diodes (LEDs)

LEDs are similar to other diodes in that they consist of two layers of semiconductor material, one n-type and one p-type. The intrinsic material is doped with different types of impurities, such as gallium, arsenic, and phosphorous to result in the wide range of colors that are available. Typical current ratings of LEDs are between 10 mA and 20 mA. Since LEDs are constructed of semiconductor materials other than silicon, the voltage across a forward-biased LED will vary between 1.0 V and about 2.2 V. Figure 31–27(a) shows the construction of a typical surface-emitting LED, while Figure 21–27(b) shows the schematic symbol of an LED.

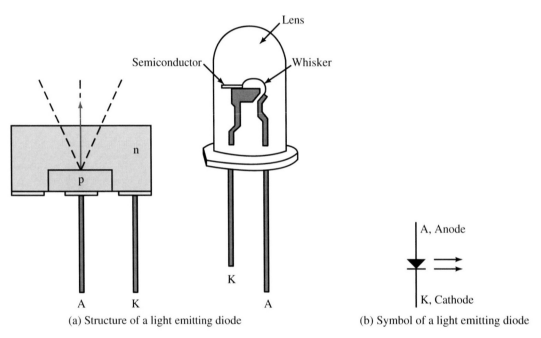

(a) Structure of a light emitting diode          (b) Symbol of a light emitting diode

**FIGURE 31–27**

When the LED is forward-biased, excess electrons from the n-type material will be injected into the p-type material, where there is an excess of *holes*. The *recombination* process between the holes and electrons causes the conduction-band electrons of the n-type material to drop from a high energy level to the lower energy level of the valence band in the p-type material. When the electron moves to a lower energy level, energy is conserved by the release of a *photon* of E/M radiation having an energy of

$$E = hf \tag{31–18}$$

In Equation 31–18, $E$ is the difference in energy between the conduction band and the valence band, $h$ is Planck's constant ($h = 6.626 \times 10^{-34}$ J·s), and $f$ is the frequency (Hz) of E/M radiation emitted. If the energy difference is large enough, the radiation will occur in the visible spectrum. LEDs have several advantages over other light sources:

- LEDs can operate from low-voltage sources. They are easily combined with logic ICs that use 5-V power supplies.

- Unlike incandescent light sources, which require filaments to heat up, LEDs react quickly to voltage changes, making them useful for digital transmission.

- LEDs have a very long life expectancy, provided that the maximum voltage and current ratings are not exceeded.

- The peak intensity of an LED can be matched to the peak sensitivity of a photodetector, making LEDs useful for data transmission.

Although LEDs have many advantages over other types of light sources, they have several disadvantages.

- LEDs are easily damaged by excessive voltage or current. Unlike other diodes, LEDs are unable to handle large reverse voltage. Typical reverse voltage for an LED is $V_R = 5$ V. If a circuit uses an alternating voltage source, it is necessary to include signal diodes across LEDs as protection.

- The brightness and peak response frequency of LEDs is dependent upon the ambient temperature.

- If an LED is used to transmit data, the pulses will spread due to the variation in the frequency of the emitted light (called *chromatic dispersion*).

- When used as displays (for calculators, or any battery operated commercial electronics), the LED is inefficient when compared to LCD (liquid crystal displays). A 7-segment display uses 7 LEDs to indicate numbers from zero to nine, and it could require as much as $7 \times 20$ mA $= 140$ mA to display a single decimal digit.

LEDs are very simple devices to design into a circuit. Manufacturers typically provide the forward current and voltage drop for a diode at a given light intensity. Light intensity for an LED operating in the visible spectrum is normally specified in the SI unit, the **candela** (cd). The candela is defined as the visible light intensity emitted from a $\frac{1}{60}$ cm$^2$ opening in a standard white-hot oven at a temperature of 2046 K. Since this amount of light is difficult to visualize, it is much easier to remember that 1 cd is approximately the amount of light that will be emitted from a candle (1 candle $= 0.981$ cd). When an LED is used in a circuit, it is generally necessary to insert a current-limiting resistor in series with the voltage source and the diode.

**EXAMPLE 31–7**

A high-intensity yellow LED providing 80 mcd of visible light is specified as having a rated voltage of 2.2 V at a current of 21 mA. Determine the current-limiting resistor that must be used to ensure that the diode does not exceed its specified operating point if the voltage source for the circuit is 5.0 Vdc.

**Solution**

The circuit appears as shown in Figure 31–28.

We use Ohm's law to solve for the current limiting resistor as

$$R = \frac{5.0 \text{ V} - 2.2 \text{ V}}{21.0 \text{ mA}} = 133 \ \Omega$$

In this example, we would likely use a 150–$\Omega$ resistor to ensure that the current through the LED remains below the rated value.

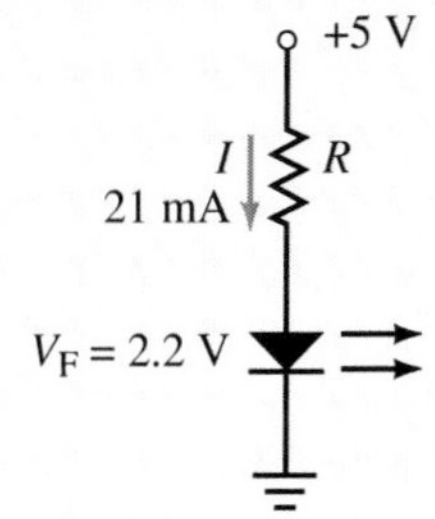

**FIGURE 31–28**

Although LEDs are used extensively as indicators, many LEDs emit light in the infrared (IR) region. These IRLEDs are easily coupled to fiber optic cable that has optimum transmission characteristics at the same frequency as that at which the light is transmitted. Since IRLEDs can be switched on and off at relatively high rates, it is possible to use the resulting system to transmit binary data (in the form of 1s and 0s) at very high rates.

However, it is not sufficient to be able to simply transmit information as light; we must also be able to recover the data. There are several devices that allow light to be converted into electrical signals.

## 31.7 Photodetectors

There are many types of devices that convert light into electrical energy. In Chapter 3, you were introduced to the photoresistor, a device having a resistance that decreased as the amount of light increased. In this section, we examine semiconductor devices that produce a voltage or current variation that is dependent on the amount of light applied to a p-n junction. In each case, the principle of operation is the same. When a photon of light strikes the p-n junction, a valence electron absorbs the energy of the photon, moving into the higher energy level. The electron is now free to move and results in increased saturation or leakage current in the device. If necessary, the resulting current may be further amplified. The most common photodetectors are the photodiode, the phototransistor, and the LASCR (light activated silicon controlled rectifier).

### Photodiodes

Figure 31–29 shows the symbol and typical current-voltage characteristics of a photodiode. Notice that the forward characteristic of the photodiode is similar to that of standard signal diode. The reverse characteristics are much different. When no light is applied to the p-n junction of the reverse-biased photodiode, there will be very little leakage current. However, as the light increases, we see a marked increase in the reverse current due to the increase in minority carriers.

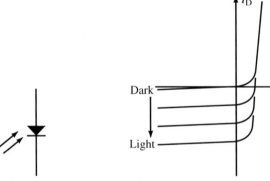

**FIGURE 31–29**　　(a) Symbol of a photodiode　　(b) Current-voltage characteristics of a photodiode

### Phototransistors

The phototransistor shown in Figure 31–30 is an npn transistor, with the base normally left open. As light strikes the reverse-biased C-B junction, the number of minority carriers increases, thereby resulting in an increase in the collector current, $I_C$. Recall that the collector current of a transistor is given as

$$I_C = \beta I_B + (\beta + 1)I_{CBO} \qquad (31\text{--}19)$$

Since the base current is zero due to the open base, the collector current is entirely dependent on the contribution due to the minority carriers, namely

$$I_C = (\beta + 1)I_{CBO} \qquad (31\text{--}20)$$

Although the collector current of a phototransistor is dependent on the light intensity and could therefore be used as an amplifier, a phototransistor circuit is normally designed to operate as a switch. The transistor is cut off when there is no light (logic "0") or saturated (logic "1") when light is present. Fig-

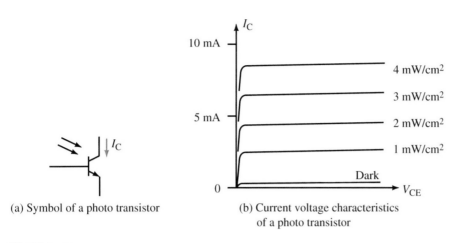

(a) Symbol of a photo transistor

(b) Current voltage characteristics
of a photo transistor

**FIGURE 31–30**

ure 31–31 shows how a photoemitter (such as an LED) can be combined with a photodetector (such as photodiode or phototransistor) as part of a fiber optic link. By using light transmission through a glass fiber, the attenuation of the signal will be very small over the length of glass fiber. Typical losses over high-quality glass fibers can be as low as 0.5 dB/km.

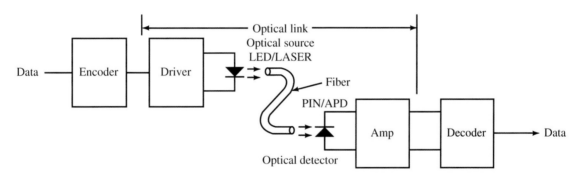

**FIGURE 31–31**    Fiber optic link uses an optical source and an optical detector to send digital signals.

Besides having very low attenuation characteristics, fiber optic transmission neither causes nor is susceptible to E/M interference. Although LEDs and photodiodes are used in data transmission, it is now much more common to use lasers as light sources and avalanche photodiodes as photodetectors. The main difference between avalanche photodiodes (APDs) and other optical detectors is that high electric fields within APDs cause freed carriers to accelerate and effectively knock other valence electrons out of the crystal lattice. This effect is called **impact ionization,** and it results in APDs providing a 30- to 100-fold increase in the number of carriers. While APDs have much faster response times that other photodetectors, they have several disadvantages:

- An avalanche photodiode is easily destroyed if the operating voltage exceeds the device breakdown voltage.
- Variation in operating temperature will adversely affect the operation of an APD.
- APDs are much more costly than other photodiodes.

## Light-Activated SCRs-LASCRs

An LASCR uses light energy to cause an SCR to fire. Once the LASCR has fired, the device will remain on until the current drops below the holding current, $I_H$.

Figure 31–32 shows an LASCR used as a light-sensitive switch. When the ambient light level drops below a certain value, the LASCR will effectively be an open circuit, allowing $C_1$ to charge through $R_1$. Once the voltage across $C_1$ is sufficient to fire the diac $D_5$, the resulting gate current causes $SCR_1$ to also fire. This results in a large current through the lamp for the balance of the half-cycle. $SCR_1$ will not conduct on the negative half-cycle of the ac supply. If sufficient ambient light is available to the LASCR, the LASCR will effectively be a short circuit, preventing $C_1$ from charging. Consequently, $SCR_1$ will not be able to fire if the ambient light is high. The sensitivity of the circuit can be controlled by adjusting the value of $R_2$. If $R_2$ has low resistance, the LASCR will be less sensitive than if $R_2$ were a larger value. The LASCR is most sensitive when $R_2$ is left open. Notice that full-wave control can be achieved if the $SCR_1$ is replaced by a triac.

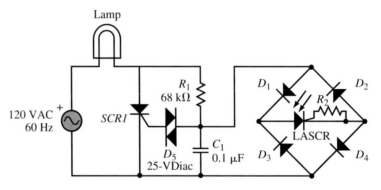

**FIGURE 31–32**   LASCR light control.

## 31.8 Optocouplers

As the name implies, an optocoupler is a photoelectric device used to couple two circuits using light as the common medium. An optocoupler generally uses an infrared emitting diode to convert electrical energy into light that is internally coupled to a photodiode, phototransistor, or other photodetector. Since the two circuits are electrically isolated, there will be no electrical interaction between the two circuits, making these circuits ideal for medical equipment and for interfacing high-voltage monitoring equipment to low-voltage microprocessor inputs. Figure 31–33 shows a typical 6-pin phototransistor optocoupler. Optocouplers can be used as either linear devices or as digital buffers.

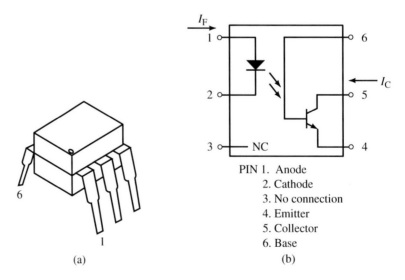

PIN 1.  Anode
     2.  Cathode
     3.  No connection
     4.  Emitter
     5.  Collector
     6.  Base

(a)                          (b)

**FIGURE 31–33**   Phototransistor optocoupler. *(Courtesy of Fairchild Semiconductor Corporation)*

We define the current transfer, *CTR*, as the ratio of output collector current to input forward current, namely

$$\text{CTR} = \frac{I_C}{I_F} \qquad \textbf{(31–21)}$$

Typical values for CTR are between 0.1 and 1.0. The following examples show typical applications of optocouplers.

EXAMPLE 31–8

Given the optocoupler circuit shown in Figure 31–34. Assume that the forward diode voltage is $V_F = 1.2$ V and the current transfer ratio of the optocoupler is CTR = 0.3:

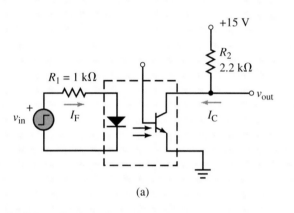

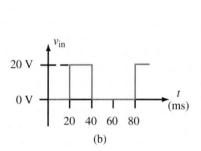

(a)                                    (b)

**FIGURE 31–34**   Digital application of an optocoupler.

a. Solve for the output voltage when the input voltage is 0 V.
b. Solve for the output voltage when the input voltage is 20 V.
c. Sketch the corresponding output voltage.

**Solution**

a. When the input voltage is 0 V, the current $I_F = 0$. Consequently, $I_C = 0$, and so we have $v_{out} = + 15$ V.

b. When the input voltage is 20 V, the diode current will be

$$I_F = \frac{20\ \text{V} - 1.2\ \text{V}}{1\ \text{k}\Omega} = 18.8\ \text{mA}$$

The collector current will be

$$I_C = (0.3)(18.8\ \text{mA}) = 5.64\ \text{mA}$$

and so the output voltage will be

$$v_{out} = 15\ \text{V} - (2.2\ \text{k}\Omega)(5.64\ \text{mA}) = 2.59\ \text{V}$$

c. The output of the optocoupler is illustrated in Figure 31–35.

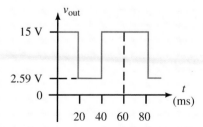

**FIGURE 31–35**

**EXAMPLE 31–9**

Given the optocoupler circuit shown in Figure 31–36. Assume that the forward diode voltage is $V_F = 1.2$ V, and the current transfer ratio of the optocoupler is CTR = 0.3:

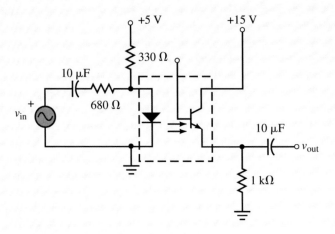

**FIGURE 31–36** Linear application of an optocoupler.

a. Determine the operating point of the phototransistor.

b. Solve for the output voltage when the input voltage is 1.0 $V_p$ and the frequency is 1 kHz.

**Solution**

a. The operating point of the phototransistor is determined by considering only the dc voltage sources. Using the same approach as the previous example, we have

$$I_F = \frac{5 \text{ V} - 1.2 \text{ V}}{330 \text{ k}\Omega} = 11.5 \text{ mA}$$

and so

$$I_{CQ} = (0.3)(11.5 \text{ mA}) = 3.45 \text{ mA}$$

The collector-emitter voltage at the operating point is now determined to be

$$V_{CEQ} = 15 \text{ V} - (1 \text{ k}\Omega)(3.45 \text{ mA}) = 11.55 \text{ V}$$

b. Since the diode ac resistance will be very small (normally $r_d \approx 7 \ \Omega$) in comparison to the 680-$\Omega$ resistance, we may ignore its effect. Consequently, the variation in the diode forward current will be

$$i_f = \frac{1.0 \text{ V}_p}{680 \ \Omega} = 1.47 \text{ mA}_p$$

The resulting variation in collector current will be

$$i_c = (0.3)(1.47 \text{ mA}) = 0.441 \text{ mA}_p$$

Since the coupling capacitor allows only the ac portion of the emitter voltage to pass to the output, we have

$$v_{out} = (0.441 \text{ mA}_p)(1.0 \text{ k}\Omega) = 0.441 \text{ V}_p$$

## 31.9 Semiconductor LASERs

As we saw in the previous section, when an electron drops from a high energy level to a lower level, a photon of light is released. In the case of LEDs, an electron can drop to its lower level at any time, releasing a photon of light spontaneously and in any direction. In the case of lasers, electrons will drop to a lower energy level when they are stimulated to do so. Hence, the word LASER is an acronym for **L**ight **A**mplification through **S**timulated **E**mission of **R**adiation.

The principle behind the operation of lasers is simple. As in the case of LEDs, an external voltage source raises the energy level of electrons within the semiconductor material. However, unlike LEDs, the number of electrons raised to this higher level is much greater. The electrons do not immediately drop to a lower level. An incoming photon with exactly the right energy level will stimulate an electron in this *metastable state* to drop to its lower energy level. When this happens, another photon having exactly the same wavelength as the original photon is created. The two photons will travel in the same direction, stimulating other electrons to also drop to a lower energy level. Hence the amplification. The external voltage source ensures that more electrons are raised to higher levels. A laser uses one totally reflective surface to ensure that light emerges from only one end. The opposite end is a partially reflective surface to sustain the stimulated emission of photons in a cavity between the p- and n-type materials. Part of the beam emerges from the partially reflective surface, as illustrated in Figure 31–37.

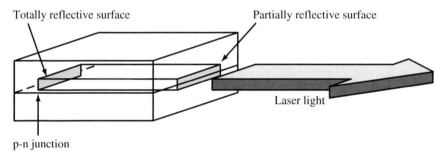

**FIGURE 31–37**   The semiconductor laser.

The beam of light that emerges from a laser will have much higher intensity that a similar beam from an LED. Additionally, the light will be **monochromatic** (having a single wavelength) and **coherent** (in phase and in the same direction). Figure 31–38 shows the major difference between an LED and a laser, each emitting light at 1330 nm. Besides having much greater intensity, a laser has a very small variation in wavelength, $\Delta\lambda$. When used to transmit digital pulses, this small variation results in a laser having less much less pulse-dispersion than an LED.

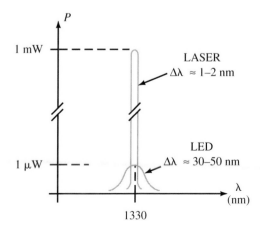

**FIGURE 31–38**   Comparison of the spectral purity and intensity of an LED and a laser.

### 31.10 Computer Analysis

In this section we examine how MultiSIM can be used to simulate the effects of triggering an SCR. We will use a variable resistor and observe how increasing the charging rate of a capacitor is used to delay the firing angle of the signal applied to the gate of the transistor.

**EXAMPLE 31–10**

Use MultiSIM to construct the circuit shown in Figure 31–39. Place an oscilloscope across the lamp and observe the voltage waveform as the variable resistor, $R$, is adjusted between 10% ($R = 5$ k$\Omega$) and 50% ($R = 25$ k$\Omega$). As the resistance value is increased, you will find that it will take longer for the capacitor to charge to a large enough voltage to cause the diac to reach its breakover voltage. This increase in time translates into an increased firing angle for the SCR. Determine the approximate firing angle for $R = 5$ k$\Omega$ and for $R = 25$ k$\Omega$.

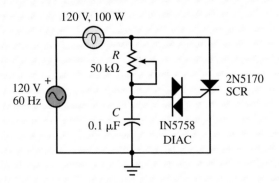

**FIGURE 31–39**

**Solution**
Once entered into MultiSIM, the circuit will appear as shown in Figure 31–40.

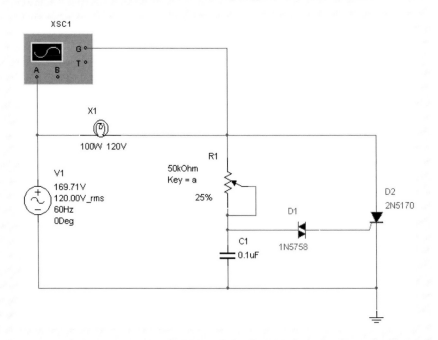

◀ MULTISIM     **FIGURE 31–40**

In order for the simulation to operate correctly, it is necessary to change the default instrument setting of EWB. The following settings will help to prevent simulation errors.

- Select the *Simulate* menu item.
- Click on *Default Instrument Settings . . .*
- In the tab labeled as *Defaults for Transient Analysis Instruments,* change the values as illustrated in Figure 31–41.

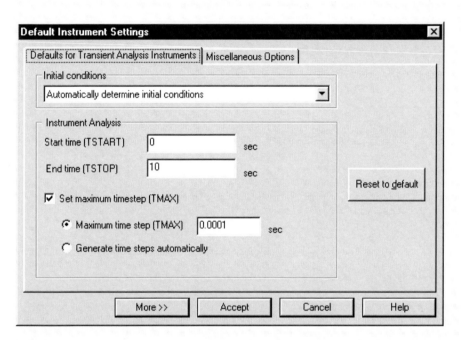

**FIGURE 31–41**

When the simulation is run, the displays for the resistor values are shown in Figure 31–42 and Figure 31–43. These results indicate that the conduction angles are

$$\theta_C = \frac{7.3 \text{ ms}}{8.33 \text{ ms}} \times 180° = 158° \quad \text{for } R = 5 \text{ k}\Omega \text{ and}$$

$$\theta_C = \frac{6.6 \text{ ms}}{8.33 \text{ ms}} \times 180° = 143° \quad \text{for } R = 25 \text{ k}\Omega$$

Therefore, the firing angles are $\theta_F = 22°$ for $R = 5$ k$\Omega$ and $\theta_F = 37°$ for $R = 25$ k$\Omega$.

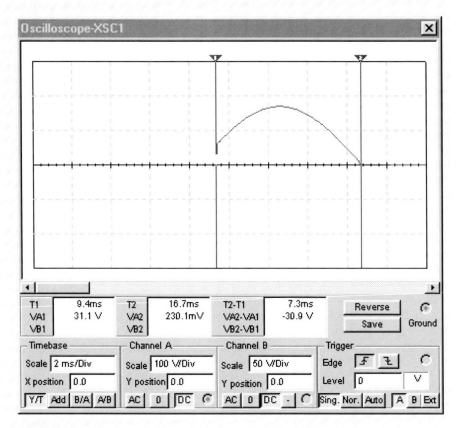

**FIGURE 31–42**

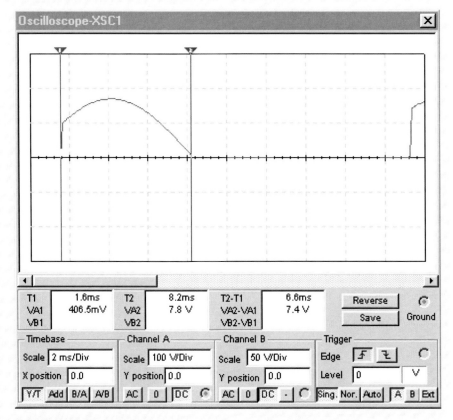

**FIGURE 31–43**

## PUTTING IT INTO PRACTICE

Part of a monitoring system in a nuclear generating station requires that you observe the status of 24-V relays. The signals entering your computer must be either 0 V to indicate that the contact is closed or 5 V, to show the contact is open. Use an optocoupler that requires $I_F = 10.0$ mA and has CTR = 0.4 to produce the desired signal at your computer. Show the complete schematic of your design.

## PROBLEMS

### 31.2 Triggering Devices

1. Given that the UJT in the circuit of Figure 31–44 has

   Valley point: $V_V = 1.8$ V     $I_V = 2.0$ mA

   Peak point: $V_P = 10.0$ V     $I_P = 4.0$ μA

   $V_D = 0.6$ V and     $I_{B2} = 2.4$ mA when $I_E = 0$

   a. Solve for the frequency of oscillation if $R_E = 6.8$ kΩ and $C_E = 0.56$ μF.

   b. Determine the values of η and $R_{BB}$ of the UJT

   c. Sketch the waveforms that appear at $V_E$, $V_{out1}$, and $V_{out2}$ (relative to ground).

2. If the UJT in the circuit of Figure 31–44 has

   Valley point: $V_V = 1.0$ V     $I_V = 1.5$ mA

   Peak point: $V_P = 10.0$ V     $I_P = 5.0$ μA

   $V_D = 0.6$ V     $R_{BB} = 6.0$ kΩ

   a. Solve for the frequency of oscillation if $R_E = 12$ kΩ and $C_E = 0.01$ μF.

   b. What is the purpose of the load resistor, $R_L$?

3. Using the UJT characteristics of Problem 1, design a UJT relaxation oscillator to oscillate at a frequency of 8.0 kHz.

4. Using the UJT characteristics of Problem 2, design a UJT relaxation oscillator to oscillate at a frequency of 6.25 kHz.

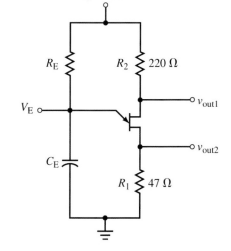

**FIGURE 31–44**

### 31.3 Silicon-Controlled Rectifiers (SCRs)

5. Refer to the illustration of Figure 31–45. Sketch the corresponding voltages $V_{AK}$ and $V_L$ if the triggering circuit provides positive-going gate pulses 5.0 ms after each zero-crossing of the applied ac voltage source.

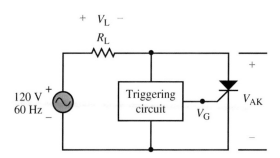

**FIGURE 31–45**

6. Repeat Problem 5 if the triggering circuit were adjusted to provide positive-going gate pulses 10.0 ms after each zero-crossing of the applied ac voltage source.

7. Refer to the illustration of Figure 31–46. Sketch the corresponding voltages $V_{AK}$ and $V_L$ if the triggering circuit provides positive-going gate pulses 5.0 ms after each zero-crossing of the applied ac voltage source.

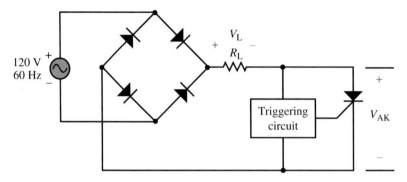

**FIGURE 31–46**

8. Repeat Problem 5 if the triggering circuit were adjusted to provide positive-going gate pulses 10.0 ms after each zero-crossing of the applied ac voltage source.

### 31.4   Triacs

9. Refer to the illustration of Figure 31–47. Sketch the corresponding voltages $V_{GT2\text{-}GT1}$ and $V_L$ if the triggering circuit provides positive-going gate pulses 5.0 ms after each zero-crossing of the applied ac voltage source. In which modes of operation does the triac operate?

10. Repeat Problem 9 if the triggering circuit is adjusted to provide positive-going gate pulses 10.0 ms after each zero-crossing of the applied ac voltage source.

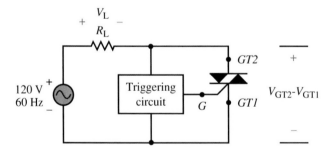

**FIGURE 31–47**

### 31.5   Power Control Fundamentals

11. A trigger circuit delays firing of an SCR until $\theta_F = 45°$. If the supply voltage is a 120-V (rms) sinusoidal, determine the rms voltage and power that is delivered to a 150-$\Omega$ load.

12. Repeat Problem 11 if the firing angle occurs at $\theta_F = 135°$.

13. A trigger circuit delays firing of a triac until $\theta_F = 60°$. If the supply voltage is a 240-V (rms) sinusoidal, determine the rms voltage and power that is delivered to a 20-$\Omega$ motor.

14. Repeat Problem 13 if the firing angle occurs at $\theta_F = 120°$.

15. An electric motor is rated as having 0.5 hp at 120 V. Assuming that the motor is 100% efficient, what must be the firing angle of a triac in order for the motor to provide 0.2 hp?

16. If an SCR circuit controls the motor of Problem 15, what must be the firing angle?

17. Use calculus to determine the rms voltage delivered to the load described in Problem 11.

18. Use calculus to determine the rms voltage delivered to the load described in Problem 14.

## 31.6   Introduction to Optical Devices

19. Green light has a wavelength of approximately 550 nm in air. Determine the frequency of this light.

20. Radiation emitted from a E/M source occurs at a frequency of $2.5 \times 10^{14}$ Hz. Determine the wavelength of this radiation in air. In which region of the E/M spectrum is this radiation (infrared, visible, or ultraviolet)?

21. A GaAsP (gallium-arsenide-phoshide) amber LED requires 20 mA of current to provide its rated intensity. If the diode has a forward voltage of 2.0 V at this intensity, determine the current-limiting resistor needed for the LED to operate from a 9.0-V source.

22. White LEDs provide bright light that requires only 10% of the power of conventional incandescent light bulbs. A typical white LED providing 3200 mcd of light requires a forward current of $I_F = 20$ mA and has a forward voltage of 3.6 V. Determine the current-limiting resistor needed for the LED to operate from a 10-V source.

## 31.8   Optocouplers

23. Given the optocoupler circuit and corresponding input voltage shown in Figure 31–48, assume that the forward diode voltage is $V_F = 1.4$ V and the current transfer ratio of the optocoupler is CTR = 0.4:

   a.  Solve for the output voltage when the input voltage is 0 V.

   b.  Solve for the output voltage when the input voltage is 15 V.

   c.  Sketch the corresponding output voltage.

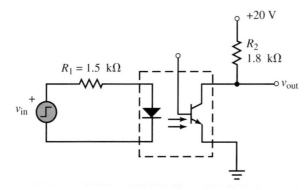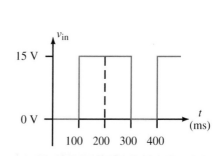

**FIGURE 31–48**

24. Given the optocoupler circuit and corresponding input voltage shown in Figure 31–49, assume that the forward diode voltage is $V_F = 1.5$ V, and the current transfer ratio of the optocoupler is CTR $= 0.4$:

    a.  Determine the operating point of the phototransistor.

    b.  Sketch the corresponding output voltage that will be observed.

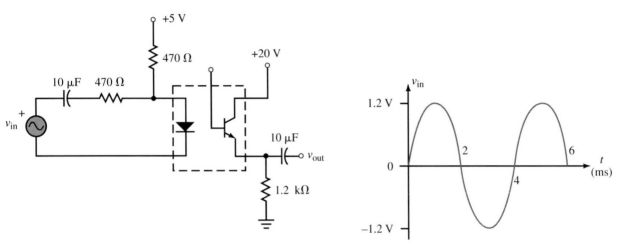

**FIGURE 31–49**

### 31.9   Semiconductor LASERs

25. What does the acronym LASER stand for?

26. Provide at least three characteristics that distinguish semiconductor lasers from LEDs.

### 31.10   Computer Analysis

27. Use MultiSIM to construct the circuit shown in Figure 31–50. Adjust the value of $R_1$ between 10% and 90%, while using the oscilloscope tool to observe the voltage across the lamp.

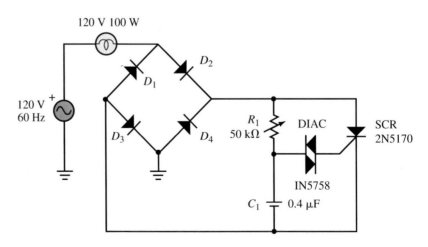

◄ MULTISIM    **FIGURE 31–50**

**ANSWERS TO IN-PROCESS LEARNING CHECKS**

**In-Process Learning Check 1**

1. Initially the anode current of the SCR is $I_A = 0$.

2. As the supply voltage increases, the voltage applied to $B_1$ of the UJT also increases. The capacitor begins to charge through resistors, $R_2$ and $R_3$. The rate of charge is determined by the value of $R_3$.

3. At some point in the positive half-cycle of the applied sinusoidal, the voltage across the capacitor will be sufficient to cause the UJT to fire. The resulting positive voltage spike across $R_4$ will trigger the SCR.

4. The SCR will conduct during the balance of the half-cycle. While it is conducting, the voltage across the SCR is $V_{AK} \approx 0V$ and so the UJT will no longer operate as a relaxation oscillator.

5. In the negative half-cycle of the applied sinusoidal, the SCR will remain off, since it can conduct in only one direction. At the same time, the UJT will not provide any pulses since $V_{B1\text{-}B2}$ must be positive in order for the UJT to oscillate.

# APPENDIX
# D

## CHAPTER 24

1. An electron in the outer (i.e., last occupied) shell of an atom.

3. Gold is a conductor. Thus, same as Figure 24–3(c).

5. See Figure 24–3. It is smaller than that of an insulator but larger than that of a conductor.

7. a. 6      b. 4

   c. Tetravalent (has 4 electrons in valence shell).

9. a. Resistance increases as temperature increases. Copper.

   b. Resistance decreases as temperature increases. Silicon.

13. a. Trivalent      b. Pentavalent

15. Holes

17. Electrons

19. As shown in Figure 24–8, antimony has 5 valence electrons, which is one more than is needed for bonding. If the electron escapes, it will not leave behind a hole because it isn't needed for bonding anyway.

21. 0.7 V

23. 0 V

25. The depletion region is formed by free electrons from the $n$-material diffusing across the junction, leaving atoms of the $n$-material near the junction with a deficiency of electrons and atoms of the $p$-material with an excess as indicated in Figure 24–14. When a forward-biased source is connected, electrons injected into the $n$-material are propelled toward the junction, replacing those originally lost; similarly, holes injected into the $p$-material are propelled toward the junction, replacing those originally lost. As the ions near the junction have their lost charges replaced, the depletion region narrows.

27. Majority

29.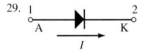

## CHAPTER 25

1. a. 0 A: 27 V      b. 4 mA: 0 V

3. Connect the diode directly across the coil with its cathode at the source end. With the switch closed, the diode is reverse-biased and does not conduct. At the instant the switch is opened, the induced voltage across the coil changes polarity so that its bottom end is $+$ with respect to its top end $-$ thus, the diode is forward-biased and conducts. Now, instead of getting a huge voltage spike across the coil (recall Figure 14–16), the diode limits it to one diode drop.

5. a. 0 A: 27 V      b. 3.84 mA: 0.7 V

7. a. 0.244 A      b. 19.2 mA

9. 0.88 V: 22.48 V

11. 1N4004 to achieve a safety margin.

13. 703 mA

15. 13° C

17. 55° C

19. 43.2 mA: 777 mW: 30 mA

21. 23.6 V to 31.1 V

23. 16.0 V to 23.3 V

25. 14.77 V: 15.53 V

29. 1.51 A: 33.9 V

31. 31.6 V

33. 0.762 V

35. 0.758 V: 19.6 V

37. 2 V: 2083 μF

39. 1.98 V: 19.0 V 0.57 V

43. b. 1.51 V: 8.51 V

45. b. 0.723 V, 8.16 V

**CHAPTER 26**

1. $I_B = 0.05$ mA, $\alpha = 0.989$, $\beta = 90$

3. $I_B = 0.0417$ mA, $I_E = 5.04$ mA, $\alpha = 0.992$

5. $\alpha = 0.990$, $I_C = 4.89$ mA, $I_B = 0.0489$ mA

9. $V_{(BR)EBO} = 6.0$ V

    Emitter-base breakdown voltage (with open collector)

    $I_E = 10$ μA, $I_C = 0$

11. 110

13. 108

15. Saturation

17. b. $I_B = 43.0$ μA, $I_C = 4.5$ mA, $\beta = 105$

    c. $I_B = 21.5$ μA, $I_C = 2.5$ mA, $\beta = 116$

    d. $I_B = 0.215$ mA, $I_C = 8.0$ mA, $\beta$ cannot be found. Transistor is in saturation.

    e. The transistor is in cutoff.

19. d. The slope becomes less negative. Also, the saturation current decreases in magnitude.

21. a. $I_{C(SAT)} = 8.0$ mA

    b. $I_B = 24.7$ μA, $I_C = 2.96$ mA, $V_{CE} = 10.08$ V

23. a. $I_{C(SAT)} = 6.15$ mA

    b. $I_B = 19.4$ μA, $I_C = 2.91$ mA, $V_{CE} = 12.64$ V

25. a. $I_{C(SAT)} = 4.49$ mA

    b. $I_B = 12.9$ μA, $I_C = 1.94$ mA, $V_{CE} = 12.5$ V

27. a. $I_{C(SAT)} = 10.0$ mA

    b. $I_B = 37.0$ μA, $I_C = 4.62$ mA, $I_E = I = 4.66$ mA, $V_{CE} = 10.68$ V

29. a. $I_{C(SAT)} = 5.00$ mA

    b. $I_B = 14.6$ μA, $I_C = 2.342$ mA, $I_E = 2.35$ mA, $I_{CE} = -10.60$ V

31. a. $I_{C(SAT)} = 7.96$ mA

    b. $I_B = 21.8$ μA, $I_C = 2.62$ mA $\approx I_E$, $V_{CE} = -10.60$ V

33. a. $I_{C(SAT)} = 7.96$ mA

    b. $I_B = 13.6$ μA, $I_C = 1.63$ mA $\approx I_E$, $I_{CE} = 12.7$ V

35. a. $I_{C(SAT)} = 7.96$ mA

    b. $I_C = 2.82$ mA $\approx I_E$, $V_{CE} = 10.3$ V

37. a. $I_{C(SAT)} = 6.12$ mA

    b. $I_C = 2.80$ mA $\approx I_E$, $I_{CE} = -16.3$ V

39. $R_C = 2$ kΩ, $R_E = 0.5$ kΩ, $R_2 = 5$ kΩ, $R_1 = 32$ kΩ

41. a. $I_{C(SAT)} = 7.5$ mA

    b. $I_C = 4.65$ mA $\approx I_E$, $V_{CE} = -11.4$ V

43. a. $I_{C(SAT)} = 14.9$ mA

    b. $I_C = 14.9$ mA (transistor is in saturation)

    c. $V_{out} \approx 0$ V

    d. $I_C = 0$ mA

    e. $V_{out} \approx 8$ V

45. Pin 2 is the base, Pin 3 is the emitter, and Pin 1 is the collector. The transistor is pnp.

47. Pin 1 is the base, Pin 3 is the emitter, and Pin 2 is the collector. The transistor is pnp.

49. a. p-channel     b. 1.28 mA

    c. 2.88 mA     d. 0 mA

51. $V_{GSQ} = -1.94$ V, $I_{DQ} = 2.15$ mA, $V_{DSQ} = 10.17$ V

53. $V_{GSQ} = -1.98$ V, $I_{DQ} = 2.03$ mA, $V_{DSQ} = 4.01$ V

55. a. $V_{GSQ} = -1.00$ V, $I_{DQ} = 6.40$ mA

    b. The MOSFET is in its depletion region.

    c. $V_{DSQ} = 7.41$ V

57. $k = 0.2$ mA/V², $I_D = (0.2$ mA/V²$)(V_{GS} - 2.0$ V$)^2$

59. $V_{GSQ} = 10.4$ V, $I_{DQ} = 14.1$ mA, $V_{DSQ} = 10.4$ V

61. Meter 1 indicates there is no base current. This will be the result of the base-emitter being an open circuit. Meter 2 satisfies the same diagnosis. The absence of base current means there can be no collector current, as indicated by Meter 3. Consequently, the transistor is in cutoff, as indicated by Meter 4.

**CHAPTER 27**

1. a. 7.96 μF     b. 1.990 V, 2.000 V

3. 74.5 μF

5. a. $I_B = 17.4$ μA, $I_C = 2.60$ mA, $V_{CE} = -7.91$ V

    c. $A_v = -222$, $z_{in} = 1350$ Ω, $z_{out} = 4$ kΩ, $A_i = 74.9$

7. a. $I_B = 19.4$ μA, $I_C = 2.91$ mA, $V_{CE} = 10.4$ V

    b. $h_{fe} = 160$, $h_{ie} = 1600$ Ω

    d. $A_v = -330$, $z_{in} = 1600$ Ω, $z_{out} = 3.3$ kΩ, $A_i = 160$

9. a. $I_B = 19.4$ μA, $I_C = 2.91$ mA, $V_{CE} = 12.6$ V

    c. $A_v = 255$, $z_{in} = 1.30$ kΩ, $z_{out} = 3.9$ kΩ, $A_i = 64.9$

    d. $v_{in} = 6.84$ mV$_p$, $v_{out} = 1.744$ V$_p$

11. a. $I_B = 16.4$ μA, $I_C = 2.62$ mA, $V_{CE} = 10.7$ V

    b. $r_e = 9.91$ Ω

    c. $A_v = -4.63$, $z_{in} = 143$ kΩ, $z_{out} = 4.7$ kΩ, $A_i = 141$

13. a. $I_B = 18.6$ μA, $I_C = 2.79$ mA, $V_{CE} = -3.23$ V

    c. $A_v = -11.8$, $z_{in} = 29.3$ kΩ, $z_{out} = 4.3$ kΩ, $A_i = 73.6$

    d. $v_{in} = 4.80$ mV$_p$, $v_{out} = 56.6$ mV$_p$

15. b. $A_v = -2.2$, $z_{in} = 134$ kΩ, $z_{out} = 4.3$ kΩ, $A_i = 63.3$

    c. $v_{in} = 4.96$ mV$_p$, $v_{out} = 11.0$ mV$_p$

17. a. $I_C = 1.93$ mA, $V_{CE} = 7.70$ V

    b. $r_e = 13.4$ Ω

    d. $A_v = -4.8$, $z_{in} = 3990$ Ω, $z_{out} = 3.9$ kΩ, $A_i = 4.91$

19. a. $I_C = 2.24$ mA, $V_{CE} = -9.50$ V

    b. $h_{ie} = 2.0$ kΩ, $h_{fe} = 150$

    c. $A_v = -6.79$, $z_{in} = 5.84$ kΩ, $z_{out} = 3.3$ kΩ, $A_i = 18.0$

21. a. $I_C = 2.3$ mA, $V_{CE} = -10.2$ V

    c. $A_v = -11.7$, $z_{in} = 6.87$ kΩ, $z_{out} = 5$ kΩ, $A_i = 16.1$

    d. 39.6 mV$_p$

23. a. $I_C = 2.41$ mA, $V_{CE} = 10.35$ V

    c. $I_{C(AC-SAT)} = 7.59$ mA, $V_{CE(AC-OFF)} = 15.2$ V

    e. 9.65 V$_{p-p}$, 4.83 mA$_{p-p}$

25. a. $I_C = 2.12$ mA, $V_{CE} = -9.12$ V
    c. $I_{C(AC-SAT)} = 5.20$ mA, $V_{CE(AC-OFF)} = -15.4$ V
    e. $12.6$ $V_{p-p}$, $4.25$ $mA_{p-p}$
27. a. $I_{C(DC-SAT)} = 3.40$ mA, $V_{CE(DC-OFF)} = -18$ V
    b. $I_{C(AC-SAT)} = 4.12$ mA, $V_{CE(AC-OFF)} = -10.00$ V
    c. $6.46$ $V_{p-p}$, $2.66$ $mA_{p-p}$
    d. $0.548$ $V_{p-p}$
29. a. $I_C = 14.8$ mA, $V_{CE} = 9.03$ V
    c. $A_v = 0.996$, $z_{in} = 30.8$ k$\Omega$, $z_{out} = 6.75$ $\Omega$, $A_i = 65.3$, $A_p = 65.1$
31. a. $I_C = 4.87$ mA, $V_{CE} = 8.7$ V
    c. $A_v = 0.991$, $z_{in} = 6.93$ k$\Omega$, $z_{out} = 9.28$ V, $A_i = 6.87$, $A_p = 6.81$
33. a. $h_{ie} = 1600$ $\Omega$, $h_{re} = 1.1 \times 10^{-4}$, $h_{fe} = 150$, $h_{oe} = 20$ $\mu$S
    c. $A_v = 0.978$, $z_{in} = 34.8$ k$\Omega$, $z_{out} = 14.1$ $\Omega$, $A_i = 72.5$, $A_p = 70.9$
35. a. $h_{ie} = 2200$ $\Omega$, $h_{re} = 1.1 \times 10^{-4}$, $h_{fe} = 140$, $h_{oe} = 12$ $\mu$S
    c. $A_v = 0.975$, $z_{in} = 6.90$ k$\Omega$, $z_{out} = 19.6$ $\Omega$, $A_i = 6.73$, $A_p = 6.56$
37. a. $1.875$ mS      b. $0.94$ mS      c. $3.35$ mS
39. a. $4.44$ mS      b. $13.3$ mS
    c. $10.3$ mS      d. $14.6$ mS
41. a. $I_{DQ} = 3.01$ mA, $V_{GSQ} = -2.26$ V, $V_{DSQ} = 13.1$ V
    b. $g_{m0} = 4.0$ mS, $g_m = 2.19$ mS
    d. $A_v = -1.51$, $z_{in} = 1$ M$\Omega$, $z_{out} = 2.2$ k$\Omega$
43. a. $I_{DQ} = 3.02$ mA, $V_{GSQ} = -1.54$ V, $V_{DSQ} = 8.39$ V
    b. $g_{m0} = 4.0$ mS, $g_m = 2.46$ mS
    d. $A_v = -4.06$, $z_{in} = 79.6$ k$\Omega$, $z_{out} = 3.3$ k$\Omega$
45. a. $I_{DQ} = 2.13$ mA, $V_{GSQ} = 1.21$ V, $V_{DSQ} = -10.10$ V
    b. $g_{m0} = 4.0$ mS, $g_m = 2.38$ mS
    d. $A_v = -4.23$, $z_{in} = 2$ M$\Omega$, $z_{out} = 2.2$ k$\Omega$
47. a. $I_{DQ} = 2.5$ mA, $V_{GSQ} = -2.5$ V, $V_{DSQ} = 17.5$ V
    b. $g_{m0} = 4.0$ mS, $g_m = 2.0$ mS
    d. $A_v = 0.667$, $z_{in} = 1$ M$\Omega$, $z_{out} = 333$ $\Omega$
49. a. $I_{DQ} = 5.76$ mA, $V_{GSQ} = -4.23$ V, $V_{DSQ} = 4.72$ V
    b. $g_{m0} = 3.75$ mS, $g_m = 3.29$ mS
    d. $A_v = 0.730$, $z_{in} = 173$ k$\Omega$, $z_{out} = 221$ $\Omega$
51. The emitter bypass capacitor is effectively an open circuit. This could be due to poor soldering or an internal fault.
53. a.  i. $I_C = 4.32$ mA, $V_{CE} = 7.16$ V
       ii. The voltage gain would remain unchanged.
    b.  i. The operating would not change.
       ii. $-450$
55. The capacitor may cause excessive noise.
    The capacitor may be damaged and possibly explode.

**CHAPTER 28**

1. Very high open-loop gain
   Very high input impedance.
   Very low output impedance.
3. $I_{C1} = 2.65$ mA, $V_{C1} = 9.17$ V
5. $86.0$ dB
7. $0.5$ $V_{p-p}$
9. $A_v = -5.0$, $z_{in} = 20$ k$\Omega$, $z_{out} = 2.25$ m$\Omega$
11. $R_1 = 12$ k$\Omega$, $R_F = 60$ k$\Omega$
13. $A_v = 6.0$, $z_{in} = 66.7$ G$\Omega$, $z_{out} = 2.25$ m$\Omega$, $v_{out} = -12.0$ V
15. $R_1 = 12$ k$\Omega$, $R_F = 40$ k$\Omega$
17. $A_v = 1$, $z_{in} = 400$ G$\Omega$, $z_{out} = 0.375$ m$\Omega$
19. $4$ mV
21. $50$ nA, $20$ nA
23. $23.9$ nA
25. $200$ kHz
27. $1$ MHz
29. $79.6$ kHz
31. $16.67$ k$\Omega$
33. $R_F$ might have failed.
    The power supply might have failed.

## CHAPTER 29

1. $v_{out} = -15$ V, $0 < t < 6$ ms
   $v_{out} = +15$ V, 6 ms $< t < 12$ ms

3. $v_{out} = +15$ V, $0 < t < 12$ ms
   $v_{out} = -15$ V, 12 ms $< t < 16$ ms

5. $v_{out} = +15$ V, $0 < t < 8$ μs
   $v_{out} = -15$ V, 8 μs $< t < 24$ μs

7. $v_{out} = -15$ V, $0 < t < 35.2$ μs
   $v_{out} = +15$ V, 35.2 μs $< t < 60.8$ μs

9. LED1 will be on whenever $v_{in} > 10$ V
   LED2 will be on whenever $v_{in} > 5$ V

11. a. $I_1 = -0.20$ mA, $I_2 = 0.45$ mA, $I_3 = -0.15$ mA, $I_F = 0.10$ mA
    b. $-2.0$ V

15. a. $4.0$ V$_{p-p}$

17. $15$ V$_p$

19. a. $v_{out} = -0.5$ V, $0 < t < 1$ ms
       $v_{out} = 0.5$ V, 1 ms $< t < 2$ ms

21. $R_{in} = 100$ Ω, $C_F = 2.5$ nF

23. $I_1 = I_3 = 1.0$ μA (to the right), $I_2 = I_4 = 1.0$ μA (to the left), $v_{out} = 1.02$ V

25. $-20.4$ mV

27. $R_1 = 1590$ Ω, $R_F = 15.9$ kΩ, $R_2 = 1770$ Ω

29. $f_L = 99.5$ Hz, $f_H = 333$ kHz

31. $R = 19.89$ kΩ, $R_1 = 99.9$ Ω

33. $v_{out} = 12.3$ V → 13.5 V, line regulation = 5.79%

35. $v_{out} = 13.5$ V → 13.7 V, load regulation = 1.58%

37. a. $v_{out} = 6.6$ V → 25 V
    b. 0.249 W

39. 54.0 dB

## CHAPTER 30

1. $B = 0.1$, $A_{vcl} = 9.80$

3. UTP $= +9.0$ V, LTP $= -9.0$ V

5. UTP $= +10.5$ V, LTP $= -4.5$ V

7. $V_{REF} = \pm 4.8$ V, $T = 6.78$ mS

9. a. 20 kΩ    b. 72.3 Hz

11. $B = 0.25$, $A = 4$

13. a. 922 Hz    b. 10.5 kΩ
    c. 43.5 kΩ    d. 69.0 kHz

15. $R = 345$ Ω, $R_F = 10.0$ kΩ

17. 100.7 kHz

19. When the crystal is subjected to mechanical pressure, an electric field is developed at right angle to the applied pressure. Conversely, if an electric field is applied, the material will deflect at right angle to the electric field.

21. Refer to Figure 30–35.

23. a. $v_{out} = V_{CC}$ and the discharge transistor will be OFF.
    b. $v_{out} = 0$ and the discharge transistor will be ON.

25. $R_B = 361$ kΩ, $R_A = 721$ kΩ

27. $v_{out} = 0$ V $0 < t < 20$ ms
    $v_{out} = 15$ V $20 < t < 56.3$ ms
    $v_{out} = 0$ V $56.3$ ms $< t$

29. $f_{0\%} = 34.1$ kHz, $f_{50\%} = 18.5$ kHz, $f_{100\%} = 2.93$ kHz

## CHAPTER 31

1. a. 267 Hz
   b. $\eta = 0.627$ $R_{BB} = 5.98$ kΩ

3. $R_E = 12.7$ kΩ (Note: Any combination of $RC = 0.127$ ms will work.)

9. Triac operates in Modes I$^+$ and III$^+$.

11. $V = 81.1$ V    $P = 43.9$ W

13. $V = 216$ V    $P = 2320$ W

15. $\theta = 120°$

17. $V = 81.064$ V

19. $5.45 \times 10^{14}$ Hz

21. 350 Ω

23. a. 20 V
    b. 13.5 V
    c. $v_{out} = +20$ V, $0 < t < 100$ ms
       $v_{out} = +13.5$ V, 100 ms $< t < 300$ ms
       $v_{out} = +20$ V, 300 ms $< t < 400$ ms
       $v_{out} = +13.5$ V, 400 ms $< t$

25. **L**ight **A**mplification through **S**timulated **E**mission of **R**adiation.